TOBACCO
AND CANCER
THE SCIENCE AND THE STORY

TOBACCO
AND CANCER

THE SCIENCE AND THE STORY

Editors

Stephen S Hecht
Dorothy K Hatsukami
University of Minnesota, Twin Cities, USA

World Scientific

NEW JERSEY · LONDON · SINGAPORE · BEIJING · SHANGHAI · HONG KONG · TAIPEI · CHENNAI · TOKYO

Published by

World Scientific Publishing Co. Pte. Ltd.

5 Toh Tuck Link, Singapore 596224

USA office: 27 Warren Street, Suite 401-402, Hackensack, NJ 07601

UK office: 57 Shelton Street, Covent Garden, London WC2H 9HE

Library of Congress Cataloging-in-Publication Data
Names: Hecht, Stephen S., editor. | Hatsukami, Dorothy K., editor.
Title: Tobacco and cancer : the science and the story / editors, Stephen S. Hecht,
    Dorothy K. Hatsukami, University of Minnesota, Twin Cities, USA.
Description: New Jersey : World Scientific Publishing, [2022] |
    Includes bibliographical references and index.
Identifiers: LCCN 2021034645 | ISBN 9789811239526 (hardcover) |
    ISBN 9789811239533 (ebook) | ISBN 9789811239540 (ebook other)
Subjects: LCSH: Cancer--Prevention. | Tobacco--Physiological effect. |
    Tobacco use--Health aspects. | Smoking.
Classification: LCC RA645.C3 T63 2022 | DDC 614.5/999--dc23
LC record available at https://lccn.loc.gov/2021034645

British Library Cataloguing-in-Publication Data
A catalogue record for this book is available from the British Library.

For any available supplementary material, please visit
https://www.worldscientific.com/worldscibooks/10.1142/12348#t=suppl

Typeset by Stallion Press
Email: enquiries@stallionpress.com

Dedicated to elimination of the tobacco and cancer pandemic

Contents

Preface

The relationship between cigarette smoking and cancer began to crystallize in the 1950s with both animal experiments and human epidemiological studies demonstrating this link. This book tells the story of the remarkable evolution of the science, how the important discoveries were made, what we know currently about the ways that tobacco causes cancer, and what approaches can be used to reduce the risk of cancer due to tobacco use. Although there are excellent books and monographs on tobacco and cancer, both in the popular press and as government summaries, none relate the scientific story at the level of non-specialist graduate and medical students, researchers, or educated popular science readers. In this book, with a primary focus on the United States, we bring together 24 renowned experts on the subject of tobacco and cancer to summarize specific aspects of this critical topic in relatively non-technical terms while also incorporating some personal insights related to the story of the discovery process. This highly authoritative book is also expected to be an excellent teaching tool and basis for a course for graduate and medical students, as well as an introduction to the field for postdoctoral fellows and new researchers.

Our goal is to touch upon the past history of the practices of tobacco manufacturing that led to the high rates of cigarette smoking, the scientific methods that were used to make the association between tobacco and cancer, the constituents responsible for causing cancer and the biological mechanisms leading to cancer, approaches to reduce cancer risk and tobacco use, and future innovative policy approaches to reduce cancer mortality caused by smoking. The authors of each of the chapters are leaders in the scientific field of tobacco control and have had significant roles in the evolution of ideas, science or policies that are described in their chapters. As a teaser, the following provides a synopsis of each chapter.

The path and inventions that led to the development and popularity of one of the deadliest consumer products, cigarettes, is a fascinating story that is illustrated in **Chapter 1** written by K. Michael Cummings, Anthony Brown and Baron Phillipson. As described by these authors, cigarettes emerged as a popular product at the turn of the 20th century for a number of reasons including the reduction in cost due to the invention that led to mass manufacturing of cigarettes, the ability to grow tobacco in challenging soil conditions, and through the use of cheap reconstituted tobacco. On top of this massive production of cigarettes, the tobacco industry launched aggressive advertising campaigns. These sophisticated Madison Avenue marketing campaigns, which included promotional activities, were aimed at both men and women and, most egregiously, at children in order to ensure a steady stream of customers. Meanwhile, cigarette manufacturers continued to perfect the cigarette by finding ways to make them taste smoother, more appealing and more addictive. What better way to recruit and retain customers? When information on the health risks of smoking began to become known, cigarette manufacturers made and deceptively promoted cigarettes that were perceived to be less harmful. To this day, cigarettes are continually mutated to capture more consumers. Tobacco companies knew of the health consequences of smoking before the information became public. But instead of owning up to their scientific discoveries, they obfuscated these associations by putting up smoke screens to generate doubt. At its peak, the cigarette manufacturers were able to capture more than 40% of the U.S. population as smokers, which resulted in the 20th century being called the "Cigarette Century." However, scientists and physicians became more concerned about the increasing incidence in cancer which appeared to be related to the increasing prevalence of smoking. What type of studies led to the final nail in the coffin that linked smoking to cancer?

Chapter 2, written by Jonathan Samet, describes the evolution of the epidemiological studies that linked lung cancer with smoking. While studies existed recognizing environmental exposures as a cause of cancer, examining the association between lung cancer and smoking did not occur in earnest until the early 20th century. By the 1930s, lung cancer rates were dramatically increasing as a result of the tobacco industry's success in capturing consumers through their marketing practices and addictive product. The rise in lung cancer cases was initially observed and reported by clinicians and later followed by epidemiological studies that were initially inconsistent in demonstrating any association between smoking and lung cancer. However, with the use of more sophisticated methodology which included case control and longitudinal cohort studies, from the 1950s to 1964, evidence was accumulating linking smoking with lung cancer. Several systematic reviews were conducted including the landmark 1964 U.S. Surgeon General's Report, which concluded that smoking causes lung cancer (in men). Over the years, smoking cigarettes was confirmed as a cause of multiple cancer types in both men and women, and secondhand smoke as a cause of lung cancer in healthy nonsmokers. However, epidemiological studies were not the only pieces of evidence that showed that tobacco use caused cancer. A series of animal studies strongly supported the human study findings.

Chapter 3, written by Karam El-Bayoumy, describes animal studies of tobacco and cancer which were performed to bolster the epidemiologic findings and also to investigate which constituents of tobacco smoke were carcinogenic. While there were scattered animal studies of tobacco extracts, juice, tar, distillate, or smoke prior to the 1950s, it was not until 1953 that the eminent scientist Ernst Wynder and colleagues convincingly demonstrated that tobacco tar caused benign and malignant tumors when painted repetitively on the shaved backs of mice. Mouse skin thus emerged as a widely used test system not only for whole tobacco smoke condensates but also for fractions of the condensate obtained through chemical separation methods. The mouse skin studies not only supported the epidemiologic research noted above but also provided a way to determine the biologically active fractions of tobacco smoke condensate, resulting in the identification of one of the main carcinogens in tobacco smoke — benzo[a]pyrene — and other constituents that acted as tumor promoters or co-carcinogens. In the next phase of animal research, systems were developed to expose laboratory animals such as mice, rats, and hamsters to cigarette smoke by inhalation. This was quite challenging because laboratory animals will not inhale cigarette smoke the way that humans do; in fact they are strongly averse to it (maybe they are smarter). Ultimately, inhalation studies of cigarette smoke were also successful in inducing tumors and leading to a better understanding of mechanisms of tobacco carcinogenesis.

What are the constituents of tobacco smoke and its condensate that cause cancer? This complex question is addressed in **Chapter 4**, written by Irina Stepanov. When you burn tobacco at about 800°C, as in a cigarette, the emitted smoke contains not only compounds that were distilled from the tobacco, but a much more complex mixture of combustion products, at least 6000 of them, that have been identified by talented chemists using all the modern methods of the laboratory. Some of these compounds have powerful cancer-causing activities, and are believed to be responsible for the different cancer types observed in users of combusted tobacco products such as cigarettes, cigars, cigarillos, and pipes. This informative chapter dissects cigarette smoke and provides an essential overview of its composition, and the ways in which this complex mixture is analyzed to identify each constituent. The chapter also discusses which carcinogens cause the multiple different cancer types from cigarette smoking. Another important topic discussed here is the ways in which sugars and other additives to tobacco to improve taste contribute to the composition of cigarette smoke.

Chapter 5, written by S. Jane Henley, Taylor Ellington, Stephen Stanfill, Kathi Mills, and Michael J. Thun focuses on smokeless tobacco. Its first sentence sets the stage for this informative chapter: "In countries around the world, people not only smoke tobacco, but also suck, chew, dip, and snort it." There are a huge variety of these products in the world — ranging from chewing tobacco and moist snuff products that are popular in parts of the U.S. to a bewildering assortment of local products and mixtures that are consumed in India and other parts of Southeast Asia. This chapter provides a brief history of smokeless tobacco use, and its deadly consequences — particularly for oral cancer — in the U.S., as exemplified in the tragic case of the all-star baseball player Tony Gwynn. The carcinogenic properties of smokeless tobacco are believed to be due mainly to a group of chemicals called "tobacco-specific nitrosamines", powerful cancer-causing agents found only in tobacco products and potentially targeted for regulation by the U.S. Food and Drug Administration.

With so much known about the dangers of cigarette smoking and other tobacco products, why on earth would anyone continue using them? The answer is: the users are addicted to nicotine. The tobacco industry knows this, so they have been endlessly inventive in coming up with new nicotine delivery systems. The currently most popular of these — e-cigarettes and heated tobacco products — are discussed in **Chapter 6**, written by Maciej L. Goniewicz. These products have the advantage of delivering nicotine without combustion. e-Cigarettes don't even contain tobacco, but rather a mixture of propylene glycol and vegetable glycerin — which when heated produces the visible vapor — as well as nicotine, and any of several thousand flavoring compounds. This chapter explains the different varieties of e-cigarette devices which have flooded the market in recent years in an ever-changing manner, from big tank systems to the currently popular Juul pods. Heated tobacco products have been intro-duced worldwide by the tobacco industry. These products heat tobacco rather than burning it; the nicotine and some of the tobacco flavors are distilled into the user's mouth. You get your nicotine fix with a reduced amount of toxicants and carcinogens. One type of heated tobacco product — Phillip Morris' IQOS — has even been authorized by the FDA as a modified risk (exposure) tobacco product.

How do tobacco products cause cancer? This intriguing question is addressed in **Chapter 7** by Stephen S. Hecht, one of the editors of this book. Tobacco products, especially the combusted ones such as cigarettes and cigars, are, as noted above, sources of a complex mixture of cancer-causing agents — at least 70 different ones are present in each puff. Some of these compounds can really mess up your DNA without even much effort, while others require some help from enzymes in your lungs or other tissues. When these compounds get bound chemically to DNA, its normal process of base pairing — G with C and A with T — can get disrupted, so you may get G pairing with T instead of with C. That is a real problem because it can lead to permanent mutations in critical genes involved in growth control! This process can get terribly out of control with the result being formation of a tumor and ultimately metastatic cancer. Scientists have dissected this process and can now follow it in the body by measur-ing certain chemicals in urine or blood. These chemicals — called bio-markers — can reflect dangerous events that occur due to tobacco smoke exposure and may be able to predict cancer development in smokers. This is important because about 10–20% of lifelong smokers will get cancer; if we knew who those individuals were, we would be better equipped to prevent this deadly disease.

As noted above, nicotine is the primary reason people use tobacco products as well as the newer nicotine delivery systems. The metabolism of nicotine is an important determinant of how much people will smoke or use other nicotine-containing products, as discussed in **Chapter 8**, written by Sharon E. Murphy. Nicotine is not a carcinogen, but it is addictive. Your body has enzymes which can convert foreign compounds like nicotine to metabolites that are more readily excreted. The enzymes that metabolize nicotine are part of the cytochrome P450 drug metabolizing enzyme family; one enzyme — P450 2A6 — is particularly important. But this enzyme has multiple different forms causing some individuals to metabolize nicotine very inefficiently. This has a significant effect on smoking because there is more unmetabolized nicotine left in the body, so there is less reason to smoke a lot of cigarettes. So, the different forms of P450 2A6 can affect how much you smoke, and it has been found that Japanese Americans in particular have more unmetabolized nicotine on board, therefore smoke less intensely, and have a lower risk for lung cancer.

The theme of ethnic differences in susceptibility to lung cancer in smokers is taken up in more detail and expanded in **Chapter 9**, written by Loïc Le Marchand. He describes the important epidemiologic studies which have demonstrated significant and intriguing differences in lung cancer occurrence in cigarette smokers from different ethnic groups. Important among these studies is the Multiethnic Cohort, the first prospective study of ethnic/racial differences in lung cancer risk related to cigarette smoking, which has been following 215,000 Hawaii and Los Angeles residents since 1993–1996. The subjects in this study come from five ethnic groups: African Americans, Native Hawaiians, Whites, Latinos, and Japanese Americans. Consistent with the data discussed in Chapter 8, Japanese American smokers have the lowest risk for lung cancer among smokers in the five ethnic groups. African Americans and Native Hawaiian smokers have a high risk for lung cancer while Whites are intermediate and Latinos have lower risk. These differences are most evident among individuals who smoke only 10 cigarettes per day; heavier smoking

(30 cigarettes per day) tends to obliterate the different risks due most likely to the high dose of smoke carcinogens.

Is it possible to prevent lung cancer in addicted cigarette smokers or ex-smokers, using specific naturally occurring or synthetic drugs? This important question is discussed in **Chapter 10**, written by Gary D. Stoner. This chapter discusses chemoprevention, the use of naturally occurring or synthetic drugs to prevent cancer in high-risk individuals such as cigarette smokers. Animal models are used extensively to test potential chemopreventive agents by administering them either before, during, or after treatment with a carcinogen. The efficacy of a chemopreventive agent is determined by comparing the extent of tumor induction in animals treated with the carcinogen alone compared to the carcinogen plus the chemopreventive agent. Laboratory animals, usually special strains of mice or rats, are used in these studies, sometimes following protocols similar to those employed in the testing of tobacco products or their constituents as described in Chapter 3. These studies have uncovered numerous naturally occurring and synthetic compounds that have the potential to prevent cancer. These chemopreventive agents include isothiocyanates found in cruciferous vegetables, selenium compounds, tea and some of its constituents, anti-inflammatory agents, kava and its constituents, and others. Some clinical trials have also been performed. These studies have produced a huge amount of important data on mechanisms and prevention of tobacco-induced cancer, but there is still no FDA approved method for prevention of smoking- or smokeless tobacco-caused cancers.

Currently one third of cancer deaths are attributed to smoking, primarily from lung cancer, which continues to be a leading cause of cancer deaths worldwide. **Chapter 11**, written by Terry Pechacek, describes the current trends in tobacco product use and cancer rates. Since the 1950s and 1960s epidemiological studies that linked smoking with cancer, large national surveys have been implemented to follow the types and patterns of tobacco use over time. Key areas of assessment in these surveys include who is using tobacco products, what products are being used, how much of the product is being used and for how long, and other lifestyle health risk factors. Knowing *who* is smoking will allow an understanding of the population groups who might be most vulnerable to cancer risk. Following trends in tobacco use over time in specific populations can provide information on the likely patterns of cancer incidence rates. Knowing *what* types of tobacco products are being used can provide awareness of what cancer types and rates might be expected in the future. Smoking by far is the predominant cause of cancer, and in the U.S., smoking rates are dramatically falling, particularly among youth (which is great news). However, e-cigarette use is increasing along with poly-tobacco use (using multiple tobacco products). How this change in types of tobacco product use might affect cancer rates is unknown and worthy of study. Knowing the *amount, frequency* and *duration* of cigarette use might inform us of how these patterns of smoking might influence cancer risk. For example, surveys show that fewer cigarettes are being smoked and the frequency of smoking has also decreased. Although this trend is promising, its impact on reducing cancer risk has been modest at best. However, research shows that cancer risk can be dramatically decreased if people quit smoking at a younger age. But only a small percentage of people are successful in quitting long-term in any one year. Why? Perhaps, the addictive effects of nicotine in tobacco products are the explanation.

With nicotine addiction comes exposure to tobacco-related carcinogens and other toxicants. Without addiction to cigarettes, there would be no cigarette manufacturing companies because people would simply not smoke. **Chapter 12**, written by Jodi Prochaska and Neal Benowitz, describes why nicotine is addictive, factors that contribute to its addictiveness and approaches to treat nicotine addiction. They describe the biological and pharmacological basis for addiction. Nicotine targets the nicotinic acetylcholine receptors resulting in a cascade of neurochemicals responsible for its reinforcing effects. The greater the magnitude and speed of nicotine delivery, the greater its reinforcing value. Unfortunately, smoking cigarettes, the most toxic tobacco product, has the greatest potential to addict because of the rapid delivery of high amounts of nicotine to the brain; whereas products such as nicotine patches or gum deliver nicotine more slowly resulting in less potential for addiction. The authors point out that cigarettes were designed by cigarette manufacturers to promote and sustain addiction. With repeated use, alterations occur in the morphology of the brain such that tobacco users develop tolerance to the effects of nicotine and experience withdrawal symptoms after cessation of smoking or other tobacco use. These morphological changes are particularly profound in the adolescent brain. Tobacco companies were well aware of the susceptibility of youth to experimentation and eventual addiction to nicotine; therefore, as noted in Chapter 1, their earlier marketing efforts were targeted towards adolescents. The younger the age of tobacco use onset, the greater the dependence on the product and the lower the likelihood of quitting. It's not just nicotine that leads to persistent use, but stimuli that are associated with nicotine begin to induce craving and motivates the person to seek nicotine. The 1988 U.S. Surgeon General's Report and subsequent reports acknowledged that nicotine is addictive, similar to other drugs of abuse. How can we treat the addicted smoker? In the U.S., beginning in the mid-1980s, medications to treat nicotine addiction became available, first nicotine gum, then followed by other nicotine replacement therapies. Non-nicotine medications such as bupropion and varenicline were also subsequently FDA approved. These medications targeted different aspects of nicotine addiction. Nicotine replacement therapies allayed the withdrawal symptoms following smoking cessation, while varenicline is a partial agonist blocking the reinforcing effects of nicotine and reducing withdrawal symptoms. Bupropion simulated the effects of nicotine with some weak nicotinic receptor antagonist effects. However, the authors point out that medications alone are not sufficient for treating nicotine addiction; behavioral and psychological aspects of addiction also need attention. The nature of these treatments has evolved over time, beginning as individual and group therapies and expanding to telephone quitlines and the use of technology such as smartphone texting and the internet to provide treatments with greater reach. Despite these tools, smoking cessation is difficult to achieve, relapse is high and treatment for smoking cessation is not sufficient. Because of the addictiveness of nicotine in cigarettes, the authors raise the idea that tobacco companies should be required to make smoked tobacco products non-addictive, thereby preventing youth from becoming addicted and facilitating abstinence among those who are already addicted. Short of this approach, policies are needed to prevent the use of tobacco products in the first place as well as to facilitate cessation.

Chapter 13, written by Michael Eriksen and Carrie Whitney, describes effective tobacco control laws, policies and regulations that have been implemented in the U.S. and around the world to reduce tobacco-caused mortality. The development and implementation of these policies and regulations began shortly after the 1964 Surgeon General's Report that linked smoking with cancer and other diseases. In the U.S., steps taken to reduce disease caused by smoking began by educating smokers with warning labels about the health hazards of smoking followed by anti-smoking or counter-advertising campaigns, then banning advertisements altogether on television and radio. This was followed by implementing smoke-free laws, increasing taxes on tobacco products, restricting marketing and promotional activities, and providing access to effective and affordable treatments to tobacco users. The implementation of these policies and laws often started with grassroots social action in localities, cities and states and in some cases, eventually reached the federal level. Similar and even stronger policies (such as plain cigarette packaging with graphic warning labels) are being implemented worldwide. Another approach that has been used to establish policies and regulations is through litigation against the tobacco companies for charges such as racketeering (deceiving the public about the health risks of smoking, marketing to children, putting profit before human welfare) and to cover healthcare costs (leading to the U.S. Master Settlement Agreement). The authors also mention the FDA authority to regulate tobacco products (see Chapter 14) and the currently controversial topic of harm reduction, that is, reducing harm by providing tobacco/nicotine products that allow consumers to switch to a less harmful product. In the U.S., the FDA rulings will be integral to the nature and role of harm reduction in the tobacco control toolbox. This chapter also makes the point that tobacco control policies are not sufficient to reduce the burden of tobacco use on cancer. The authors point out that we also need to consider ways to enhance cancer screening such as low dose computed tomography scans for lung cancer, and to use precision medicine to treat cancer patients.

What if a regulatory agency could tell tobacco companies that any introduction of new tobacco products in the marketplace must demonstrate public health benefit? What if a regulatory agency could require a tobacco company to reduce the appeal, toxicity and addictiveness of a tobacco product? **Chapter 14**, written by David Ashley, describes the

U.S. FDA authority to regulate tobacco products. The overall goal of tobacco product regulation is to benefit or protect public health for both users and non-users of tobacco products. This chapter describes various pathways that FDA can take to regulate tobacco products that can potentially result in reducing cancer and other diseases caused by tobacco. Key among these pathways is the premarket tobacco application (PMTA) and the issuance of product standards. Any new product that is introduced in the U.S. marketplace after February 15, 2007 for cigarettes, cigarette tobacco, roll your own tobacco and smokeless tobacco and any other tobacco-derived products (e.g., e-cigarettes, tobacco heating systems, waterpipes, etc.) requires manufacturers to submit a PMTA. The manufacturers need to demonstrate that the introduction of this product to the marketplace would be "appropriate for the protection of public health." Tobacco companies are also allowed to make a modified risk claim for their tobacco products if they are shown to significantly reduce the risk for tobacco related disease (reduced risk claim) or reasonably likely to reduce the risk for disease (modified exposure claim). These claims are one means of educating consumers about the relative risk of products. A potentially more impactful regulation is the FDA's authority to establish product standards. These standards could involve reducing nicotine to minimally addictive levels (see Chapter 12), reducing carcinogens and other harmful and potentially harmful constituents in the tobacco and/or in smoke emissions (e.g., tobacco-specific nitrosamines), eliminating constituents that result in increasing the appeal of a tobacco product leading to uptake among youth or greater dependence (e.g., characterizing flavors such as menthol in cigarettes) or removing specific cigarette design features that are associated with greater harm (e.g., filter ventilation). The author describes in detail the requirements and review process for authorizing the marketing of a product via the PMTA, a substantially equivalent product (e.g., the modified product is similar to an existing or predicate product on the market) and product standards. The authority to regulate tobacco products is also possible in countries that signed the World Health Organization Framework Convention on Tobacco Control. In this treaty, Articles 9 and 10 allow government authorities to regulate the contents and emissions of tobacco products and require manufacturers and importers of tobacco products to disclose information on contents and emissions of tobacco products to these authorities. The regulation of tobacco products can potentially be a game changer in reducing disease burden of tobacco products.

What should be the "endgame" for tobacco and what are the ways to achieve this endgame? **Chapter 15**, written by Kenneth Warner, describes many innovative ideas that can complement and exceed the existing evidence-based tobacco control policies and regulations. Dr. Warner quotes Ruth Malone, who has described the strategies to achieve the endgame as "big-picture radical ideas that seek to propel the tobacco control movement more quickly towards a time when the global tobacco disease pandemic…will be ended." He further states that she considers endgame thinkers "the visionaries of the tobacco control movement." What are some of these radical ideas? Endgame, which could mean the end of all tobacco use or all combusted tobacco use, has been described as targeting different categories of intervention: 1) general supply side; 2) product-specific; 3) consumer-specific; and 4) a combination. To whet the reader's curiosity, one radical supply-side reduction proposal is to establish a government authorized agency to set time-specific and company-specific targets for reducing smoking prevalence and cigarette sales; failure of companies to do so would result in a fine. A product-specific intervention has been described previously, that is, to reduce nicotine in all combusted tobacco products to minimally addictive levels. Another idea is to increase the pH of the cigarette smoke (≥ 8) so that it is too harsh to inhale. A consumer-specific intervention includes restricting any tobacco sales among individuals born after a certain year (e.g., 2010). There are many other fascinating and bold ideas described in this chapter; these ideas, some of which can be considered audacious, are needed to outpace the tobacco industry in their efforts to addict and profit.

We hope you enjoy this book as much as we have, and we want to thank the chapter authors for their thoughtful contributions. We also hope that the information provided here will stimulate new investigators to contribute to the science of tobacco and cancer. We still have a lot of work to do. As of 2021, about a half-million people in the U.S. die per year from smoking-related disease (about 135,000 from lung cancer) and about 7.7 million worldwide. It is our hope that the current and future generations of scientists, policy makers and tobacco control advocates will contribute to making smoking cigarettes an obsolete behavior and ensuring the reduction of harm of other tobacco products.

We thank Bob Carlson for his superb work in managing this project.

Stephen S. Hecht
Dorothy K. Hatsukami
Minneapolis, 2021

Stephen S. Hecht, PhD, is Wallin Professor of Cancer Prevention at the University of Minnesota and an American Cancer Society Research Professor. He is an internationally recognized expert on carcinogens in tobacco products and their mechanisms. He is the co-discoverer of tobacco-specific nitrosamines, causative agents for tobacco-induced cancer. His current research focuses on the relationship of human carcinogen and toxicant metabolites and DNA adducts to cancer risk.

He has a BS in chemistry (Duke University) and a PhD in organic chemistry (MIT). Prior to moving to the University of Minnesota in 1996, he conducted research at the American Health Foundation cancer prevention research institute in Valhalla, NY, where he was Director of Research from 1987 to 1996.

He received the AACR Award for Excellence in Cancer Prevention Research in 2006, and the Founders Award from the Division of Chemical Toxicology, American Chemical Society in 2009. He was elected an American Chemical Society Fellow in 2009, a Fellow of the American Association for the Advancement of Science in 2014, and was Editor-in-Chief of *Chemical Research in Toxicology* 2013–17. He has received a Merit Award and an Outstanding Investigator Grant from the National Cancer Institute.

He has published over 900 papers in the scientific literature.

Dorothy K. Hatsukami, PhD, is Forster Family Chair in Cancer Prevention and Professor of Psychiatry and Behavioral Sciences at the University of Minnesota. She is internationally recognized for her expertise in tobacco addiction and its treatment and tobacco regulatory science, focused on ways to reduce tobacco harm. Her scientific work has involved characterizing tobacco and nicotine dependence, evaluating different pharmacological treatments including the nicotine vaccine and combination medications, and evaluating the toxicity, abuse liability and appeal of different tobacco products. Her recent primary focus has been to generate the science to support the regulation to reduce nicotine in cigarettes to make them minimally addictive.

She has a BA in psychology (University of California, Berkeley) and a PhD in clinical psychology (University of Minnesota). She joined the faculty at the University of Minnesota upon receiving her PhD.

She has received awards from the Society for Research on Nicotine and Tobacco, American Psychological Association (Division 28) and the College on Problems on Drug Dependence. She has served on a number of advisory boards for the US governmental agencies, including the Food and Drug Administration, National Institute on Drug Abuse and currently serves on the World Health Organization, Study Group on Tobacco Product Regulation and the National Cancer Institute, Board of Scientific Advisors.

She has over 500 publications.

© 2022 World Scientific Publishing Company
https://doi.org/10.1142/9789811239533_0001

Chapter 1

History of the Evolution of Tobacco Products

K. Michael Cummings*, Anthony Brown[†] and
Baron Philipson[‡]

1. Introduction

Tobacco has been used by humans for hundreds of years — mostly smoked, chewed, or snorted. The main reason people use tobacco is to obtain nicotine, the psychoactive and addictive substance that both stimulates and calms the body.[1] The way tobacco products are designed can influence the bioavailability of nicotine.[2] Not all tobacco products deliver nicotine in the same way.

The tobacco plant encompasses many different species in the genus *Nicotiana*.[3] Nicotine was first isolated from tobacco in 1828, but the medicinal qualities of tobacco were recognized much earlier. Even before Columbus and his sailors came to the New World, tobacco use was

---

*Department of Psychiatry & Behavioral Sciences, Medical University of South Carolina, Charleston, SC, 29425, USA. cummingk@musc.edu

[†]Department of Health Behavior, Division of Cancer Prevention and Population Sciences, Roswell Park Cancer Comprehensive Center, Buffalo, NY 14263, USA. Anthony.Brown@ RoswellPark.org

[‡]Legaleze Litigation Consulting and Graphics, 3860 West Commercial Boulevard, Fort Lauderdale, FL 33309, USA. bphilipson@Legaleze.com

widespread among native populations in the Americas who used tobacco in religious ceremonies and as medicine.[1,2,4] Cigarettes and cigars appear to have had antecedents in Mexico and Central America around the 9th century in the form of reeds and smoking tubes.[1,2,4–6] When tobacco plants were exported back to Europe, it was apparent that the tobacco oil had potent pharmacological effects. By 1830, the practice of rolling tobacco leaves in paper and smoking it had become a common practice. In France these tubes of tobacco were referred to as a *cigarette*.[4,5] Sometime in the 1840s, cigarette-making factories began to spring up from Saint Petersburg, Russia, to London, England. It was around this time that Philip Morris began to make custom cigarettes from his London tobacco shop.[7] The first factories in the United States were established in New York City and along the eastern seaboard beginning in the 1860s.

However, early cigarettes were not like their counterparts today. Early cigarettes typically were made from a single blend of oriental tobacco with sugar and additives to retain moisture for hand rolling.[2,5,6,8] During the early decades of the 20th century, lung cancer was a rare disease with only a few hundred cases documented annually in the United States.[9] However, as cigarettes grew in popularity so did lung cancer[10] (see Figure 1).

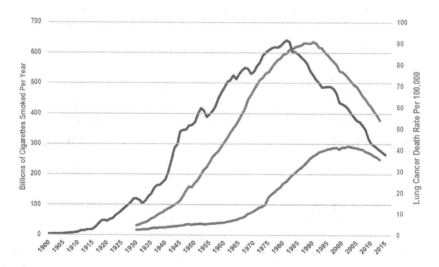

Figure 1:   US cigarette consumption and lung cancer: blue curve is cigarettes smoked per year; orange and red are death rates in men and women.

2. Why Did Cigarettes Become the Dominant Form of Tobacco Consumed in the 20th Century?

Cigarettes and their variants, such as roll-your-own cigarettes, pose the highest risks for disease because their design allows for mildly acidic smoke to be readily inhaled into the lungs with less discomfort than the more alkaline smoke found in most pipes and cigars where the nicotine is mostly absorbed through the tissues in the mouth.[2] The surface area of your mouth is roughly the size of a tennis ball in contrast to your lungs, which have the surface area of a tennis court. Thus, getting nicotine into the large surface area of the lungs allows for rapid uptake of nicotine making cigarettes especially addictive[1,11] (see Box 1).

In 2018, factory-made cigarettes accounted for about 90% of tobacco sales worldwide, followed by other smoked tobacco products such as cigars, bidis, hookah and pipe tobacco (~6%), various types of oral tobacco (~2%), nicotine vaping products (1.2%), and heated tobacco products (0.8%).[12] Until the 20th century, cigarettes were not the dominant form of tobacco consumed; instead most tobacco was used for making cigars, pipe and chewing tobacco.[13] There are several factors that

Box 1:   Quote from Colin Greig BAT document.

Excerpts from a presentation given by Colin Greig, product applications group at British American Tobacco (BAT).[11] The June 1984 conference was restricted to BAT affiliated scientists and executives, including scientists from BAT's American affiliate, Brown & Williamson. The focus of the conference was new product development.

In his summary Mr. Greig concludes by saying....

"So — give them what they want taste and value. And always remember that, while King James I issued his famous 'Counterblaste to tobacco,' in 1604, it is nicer from our point of view to remember Oscar Wilde's words in the picture Dorian Gray... 'A cigarette is the perfect type of perfect pleasure. It is exquisite and leaves one unsatisfied. What more can one want.'

Let us provide the exquisiteness, and hope that they, our customers continue to remain unsatisfied. *All we would want then is a larger bag to carry the money to the bank.*"

contributed to the growth of cigarettes in the United States and world-wide.[5-7] Among these factors are (1) the invention of flue curing, which made it possible for cigarette smoke to be inhaled; (2) the mechanization of cigarette production which lowered the costs of producing cigarettes; (3) the break-up of the American Tobacco Company (ATC) monopoly which spurred product innovation and competition in marketing; (4) the invention of matches and lighters which made smoking convenient; and (5) the military, Madison Avenue, and mass marketing that allowed for the emergence of product branding of what otherwise were homogeneous products. Each of these factors is briefly described below.

2.1. *The invention of flue curing*

Curing of tobacco has always been a process necessary to prepare tobacco leaf for consumption because when the green tobacco leaves are first picked they are too wet to ignite.[2,3,5,14,15] Different curing methods were devised to dry out the tobacco leaves including leaving them in the sun to dry (i.e., sun curing) or hanging in barns so the air would dry the leaves (i.e., air curing). In the early 1800s, tobacco growers experimented with different curing processes in order to develop milder varieties of the tobacco. However, it was really the discovery and adoption of flue curing of tobacco around 1839 that would eventually make cigarettes the pre-ferred type of tobacco product.[2,5,14] Early flue curing of tobacco leaves used charcoal and wood-fueled fires to carry heat through flues inside the barn. The dry heat that was carried by the flues throughout the barn sped up the removal of moisture from the tobacco leaves that were hung on sticks inside the barn.

In the 1950s, cigarette makers began heating the tobacco leaves in metal shipping containers using liquid propane gas, much like a propane gas grill[5] (see Figure 2). It was later discovered that failure to adequately ventilate the tobacco curing containers allowed nitric oxide to build up inside thus increasing the levels of carcinogens found in the tobacco.[16] The heat turns the green leaf to a golden yellow color. The flue-cured tobacco leaves retained more sugar and created a milder tobacco smoke which is why flue-curing became popular.[2,3,5,15]

Figure 2:   Flue curing images old vs. new.

Tobacco farmers quickly discovered that Bright tobacco that was flue cured would grow well in sandy loose soil where other species of tobacco would not grow so easily. With flue curing, formerly unproductive farms in soil-depleted areas of the Carolinas and adjoining Virginia began to produce large quantities of Bright flue-cured tobacco. The mild Bright tobacco quickly began to grow in demand. In the United States, R.J. Reynolds is credited with incorporating Bright flue-cured tobacco into cigarettes creating what became known as the American blend which combined Bright, Burley and Oriental tobaccos into its Camel brand cigarettes in 1913.[2,5,6] Bright tobacco was adopted as the preferred tobacco in cigarettes smoked by Canadians and Europeans.[17] However, the real importance of flue curing was that it helped make the smoke less harsh and easier to inhale into the large surface area of the lungs thereby delivering nicotine rapidly to the smoker's brain.[2,5]

Cigarettes are deadly not only because of the many toxic chemicals produced when the tobacco is burned, but also because of the speed of the delivery of nicotine which reaches the brain within 10 seconds.[1,2,5,11,18] This instantaneous hit to the brain releases feel-good chemicals affecting the smokers' mood. The extra sugar retained in flue-cured tobacco reinforces the impact of nicotine. Speed of nicotine delivery is one of the reasons cigarettes are so addictive and hard to stop using. Once someone develops physical dependence to the drug (nicotine), they begin to need the drug frequently to feel normal.[1] Most cigarette packs sold in the

United States have contained 20 cigarettes because, as one tobacco industry scientist observed, most smokers smoke about 20 cigarettes per day.[18] However, in the past 20 years the average number of cigarettes consumed by daily smokers has fallen to an average of about 14 cigarettes per day most likely in response to higher cigarette prices and clean indoor air laws that have impeded the ability of a smoker to light up as frequently during the day.[10] With an average of 10 puffs per cigarette and 20 cigarettes per day, that is the equivalent of 200 nicotine dose administrations daily.[1] It is the repeated exposure to the toxicants in cigarettes that makes them so deadly, but without nicotine on board, smokers would not feel the need to smoke so frequently.[19] The invention of flue-cured tobacco and its introduction into cigarettes helped make cigarette smoke inhalable and thus highly addictive and deadly.

2.2. *Mechanization of cigarette production and perfection of the cigarette design*

In the 1870s, cigarettes were not very popular in part because hand rolling each cigarette was time consuming and labor intensive. An efficient hand roller, usually a low-paid immigrant, could roll up to 2,000 cigarettes per day.[5] However, the high cost of cigarette making changed in 1884, when James Buchanan Duke took a chance on inventor John Bonsack's cigarette-making machine that had the potential to produce cigarettes 50 times faster than a hand roller[5] (see Figure 3).

With automation, Duke was able to lower prices below those of competitors and build market share to such a point that he would absorb his top tobacco company competitors. In 1890, Duke established the American Tobacco Company (ATC).[5,6] ATC expanded its possession of nearly all aspects of tobacco product production. Producers of plug chewing tobacco (i.e., leaves were pressed into a brick-like mass for oral use) and smoking tobacco were acquired through stock or cash purchases and the ATC monopoly was born.[5,6]

Cigarette companies have developed sophisticated research programs to improve manufacturing efficiency.[3,8,20] Today, most modern manufactured cigarettes are filtered, include additives that facilitate smoke inhalation, and contain enough nicotine in the tobacco blend to induce and

Figure 3: Images of cigarette making — Hand rolling, Bonsack machine, modern equipment.

sustain nicotine dependence in users.[2] While publicly downplaying the role of nicotine in the cigarette, inside the companies, the important role of nicotine in cigarette design has always been front and center.[21] A previously secret R.J. Reynolds internal business report by Dr. Claude Teague, a senior scientist, gives a candid account of the business of cigarette manufacturing: *In a sense, the tobacco industry may be thought of as being a specialized, highly ritualized and stylized segment of the pharmaceutical industry. Tobacco products, uniquely, contain and deliver nicotine, a potent drug with a variety of physiological effects.*[22] Nicotine within the cigarette rod is highly controlled. Nicotine levels in tobacco vary among different tobacco species, within species from plant to plant, and leaf location of individual plants.[3,15] The finished cigarette has precisely the amount of nicotine that the manufacturer desires.[23] Much research has focused on tobacco blending, the use of additives, and product engineering. Hundreds of additives are used in the making of cigarettes. Additives are not natural to tobacco. They include substances, mixtures, and materials that are *added to* make the finished product.

Cigarette additives include filters, adhesives, inks, paper, ash modifiers to control the burning of the cigarette, humectants to prevent the tobacco from drying out, pH modifiers to alter nicotine absorption into the body and affect the chemosensory properties of the smoke, and flavorings.[2,5,8,20,22] Menthol is a common flavoring additive in many cigarette brands and helps to mask harsh smoke. In the 1950s, cigarette companies began to introduce reconstituted tobacco into cigarette production[8] (see Figure 4). The reconstituted tobacco was made from pieces of tobacco leaf such as dust, stems and other byproducts that had previously been discarded as waste.[2,8] With reconstitution these waste products are finely ground and processed with liquids and rolled into a flat sheet of uniform thickness, cut into strips and added to the tobacco rod. During the reconstitution process nicotine is extracted and then reapplied to the sheet along with other additives giving the manufacturer precise control over the amount of nicotine in the overall blend.[2,5,24] Continued advancements in the mechanization of cigarette making have taken place during the 20th century. The original Bonsack cigarette-making machine could produce about 120,000 cigarettes per day. By comparison, today's

Figure 4:   Reconstituted tobacco images.

cigarette-making equipment can produce more than 20,000 cigarettes per minute — 100 times more than the original Bonsack machine.[5] This is the reason why cigarettes are so cheap to produce and so profitable to make. When investor Warren Buffet was asked why he liked the cigarette business, he allegedly was quoted as saying, *It costs a penny to make. Sell it for a dollar. It's addictive.*[25]

2.3. *Break-up of the American Tobacco Company monopoly*

By the beginning of the 20th century, the ATC controlled four-fifths of all tobacco markets in the United States.[5,6] In 1908, the near monopoly of the tobacco market caught the attention of government regulators, when the United States Department of Justice filed suit against the ATC for violations of the Sherman Anti-Trust Act. In October of 1911, the company was dissolved and broken into four competing companies, including American Tobacco Company, R.J. Reynolds Tobacco Company, Liggett & Myers Tobacco Company, and P. Lorillard Company[5,6] (see Figure 5).

These four companies would come to dominate the cigarette business over the next 50 years. The genesis of each of the companies along with two other smaller companies that emerged as major cigarette manufacturers in the United States is briefly described below.

2.3.1. *American Tobacco Company*

The origins of the ATC predate the Civil War.[26] Like many tobacco companies during this period, the ATC focused on the manufacturing of cigars and chewing tobacco.[6,26] However, as cigarettes began to gain prominence after the Civil War, thanks to the popularity of Bright flue-cured tobacco, James Buchanan Duke quickly moved in to automate the cigarette business, as described above. Lucky Strike, which became the American Tobacco Company's best-selling cigarette, was originally a chewing tobacco manufactured and sold by the R.A. Patterson company.[6,26] In the early 1900s, after R.A. Patterson was absorbed by the ATC, the brand evolved into a cigarette. Lucky Strike adopted the "American blend" in 1916. In 1917, the brand introduced the slogan "It's Toasted" to tout the

Figure 5:   Break-up of ATC in 1911 — Newspaper headline.

mildness of the smoke. By 1931, Lucky Strike with its unique "humidor package" was the No. 1 selling brand in America. In 1939, American Tobacco launched a new cigarette innovation, the first 85-mm cigarette brand, Pall Mall, an unfiltered cigarette which promised mildness due to the cigarette's extra length. Up to that time unfiltered cigarettes were 70 mm in length.[6] The Pall Mall brand became popular in the 1940s and combined with Lucky Strike made the ATC the #1 cigarette manufacturer in the United States by the early 1950s.[27]

2.3.2. *R.J. Reynolds Tobacco Company (RJR)*

The R.J. Reynolds Tobacco Company (RJR) was founded in 1875 by Richard Joshua Reynolds who started a chewing-tobacco manufacturing operation in Winston, N.C.[28] RJR was absorbed into the ATC in 1904.[6] Following the break-up of ATC, RJR introduced its Camel cigarette brand

Figure 6: 1913 Camel cigarettes.

in 1913[5,6] (see Figure 6). Camel contained "the American blend" of tobacco, Bright flue-cured tobacco combined with burley tobacco and oriental (also referred to as Turkish) tobacco.[2] RJR also was the first company to introduce the 20-cigarette pack box. Supported by an aggressive advertising campaign, Camel cigarettes became the first nationally popular cigarette brand in the United States.[27,29]

2.3.3. *Liggett & Myers Tobacco Company (L&M)*

In the 1880s Liggett & Myers (L&M) was the world's largest manufacturer of plug chewing tobacco. Not until the 1890s did the company begin producing cigarettes.[6] From 1899 to 1911, L&M was part of the American Tobacco Company, but reemerged after the break-up of the ATC monopoly in 1911 as Liggett & Myers Tobacco Company, headquartered in Durham, N.C. In 1916, L&M reintroduced its Chesterfield cigarette brand, using the "American blend" and sold it in a foil pack to retain freshness.[6]

2.3.4. P. Lorillard Company (Lorillard)

P. Lorillard Company (Lorillard) is among the oldest tobacco manufacturers in the United States, dating back to the 1760s, when a French immigrant, Pierre Lorillard, opened a factory in New York City.[6] The factory later moved its manufacturing operations to Jersey City, New Jersey. Lorillard made pipe tobacco, cigars, plug chewing tobacco, and snuff when it was absorbed by ATC. In 1911, when Lorillard became an independent company again, they purchased the Murad cigarette brand, but also continued to sell Beech-Nut chewing tobacco. However, under new leadership in the 1920s Lorillard prioritized the sale of its newly created Old Gold cigarette brand instead of chewing tobacco.[6] In 1956 Lorillard moved its manufacturing operations to Greensboro, N.C.

After the break-up of the ATC monopoly, until the early 1950s, Camel (made by RJR), Chesterfield (made by L&M), Lucky Strike, Pall Mall (both brands made by ATC), and Old Golds (made by Lorillard) were the best-selling cigarettes in America demonstrating the influence of advertising[27] (see Box 2). Of course, other smaller cigarette companies attempted to break into the business, but none were as successful as the four companies described above until things changed in the 1950s. Two of the smaller cigarette companies that emerged as important industry leaders after the 1950s were Philip Morris and Brown & Williamson. The genesis of these companies is briefly described below.

2.3.5. Philip Morris (PM)

In 1902, Philip Morris (PM), opened his first shop in New York City. Philip Morris was a minor cigarette industry player at that time.[5-7] When the American Tobacco cartel was dissolved in 1911, US financier George J. Whelan, formed Tobacco Products Corporation, which absorbed some of the smaller tobacco firms not already organized into the big-4 tobacco companies. Whelan purchased the US business of PM in 1919 and formed a new company to manage its assets: Philip Morris & Company Ltd., Inc., owned by the shareholders of Tobacco Products Corporation.[7] Tobacco Products Corporation was set up with the support of successful tobacco salesmen of the time, Reuben M. Ellis and Leonard B. McKitterick. However, with the stock market crash of 1929, Whelan met financial

Box 2:   Quote from 1953 Burgard study on cigarette advertising.

Excerpts from J.W. Burgard's History of Cigarette Advertising study from 1953.[27] The report was made available to Ted Bates Advertising account groups that handled the advertising for Brown & Williamson tobacco company. The report provides a detailed analysis of cigarette brand advertising and advertising expenditures by brand up through 1953. The report comments on the role of advertising in cigarette sales.

The cigarette industry dramatically demonstrates the force of advertising in the United States today. We have millions of individual purchases every day of the year and every consumer is presold, specifying his brand by name. The rise and fall of every brand of consequence has been traced in detail and their year to year success or failure shown to be the direct result of consumer advertising.

collapse and Ellis assumed control of PM. In 1930, Ellis and McKitterick purchased the stock needed to gain control of PM. The company marketed the cigarettes English Ovals, Marlboro, and Paul Jones as well as some pipe tobacco, and owned a single manufacturing facility in Richmond, Virginia.[7]

2.3.6. *Brown & Williamson (B&W)*

In the late 1870s, Brown Brothers Tobacco Manufacturing Co. was the largest tobacco company in Mocksville, N.C. It was operated by George Brown and his brother, Rufus, who were sons of a tobacco merchant. In 1893, George Brown formed a new partnership with his brother-in-law, Robert Williamson, whose father owned two tobacco factories. The new company was called Brown & Williamson.[6] In 1925, Brown & Williamson purchased J.G. Flynt Tobacco Co., including the popular Sir Walter Raleigh smoking tobacco. Brown & Williamson (B&W) was acquired by British American Tobacco (BAT) of London in 1927. That same year, construction on a new (B&W) factory in Louisville, Kentucky began. Raleigh, B&W's first national cigarette brand, was launched in 1928. Kool cigarettes, the first US menthol brand, gained nationwide distribution in 1933. Viceroy followed in 1936 as the first cork-tipped filter product. In 1952, B&W was the first company to introduce a cellulose acetate filter, which was quickly adopted by other cigarette manufacturers for their new filtered tip cigarettes.

2.4. *Invention of matches and lighters*

Without fire there is no smoke, so it is logical that the growth of cigarettes was aided by the invention and mass production of safety matches, and later by the introduction of portable lighters that made lighting up a cigarette safe and convenient. These advances happened at around the same time that cigarettes were becoming popular.[5] Match-making factories were originally established in Sweden in the 1860s, and the technology was later exported to the United States. Paper matchbooks were first introduced in America by Joshua Pusey in 1889; Pusey sold the rights to his invention to the Diamond Match company in 1896.[5] Various types of lighters were introduced around the time of World War I with improvements in design and convenience (see Figure 7). The Zippo lighter introduced in 1932 became popular because of its windproof wick and slick design.[5]

2.5. *The military, Madison Avenue, and mass marketing*

2.5.1. *Expansion of the cigarette market — The military*

While there are many factors that contributed to the growth of cigarettes, its endorsement by the United States military played a critical role. World War I made America a global power. When asked what America needed to win the war, the commander of American Forces, General John Pershing, said *Tobacco as much as bullets.*[5] Patriotic advertising, clever packaging, free-giveaways, and increased production allowed cigarettes to supplant cigars and chewing tobacco as the preferred type of tobacco consumed[5,6] (see Figure 8). Many previously anti-cigarette organizations that in the early decades of the 20th century had supported the Women's Christian Temperance Union's call to ban smoking and other forms of tobacco, withdrew their support and instead began supporting efforts to raise funds to distribute cigarettes to troops.[5,6] When the war was over, a new generation of young men had been introduced to inhalable, highly addictive cigarettes. The provision of free cigarettes to soldiers became a standard practice in subsequent wars. So popular were cigarettes during

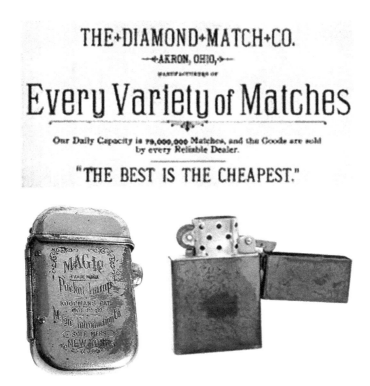

Figure 7: Images of matches and lighters for smoking.

World War II, cigarette manufacturers were required to turn over 18% of their total production to the military.[5] Despite evidence that cigarettes were a major cause of lung cancer and other serious diseases, cigarettes continued to be provided to active-duty military in K- and C-rations until 1975.[10] Cigarettes are still available without federal excise taxes in military commissaries.[10]

2.5.2. *Expansion of the cigarette market — Women*

As many young men had taken up smoking after World War I, cigarette makers turned their attention to recruiting women to further expand their profits.[30] Women were initially depicted in cigarette advertisements as non-smoking admirers of smoking men; by 1927 advertisements with women smoking began to appear in newspapers, magazines and on

Figure 8: Images of military cigarette marketing in World Wars I and II.

billboards.[5,30] One of the earliest and most famous cigarette advertising campaigns directed at women was Lucky Strike's "Reach for A Lucky Instead of A Sweet" (see Figure 9). In 1928, George Washington Hill, the president of the ATC, realized the potential market that could be found in women. ATC hired Edward Bernays, known as the father of public relations, to help him recruit women smokers. In 1929, Bernays paid women to smoke their "torches of freedom" as they walked in the Easter Sunday Parade in New York City[6] (Figure 10). This was a shock, because until that time, women were only permitted to smoke in certain places such as in the privacy of their own homes. Women were called upon to join in the march declaring "Women! Light another torch of freedom!" The targeting of women in tobacco advertising was a success as female smoking rates more than tripled from 5% to 18% between 1923 and 1935 and continued to rise throughout the next several decades with specific brands of cigarettes created just for women (e.g., Virginia Slims, Eve, Silva Thins)[5-7,30] (see Figure 11). The rapid uptake of cigarette smoking by women, which lagged men by about 15 years, is one of the reasons that the early studies implicating smoking as a cause of lung cancer found higher rates of lung cancer in men than in women.[10,13] The gap in disease risk between men

Figure 9: Chesterfield ad blow smoke my way and Lucky Strike ad encouraging woman to reach for a Lucky.

Figure 10: Picture of women smoking in 1929 NYC parade — Torches of freedom.

Figure 11:   More contemporary examples of female cigarette marketing.

and women narrowed over time as women began to smoke more[10] (see Figure 1).

2.5.3. *Expansion of the cigarette market — Children*

Children were another critical target of the cigarette advertisers who quickly recognized that smoking patterns are typically established during the teenage years.[5–7,10,30–32] Publicly, cigarette makers have always claimed that advertising was aimed only at established adult smokers, with the goal of capturing potential "brand-switchers".[32] However, internal business records of the companies have revealed that cigarette manufacturers long recognized the critical importance of directing marketing efforts to attract underage smokers. A 1984 internal marketing report tracing the rise and fall of popular youth cigarette brands from the 1930s onward observed that, *Younger adult smokers are the only source of replacement smokers; that less than one-third of smokers started smoking regularly after age 18, and only 5% started after age 24.*[33] The report goes on to explain that future cigarette sales will largely be determined by a company's ability to capture a share of the young adult market.[33] In other internal documents the terms "young adult, YA" "young adult smoker, YAS" and "first usual brand young adult smokers, FUBYAS" were code for 18 and younger.[32]

Marketing documents from as early as the 1920s reveal efforts by cigarette companies to deploy sales personnel to recruit teenage smokers through trade building[34–36] (i.e., sampling) (see Figure 12). At the beginning of the school year, cigarette promotions were strategically located in stores near high schools and prep schools and student leaders were recruited to help promote cigarette brands. Cigarette companies also were notorious for sponsoring special promotional activities to attract younger smokers during spring break, in places like Fort Lauderdale and Daytona Beach and co-sponsoring sporting events and concerts.[32] The internal business records of the cigarette companies revealed that cigarette companies researched and implemented marketing strategies to attract young smokers. Cigarette brands themselves were engineered in ways to attract the attention of beginning smokers (i.e., extra length for mildness, the use of flavors, the use of filters, low impact blends so as not to overwhelm the

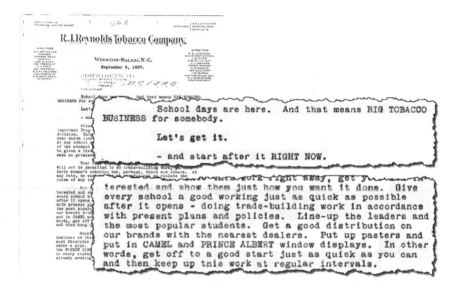

Figure 12: RJR trade building memos aimed at high schools and prep schools 1926–1927.

novice smoker, etc.), packaging (i.e., size, color and design), and advertising (i.e., media placements and themes and imagery) and were developed specifically to appeal to beginning smokers.[32] In the 1970s, the manufacturer of Newport cigarettes, a brand that was growing in popularity among teenagers observed that, *the base of our business is the high school student.*[37]

2.5.4. *Mass marketing dominance*

From the very beginning, cigarette makers have uniquely recognized the importance of advertising and mass media[5,30] In the 1920s, cigarette companies were among the first to sponsor radio shows linking their brands with popular celebrities of the era. For example, comedian Jack Benny hosted the Lucky Strike Radio Hour reaching millions of listeners each week.[5] As movies became a popular form of entertainment, cigarette makers worked with Hollywood producers to create tie-ins, paying actors and studios for brand endorsements.[5,30,38] Actors, singers, and athletes were featured in newspaper, magazine and billboard advertising helping to

Figure 13:   Movie stars featured in cigarette ads 1940–1950.

normalize smoking as an acceptable lifestyle choice. In the 1930s, until the 1960s, smoking was literally a rite of passage for most boys and girls growing up in America.

As television viewing became commonplace in the 1950s, cigarette makers were also early and frequent sponsors of TV shows, sponsoring some 80 TV shows ranging from sitcoms (i.e., "I Love Lucy" — PM; Dick Van Dyke Show — Lorillard; Beverly Hillbillies — RJR), to variety shows (i.e., "Lucky Strike Hit Parade," — ATC; Jackie Gleason — PM), to sporting events (i.e., Wide World of Sports, the 1960 Olympics — Lorillard; NFL football — PM), to dramas (i.e., Combat and Twilight Zone — ATC; Perry Mason — PM)[31,39] (see Figure 14). Cigarettes were advertised on network and local television, on radio, in magazines and newspapers, in outdoor media, and by many types of point-of-sale advertising. So ubiquitous was cigarette advertising that a 1967 Federal Trade Commission Report warned that *Cigarette advertising reaches virtually all Americans who can either read or understand the spoken word...so pervasive is cigarette advertising that it is virtually impossible for Americans of any age to avoid cigarette advertising.*[31]

Figure 14:   Images of smoking TV sponsorships.

Concern about cigarette advertising impacting children led Congress to eventually ban it on television and radio.[30] The ban went into effect January 2, 1971. However, cigarette companies simply shifted their marketing dollars to newspapers, magazines, sports sponsorship (e.g., NASCAR — RJR, Virginia Slims Tennis — PM), concerts (i.e., Kool Jazz Festival — B&W), brand placement in movies (e.g., Superman — PM), and billboards[30,40] (see Figure 15). In 1980, about half of all billboards in the United States were cigarette advertisements. A 1981 FTC report observed that cigarette companies spent more to advertise cigarettes in a single day than public health authorities spent combined in an entire year

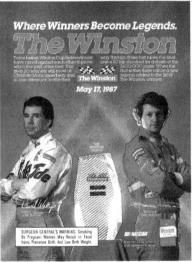

Figure 15: Images of post 1971 marketing of cigarettes. Clockwise from top left: PM Europe's Product Placement of Marlboro in the movie Superman II; B&W's sponsorship of the Kool Jazz Festival; RJR's sponsorship of NASCAR Winston Cup auto racing; PM's sponsorship of woman's professional tennis.

Figure 16: Images of direct consumer marketing — Camel cash and Marlboro miles. Top row, RJR's Camel cash campaign with catalog to redeem Camel cash coupons; Bottom row, PM's Marlboro miles campaign where smokers received miles to redeem for gifts and prizes displayed in various catalog and marketing promotions.

to educate the public about the dangers of smoking.[40] Efforts to reduce the impact of cigarette advertising have resulted in incremental restrictions on different forms of marketing over the years. For example, when advertising restrictions were extended in the 1990s to limit targeting of children, cigarette companies had already started to shift their marketing into direct consumer advertising, with micro-targeting often using price discounts and incentives to promote their cigarettes brands[30] (see Figure 16). Also, as cigarette smoking has increasingly become a behavior seen more among the poor, cigarette companies have used sophisticated price discounting strategies to induce and retain smokers who were more price sensitive. An analysis of cigarette advertising expenditures between 1940 and 2004 found that cigarette companies collectively spent about $250 billion to advertise their brands, an amount that exceeds any other consumer product sold in America.[30]

2.6. *The double-edged sword of cigarette taxes*

Increasing cigarette taxes is an effective way to reduce cigarette consumption, especially among those who are not already addicted so they are discouraged from starting.[41] Cigarette taxes also disproportionately impact those who can least afford to smoke, which is why these taxes are often referred to as regressive. Public health groups have advocated for higher cigarettes taxes to reduce smoking because it works.[41,42] A 10% increase in the purchase price of cigarettes typically reduces cigarette sales by about 4% overall. However, taxing cigarettes also has a more ominous consequence which is often not discussed, which is that governments become dependent on tax revenues, which makes them less inclined to discourage smoking.[5,43]

Tobacco taxes are an easy source of revenue for governments (see Box 3). Tobacco taxes date back to 1619 when King James I of England first levied taxes on tobacco.[4] The Revolutionary War was fought in part over tobacco taxes (i.e., taxation without representation). After the Civil War, tobacco taxes accounted for about one-third of the US government's income.[5] Cigarettes are an especially easy commodity to tax since there are only a handful of manufacturers, and the product is sold in standardized packs. Taxing of cigarettes is not unique to the United States. In Germany, the Nazis used cigarette taxes to help finance their war efforts.[5] The United States government has also relied on taxing cigarettes to finance the expenses of wars, beginning initially with the Korean War and in subsequent military conflicts. Even in peacetime, politicians have relied on tobacco tax revenues (mainly from cigarettes) to fund all kinds of special programs, even those like subsidies to farmers, price supports and agricultural assistance that only served to keep cigarette prices low and consumption growing. In parts of Africa (e.g., Malawi) and rural China, government officials have become so dependent on tobacco tax revenues that there is little incentive for them to support programs and policies that would discourage people from using tobacco.[44] Even in high income countries, tobacco taxation remains a double-edged sword preventing enactment of truly effective tobacco control policies for fear that tax revenues might decline.[5] Differential taxation of tobacco products based on harm has been suggested to shift consumers away from cigarettes to lower

Box 3:   Cigarette tax revenues collected annually in the US.

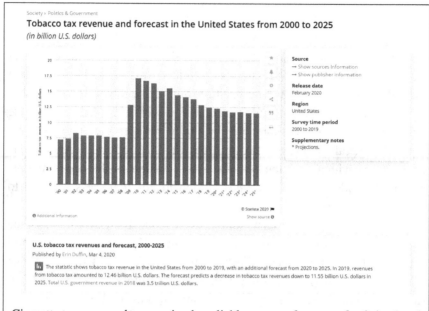

Society › Politics & Government

Tobacco tax revenue and forecast in the United States from 2000 to 2025
(in billion U.S. dollars)

Source
→ Show sources information
→ Show publisher information

Release date
February 2020

Region
United States

Survey time period
2000 to 2019

Supplementary notes
* Projections.

© Statista 2020

U.S. tobacco tax revenues and forecast, 2000-2025
Published by Erin Duffin, Mar 4, 2020

The statistic shows tobacco tax revenue in the United States from 2000 to 2019, with an additional forecast from 2020 to 2025. In 2019, revenues from tobacco tax amounted to 12.46 billion U.S. dollars. The forecast predicts a decrease in tobacco tax revenues down to 11.55 billion U.S. dollars in 2025. Total U.S. government revenue in 2018 was 3.5 trillion U.S. dollars.

Cigarette tax revenue has remained a reliable source of revenue for federal and state level governments. The applied taxes from cigarette sales alone for 2018 yielded $17.4 billion in revenue. The average of the revenue generated from 2009–2018 yielded $16.8 billion per year during that time period.

Source:https://chronicdata.cdc.gov/Policy/Table-of-Gross-Cigarette-Tax-Revenue-Per-State-Orz/rkpp-igza/data

risk non-combustible alternative nicotine products.[45] Such a tax scheme would allow governments to continue to collect tax revenues, while at the same time incentivizing consumers to switch away from the most danger-ous forms of tobacco, cigarettes, to lower risk alternatives such as oral snus and nicotine vaping products (see Chapter 6). However, until politi-cians accept the fact that the costs of smoking outweigh the benefits gained from collecting cigarette tax revenues, government sponsored efforts to markedly reduce smoking will likely continue to be limited.[5] This harsh reality helps to explain why nearly 70 years after unequivocal evidence linking smoking to lung cancer and other serious illnesses has been documented, cigarettes remain the dominant tobacco product sold in America and around the world.[10,12,46]

2.7. *Discovery of the health risks of cigarette smoking — When did they know?*

Cigarette manufacturers have only recently acknowledged the medical and scientific consensus that smoking causes serious diseases such as lung cancer, respiratory disease and heart disease.[10,46] For most of the past 100 years, cigarette manufacturers told the public that their products were not injurious to health.[5–7,10,47] Before the 1950s, neither the public nor most physicians appreciated the significant health threat from smoking. Cigarette advertising in the 1930s and 1940s often included health claims, such as "They don't get your wind" (Camel, 1935), "gentle on my throat" (Lucky Strike, 1937), "play safe with your throat" (Philip Morris, 1941), and "Fresh as mountain air" (Old Gold, 1946).[46] Brown and Williamson used baseball legend Babe Ruth to pitch Raleigh cigarettes, with the claim that "Medical science offers proof positive…No other leading cigarette is safer to smoke!" (1946).[5] Ironically, Babe Ruth later died of throat cancer.

Except for a brief period around the Great Depression, per capita cigarette consumption increased steadily from 1900 until 1953, by which time 47% of American adults were smoking cigarettes (58% of males and 36% of females), including half of all physicians.[46] The rapid rise in lung cancer deaths from a few hundred cases per year to several thousand per year by the early 1930s stimulated scientific theories about the possible causes for its increased occurrence, but cigarette smoking was only one of many possible causes implicated. Between 1920 and 1940, a chemist named Angel Honorio Roffo published several scientific papers demonstrating that cancers could be experimentally induced by exposing animals to tar from burned tobacco[5] (see Figure 17). Roffo and his colleagues further demonstrated that cancer could be induced by using nicotine-free tobacco, meaning that tar, with or without nicotine, was carcinogenic.[5,48] Research linking smoking to the rise in lung cancer deaths began to mount during the 1950s, with several landmark publications in leading medical journals, as described in the next chapter. By 1957, the scientific evidence from multiple sources, including biological studies, chemistry, pathology, and human epidemiology had converged to implicate cigarette smoking as a causative factor for lung cancer, leading to the first official statement from the US Public Health Service.[46,47] By 1960, Joseph Garland, editor of the

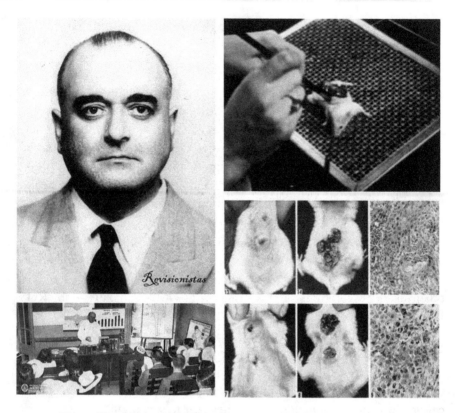

Figure 17:   Mouse skin painting and picture of Angel Honorio Roffo.

New England Journal of Medicine wrote, *No responsible observer can deny this association, and the evidence is now sufficiently strong to suggest a causative role.*[49]

It is now clear from a review of previously secret internal tobacco company records that cigarette companies knew and for the most part accepted the evidence that cigarette smoking was a cause of cancer by the late 1950s.[5–8,10,46,47] The documents also reveal that the cigarette companies helped manufacture what became known as the smoking controversy, by funding a public relations campaign that was intended to obfuscate and prolong the debate about smoking and health.[5,6,10,46,47]

In their public statements, cigarette companies held to the position that cigarettes had not been proven to be injurious to health. For example,

CIGARETTE CONCERN SCOUTS CANCER LINK

American Tobàcco Head Says There Is No Proof Smoking Causes Disease in Lungs

---

'LOOSE TALK' IS ASSAILED

Hahn Notes That Experts Differ on Causes of Increases in Respiratory Ailments

Figure 18: November 1953 *New York Times* headline — Loose talk (ATC).

a November 1953 press release issued by the ATC, stated, "…no one has yet proved that lung cancer in any human being is directly traceable to tobacco or its products in any form"[47] (see Figure 18). In 1954, Philip Morris Vice President George Weissman announced that if the company had any thought or knowledge that they (PM) were selling a product harmful to consumers, that they would stop business immediately.[47,50] However, senior scientists and executives at cigarette companies knew about the potential cancer risk of smoking as early as the 1940s, and evidence now shows that most had concluded that smoking caused cancer by the late 1950s.[6,46–48]

A 1939 memorandum from the ATC Research Director Hiram Hanmer noted, *We have been following Roffo's work for some time, and I feel that it is rather unfortunate that a statement such as his [implicating smoking in cancer] is widely disseminated.*[51] A few years later, H.B. Parmele, a scientist working for the Lorillard Tobacco Company, wrote a report to the company's manufacturing committee observing that *Certain scientists and medical authorities have claimed for many years that the use of tobacco contributes to cancer development in susceptible people. Just enough evidence has been presented to justify the possibility of such a presumption... benzopyrene is presumed to be a combustion product of burning tobacco and, by animal experiments, it has been shown to possess definite carcinogenic properties.*[52]

In 1953, a chemist at RJR, Claude Teague, produced a literature survey on smoking and cancer referencing 78 papers, which offered the following conclusion, *"...studies of clinical data tend to confirm the relationship between heavy and prolonged tobacco smoking and incidence of cancer of the lung"*.[53] Three scientists from the British ATC reported in 1958 on the results of a visit to the United States and Canada, investigating the extent to which cigarette industry and non-industry scientists accepted the premise that cigarette smoke was a cause of lung cancer. Multiple meetings were held over 3 weeks with more than 40 scientists. The internal report concluded that, *With one exception [HSN Green, a pathologist at Yale University] the individuals with whom we met believed that smoking causes lung cancer, if by 'causation' we mean any chain of events which leads finally to lung cancer and which involves smoking as an indispensable link.*[54]

In 1961, the Arthur D. Little Company provided a confidential report to Liggett & Myers Tobacco Company which stated that there are *biologically active materials present in cigarette tobacco. These are: a) cancer causing; b) cancer promoting; and c) poisonous.*[55] A 1961 presentation to the R&D committee at Philip Morris acknowledged that there was evidence that smoking may be a causative factor in lung cancer and included a partial list of carcinogens identified in cigarette smoke.[56] A 1962 report by RJR scientist Dr. Alan Rodgman characterized the amount of evidence accumulated to indict cigarette smoking as a health risk as "overwhelming" while the evidence challenging such an indictment was "scant".[57]

Unfortunately, the cigarette companies rejected the opportunity to publicly acknowledge what they knew to be true. Instead they diverted their extensive resources into creating and promoting filtered cigarettes to allay consumer health concerns[5–7,10,13,30,31,40] (see Figure 19). The

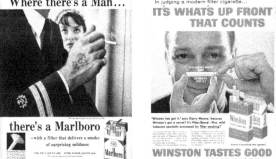

Figure 19:   Collage of filter tip cigarette marketing in 1950s/1960s.

emergence of filtered cigarettes was a direct response to the publicity linking smoking and cancer, and consumers reacted by shifting to filter-tipped cigarettes. In 1952, filtered cigarettes accounted for less than 2% of sales; by 1957 this had grown to 40% and would surpass 60% by

1966.[5,46] The switch to filter-tipped cigarettes demonstrated that cigarette smokers were willing to change products in pursuit of reduced health risks. Consumers switched to filtered cigarettes largely based on manufacturers' explicit and implied marketing claims that using filter cigarettes was associated with lower risk compared to using unfiltered cigarettes.[5-7,31,40,58] Epidemiologic studies comparing the cancer risks of those smoking filtered and unfiltered cigarettes even suggested there might be a benefit from switching to a filtered cigarette.[59,60] However, these studies failed to consider that filtered tipped cigarettes burned less tobacco compared to unfiltered cigarettes; the filter itself made no difference.[61-63] In fact, in their own internal business records, the cigarette companies acknowledged that the advertised benefits of filters were more illusory than real.[64]

The move to filtered and later lower tar cigarettes helped revive cigarette sales and rewarded the companies that had managed to successfully switch their marketing focus to filtered and low tar brands (i.e., RJR, PM, Lorillard, and B&W). However, neither the filter nor the promised delivery of low tar offered any real health benefit.[58,62-64] Filtered cigarettes achieved lower tar delivery by reducing the amount of tobacco burned, but because addicted smokers smoke for nicotine, most who switched from unfiltered to filtered brands found themselves compensating by smoking more frequently or subtly changing how they puff on a cigarette to get their needed nicotine delivery.[58,63-65] Low tar brands, which became popular in the 1970s and 1980s, mostly used tiny invisible filter vents in the filter tip to reduce the machine measured tar levels which smokers relied upon for selecting their cigarettes but allowed smokers to puff more intensely so there was no real reduction in exposure to the harmful chemicals.[63]

American Tobacco and Liggett & Myers, which had been market share leaders in the first half of the 20th century, were late to introduce filtered cigarette brands in the 1950s and as a result steadily lost market share to other cigarette manufacturers to the point where they became insignificant players in the cigarette business by the end of the 20th century.[5-7,29,30,66] In the early 1990s the ATC was absorbed by Brown & Williamson, which was later bought by R.J. Reynolds Tobacco Company in 2004 and renamed Reynolds American Inc.[67] Liggett & Myers was relegated to a minor status in the industry, selling off their most profitable brands to industry leader Philip Morris.[66] In 2014, Reynolds American acquired Lorillard Tobacco Company, with the controlling share of Reynolds American shifting to British American Tobacco.[68] In 2020, British American Tobacco and Philip Morris USA dominate the United States cigarette market.

2.8. *The era of tobacco control*

The 1964 Surgeon General's report marks the beginning of the era of tobacco control[10,46] Declining smoking rates in the US correspond to increased public awareness of the dangers of smoking, changing social norms about smoking and other tobacco products, and increased governmental actions to regulate the use, sale, and advertising of tobacco.[69] In 1966 the first cautionary label appeared on cigarette packs, stating that cigarette smoking *may be hazardous to your health*.[70] The warnings were updated in 1970 and again in 1985, although their effectiveness has been the subject of much scientific debate. In 1967, anti-smoking advertisements began to air on television as part of a Federal Communications Commission Fairness Doctrine ruling requiring broadcasters to run one anti-smoking advertisement for every three cigarette ads aired.[41] Cigarette ads were banned from television and radio in 1971, and soon after, the ban was extended to include small cigars.[41]

In 1968, the National Cancer Institute launched a 10-year research initiative to develop a less hazardous cigarette.[71] The cigarette industry was invited to participate in the research effort and responded by sending scientists to participate as advisors. However, internal company documents reveal that the industry's intent in participating in the less hazardous cigarette program was more to steer the direction of the research away from any real solutions that would have reduced cigarette sales.[72] Instead, the industry acknowledged internally that the real purpose of supporting research was for public relations purposes and to keep the false idea alive that there was a controversy about whether smoking caused any human disease.[73–75] Fear of telling the truth about cigarettes due to liability and regulatory concerns prevented cigarette companies from acting on real research solutions to the cigarette problem even though individually

Figure 20:   1964 SG report — Press event and news coverage (guilty as charged).

several of the companies internally developed plans and even tested products that could have replaced their defectively engineered cigarettes.[46,76]

Of course, what was missing during this period was any real regulatory oversight of the cigarette industry and its products. Indeed, cigarette companies often told government officials that they could regulate themselves, which of course did not occur to benefit public health.[46] As evidence regarding the health consequences of secondhand smoke strengthened in the 1970s and 1980s, policies limiting where people could use cigarettes also became more common.[69] The 1988 Surgeon General's Report helped to further stigmatize cigarette smoking by labeling nicotine addictive.[1] The report was important because it was the first Surgeon General report to focus on the question of why people persist in smoking despite recognition of its harms. The main conclusion of the report was that smoking was not just a "habit" but was in fact addictive in ways like heroin, cocaine and other drugs of abuse. When company whistleblowers finally came forward in the 1990s and told the world that cigarette companies had come together "linking arms" to sponsor a nearly 50-year long mass deception campaign, attitudes about the cigarette companies shifted further in favor of public health.[5–7,46]

In the mid-1990s, a lawsuit filed against cigarette companies by various state attorneys general gained momentum to recoup public tax dollars expended on Medicaid for treating smoking caused diseases, as did other lawsuits filed on behalf of injured smokers.[77] In 1997, Bennett S. LeBow, chairman of Brooke Group Ltd., Liggett's parent firm (formerly known as the Liggett & Myers Tobacco Company), broke ranks with the other cigarette companies and admitted that cigarette companies had deceived the American public about the addictiveness and dangers of cigarettes[78] (see Figure 21). At the time, Liggett was the smallest of the cigarette companies with only 2% of the market. However, with the cigarette company conspiracy finally revealed, the jig was up, and the other companies eventually would acknowledge the health dangers of smoking.

In 1998, the attorneys general of 46 states and cigarette makers reached an historic agreement to settle the various state lawsuits under what is known as the Master Settlement Agreement (MSA).[77,79] Four other states reached individual state settlements with cigarette manufacturers prior to the MSA. The MSA required cigarette companies to pay billions

Figure 21:   Newspaper clip covering Bennett LeBow Liggett.

Box 4:   TIRC/CTR and TI who, when, why.

The Tobacco Industry Research Committee (TIRC) was founded and funded cooperatively by nine of the American cigarette and tobacco products manufacturing companies in December 1953. In 1958, the Tobacco Institute (TI) was formed to be a trade association as part of the industry's efforts in public relations and lobbying. In March 1964, the Tobacco Industry Research Committee changed its name to the Council for Tobacco Research (CTR).

An internal secret Philip Morris document from 1978 sets forth the history of the CTR: *CTR began as an organization called Tobacco Industry Research Council [sic] (TIRC). It was set up as an industry "shield" in 1954.* Referring to special projects of the CTR: *On these projects, CTR has acted as "front."*[75]

As part of the terms of the Master Settlement Agreement, the TI and CTR were disbanded.

of dollars in perpetuity to reimburse states for their Medicaid expenditures allocated to treat smoking caused diseases. The MSA also required companies to agree to marketing restrictions on cigarettes and disband their jointly funded public relations and research programs (i.e., the Tobacco Institute and Council for Tobacco Research) (see Box 4). As part of the deal, states agreed not to pursue future efforts to recoup public health expenditures for treating diseases caused by tobacco. Importantly, the MSA required the release of previously secret internal company records, revealing much of what companies had known about smoking and disease, the marketing of cigarette brands, and the engineering of cigarettes to make them hard to stop using.[5] At the same time, though, the MSA protected the major cigarette companies from competition; and since the MSA the companies have become even more profitable.[7]

The MSA included as one of its key provisions the requirement to post over 30 million pages of industry documents online.[5] These documents revealed evidence that the tobacco industry had for decades known and accepted the fact that cigarettes caused premature death, considered tobacco to be addictive, and that their programs to support scientific research on smoking and health had been a sham.[5–7,10,47,50] Shortly after the release of their internal business records, the cigarette companies quietly adjusted their decades-long position that cigarettes were not harmful or addictive. In October 2000, Philip Morris on its website stated, *an overwhelming medical and scientific consensus that cigarette smoking causes lung cancer, heart disease, emphysema and other serious disease in smokers.*[80] Around this time Philip Morris would be the first major cigarette company to break from the rest of the industry acknowledging that there needed to be US Food and Drug Administration oversight of the industry.

2.9. *Cigarettes in the 21st century*

Following the MSA, state and local governments increasingly adopted comprehensive clean indoor air laws to protect non-smokers from second-hand smoke, some resources were allocated to enforce laws preventing the sale of tobacco products to minors, most states set up dedicated telephone quit lines for smokers to call to get help to stop smoking, and some states funded robust public education campaigns intended to discourage smoking.[69]

However, less was accomplished than might have been expected. Few states put any significant proportion of MSA or tax collections into efforts to combat the smoking epidemic.[46] Even though political support for the cigarette companies has diminished, the long ingrained political power of cigarette companies due in large part to tobacco tax revenues has continued to stall action for real change. However, the evolving marketplace of lower risk nicotine products represents a new opportunity to dramatically transform the cigarette business in ways that were never imagined when the war on tobacco was raging decades ago.[10,46]

Product innovations and the internet have allowed for a growing spectrum of lower risk nicotine delivery products to reach consumers, threatening to replace cigarettes as the dominant form of nicotine delivery consumed in much the same way that cigarettes had replaced cigars, pipe and chewing tobacco nearly 100 years ago (see Figure 22). In the early part of the 21st century, nicotine vaping products (also referred to as electronic cigarettes, or e-cigarettes, (see Chapter 6) began to be sold over the internet by Chinese manufacturers, although their popularity in the United States did not to start to grow significantly until after 2010.[46] In 2018,

Figure 22: The left hand column includes pictures of oral tobacco products, those in the middle column are e-cigarettes, and the right hand column shows heated tobacco products.

nicotine vaping products accounted for ~4% of the nicotine product market in the United States with millions of customers, mostly current cigarette smokers, using them to quit or reduce their cigarette smoking.[12] The growing demand for alternative nicotine products has spurred competition, which in turn stimulated product innovation and kept prices low. Dedicated retail outlets known as vape shops began selling vaping products around the globe.

The shift away from deadly cigarettes was something cigarette manufacturers long feared but acknowledged internally. A 1982 memo from R.J. Reynolds discussing the dynamics of the cigarette market at the time acknowledged that, *we cannot ever be comfortable selling a product which most of our customers would stop using if they could. That is to say, if the exit gate from our market should suddenly open, we could be out of business almost overnight.*[81] The memo goes on to say that Reynolds planned to remain in the conventional cigarette business as long as possible, but recognized that at some future time, they would need to be prepared to shift away from conventional cigarettes to other products which met the same needs cigarettes met, *but without the associated negatives.*[81] In the first decade of the 21st century, both R.J. Reynolds and Altria (i.e., Philip Morris) acquired smokeless tobacco manufacturers, perhaps to hedge their bets on how the cigarette business might be transformed in the future.[46] Since 2010, cigarette companies have also started to market their own nicotine vaping and heat tobacco products to keep pace with the evolving marketplace of lower risk nicotine products available to consumers.

In 2009, Congress finally passed the Family Smoking Prevention and Tobacco Control Act, which gave the Food and Drug Administration (FDA) regulatory authority over cigarettes and smokeless tobacco[82] (see Box 5, Chapter 13). The Tobacco Control Act was written in part to rein in the cigarette industry's decades of fraud, conspiracy and misrepresentation, which at the time was fully understandable. However, the statute, a

Box 5:   FDA regulation of tobacco products.

Under the Family Smoking Prevention and Tobacco Control Act, the FDA was given authority to regulate tobacco products. This authority includes establishing standards, reviewing products before their introduction to the market and restricting tobacco product marketing and advertising. The act provided for the FDA to regulate levels of nicotine in tobacco products but prohibited FDA authority to require the removal of nicotine from tobacco products.

long time in the making, was in many ways outdated on the day it was signed into law, particularly because new nicotine delivery products did not have much presence in the marketplace and potential benefits and/or risks were unknown.[46] The Tobacco Control Act was passed with the active participation and support of Altria, the parent company of Philip Morris USA, which at the time controlled half the cigarette market. Altria's support for the Tobacco Control Act likely stemmed from the fact that the law provided protection for cigarettes that were on the market as of 2007, while also making it extremely difficult to introduce new lower risk alternative nicotine products that had the potential to accelerate a decline in cigarette use, the leading preventable cause of death.[46] Public health groups' support for the Tobacco Control Act mainly focused on limiting ways cigarettes and other tobacco products were marketed, especially with regards to youth and young adults.

In July 2017, the FDA announced an innovative new framework for regulating tobacco products.[83] The science-based strategy recognized that there is a continuum of risk across different nicotine delivery products and suggested that public health could be markedly improved by reducing the addictiveness of combustible tobacco products while at the same time for those smokers who want or need nicotine increasing access to less harmful tobacco and nicotine products (i.e., both consumer and medicinal nicotine products). However, politics and skepticism about the ability to transform the cigarette business have slowed the evolution of the marketplace, keeping cigarettes as the dominant product, despite the well-documented health risks.[46]

Today, public health groups are in a unique position to align market forces with public health goals to reduce the premature deaths caused by cigarettes. However, this requires embracing risk-proportionate regulation and taxation policies along with providing consumers with accurate public messaging on product relative risks.[46] However, public health groups have not fully embraced risk-proportionate regulation in part because of concerns about youth uptake of nicotine as well as the uncertainty of long-term benefits and/or risks of presumed lower risk nicotine delivery products. Thus, while disruptive technology represents a huge potential threat to the profitability of cigarettes, it is unclear what may happen in the coming decades. However, what we do know is the status quo is not acceptable with nearly one billion daily smokers across the globe, an annual death toll of about eight million smoking-related deaths per year, and a projected cumulative death toll of nearly one billion by the end of the 21st century (10× higher than the number of deaths due to smoking in the 20th century). Chapter 14 discusses possible solutions to the projected death toll from smoking in the 21st century.

References

1. U.S. Department of Health and Human Services. *The Health Consequences of Smoking: Nicotine Addiction. A Report of the Surgeon General.* (Washington, DC: U.S. Department of Health and Human Services, Centers for Disease Control, Center for Health Promotion and Education, Office on Smoking and Health, 1988).
2. Slade J. Nicotine Delivery Devices. In: Slade J, Orleans CT, eds. *Nicotine Addiction: Principles and Management.* (New York: Oxford University Press, 1993, pp. 3–23).
3. Davis DL, Nielsen MT. *Tobacco: Production, Chemistry and Technology.* (Oxford: Blackwell Science Ltd., 1999).
4. Norman LS. (1932). *Tobacco's Early History.* Retrieved from Truth Tobacco Industry Documents: https://www.industrydocuments.ucsf.edu/docs/pgwm0178
5. Proctor RN. *Golden Holocaust: Origins of the Cigarette Catastrophe and the Case for Abolition.* (Berkeley: University of California Press, 2011).
6. Brandt A. *The Cigarette Century: The Rise, Fall, and Deadly Persistence of the Product That Defined America.* (New York: Basic Books, 2007).
7. Kluger R. *Ashes to Ashes. American's hundred-Year Cigarette War, the Public Health, and the Unabashed Triumph of Philip Morris.* (New York: Alfred A. Knopf, Inc., 1996).
8. Unknown. (1986, December 31). *RJR Research and Development Activities Fact Team Memorandum: Volume 1.* Retrieved from Truth Tobacco Industry Documents: https://www.industrydocuments.ucsf.edu/docs/qylb0024
9. U.S. Department of Health, Education, and Welfare. *Smoking and Health. Report of the Advisory Committee to the Surgeon General of the Public Health Service.* (Washington, DC: U.S. Department of Health, Education, and Welfare. Public Health Service, 1964).
10. U.S. Department of Health and Human Services. *The Health Consequences of Smoking — 50 Years of Progress. A Report of the Surgeon General.* (Atlanta, GA: U.S. Dept. of Health and Human Services, Centers for Disease Control and Prevention, National Center for Chronic Disease Prevention and Health Promotion, Office on Smoking and Health, 2014).

11. Greig C. (1984, June 28). *Structured Creativity Conference: Delegate Presentations.* Retrieved from Truth Tobacco Industry Documents: https://www.industrydocuments.ucsf.edu/docs/fybf0207

12. Smokefree World Foundation. (2018, October 19). *Global Trends in Nicotine.* Retrieved from www.smokefreeworld.org: https://www.smokefreeworld.org/advancing-industry-transformation/global-trends-nicotine

13. National Cancer Institute. *Changes in Cigarette-Related Disease Risks and Their Implication for Prevention. Tobacco Control Monograph No. 8.* (Bethesda, MD: U.S. Department of Health and Human Services, National Institutes of Health, National Cancer Institute 1996).

14. Tilley NM. *The Bright Tobacco Industry, 1860-1929.* (Chapel Hill, NC: University of North Carolina Press, 1948).

15. Tso TC. *Physiology and Biochemistry of Tobacco Plants.* (Strougsburg, PA: Dowden, Hutchinson and Ross, 1972).

16. Fisher B. Curing the TSNA problem. *Tobacco Reporter* 2000;August 2000:51–56.

17. Ashley DL, O'Connor RJ, Bernert JT, *et al.* Effect of differing levels of tobacco-specific nitrosamines in cigarette smoke on the levels of biomarkers in smokers. *Cancer Epidemiol Biomarkers Prev* 2010;19:1389–1398.

18. Dunn WL Jr. (1972). *Motives and Incentives in Cigarette Smoking.* Retrieved from Truth Tobacco Industry Documents: https://www.industrydocuments.ucsf.edu/docs/zhfg0117

19. U.S. Department of Health and Human Services. *How Tobacco Smoke Causes Disease: The Biology and Behavioral Basis for Smoking-Attributable Disease: A Report of the Surgeon General.* (Atlanta, GA: U.S. Department of Health and Human Services, Centers for Disease Control and Prevention, National Center for Chronic Disease Prevention and Health Promotion, Office on Smoking and Health, 2010).

20. American Tobacco Company. (1935). *Improving the Taste and Character of Cigarette Tobacco With a View to Removing Irritants and Producing a Light Smoke: A Chapter in Laboratory Research.* Retrieved from Truth Tobacco Industry Documents: https://www.industrydocuments.ucsf.edu/docs/sxwv0024

21. Levy DL, Cummings KM, Heckman BW, *et al.* The public health gains had cigarette companies chosen to sell very low nicotine cigarettes. *Nicotine Tob Res* 2020;23:438–446.

22. Teague CE Jr. (1972, April 14). *Research Planning Memorandum on the Future of the Tobacco Business and the Crucial Role of Nicotine Therein.*

Retrieved from Truth Tobacco Industry Documents: https://www.industry-documents.ucsf.edu/docs/stdb0184

23. Griffith RB. (1963, September 18). *Letter from RB Griffith to John Kirwan regarding Neil Gilliam's presentation at Chelwood.* Retrieved from Truth Tobacco Industry Documents: https://www.industrydocuments.ucsf.edu/docs/jglw0200

24. Rodgman AJ. (1959, November 2). *The Optimum Composition of Tobacco and Its Smoke.* Retrieved from Truth Tobacco Industry Documents: https://www.industrydocuments.ucsf.edu/docs/fxkp0034

25. Lubitz L. (2019, June 25). *Investopedia.* Retrieved from *New York Times*: https://www.investopedia.com/articles/stocks/08/buffett-best-buys.asp#:~:text=Choosing%20Investments%20With%20Long%2DTerm,It's%20addictive

26. Porter PG. Origins of the American Tobacco Company. *Bus Hist Rev* 1969;43:59–76.

27. Burgard JW. (1953). *A Study of Cigarette Advertising.* Retrieved from Truth Tobacco Industry Documents: https://www.industrydocuments.ucsf.edu/docs/qymm0104

28. Unknown. (1999, April). *RJR History, Hallmarks of Company Heritage.* Retrieved from Truth Tobacco Industry Documents: https://www.industry-documents.ucsf.edu/docs/sznf0086

29. Tindell JE. (1966, February 13). *Cigarette Market History and Interpretation and Consumer Research: MMTP presentation.* Retrieved from Truth Tobacco Industry Documents: https://www.industrydocuments.ucsf.edu/docs/glbn0130

30. National Cancer Institute. *The Role of the Media in Promoting and Reducing Tobacco Use. Tobacco Control Monograph No. 19.* (Bethesda, MD: U.S. Department of Health and Human Services, National Institutes of Health, National Cancer Institute, 2008).

31. FTC. *Report to Congress Pursuant to the Federal Cigarette Labeling and Advertising Act* (Washington, DC: U.S. Federal Trade Commission, 1967).

32. Cummings KM, Morley C, Horan J, Steger C, Leavell NR. Marketing to America's youth: Evidence from corporate documents. *Tob Control* 2002;11:i5–i17.

33. Burrows S. (1984, February 29). Strategic Research Report. Younger Adult Smokers Strategies and Opportunities. Retrieved from Truth Tobacco Industry Documents: https://www.industrydocuments.ucsf.edu/docs/kqwv0001

34. RJR. (1926, May 17). Letter to salesman -immediate attention required. Retrieved from Truth Tobacco Industry Documents : https://www.industry-documents.ucsf.edu/docs/pyyd0083

35. RJR. (1927, September 9). Letter to salesman — school days are here. Retrieved from Truth Tobacco Industry Documents: https://www.industry-documents.ucsf.edu/docs/nyyd0083

36. RJR. (1928, June 13). Letter to salesman — regular school is over. Retrieved from Truth Tobacco Industry Documents: https://www.industrydocuments.ucsf.edu/docs/myyd0083

37. Achey TL. (1978, August 30). Product Information. Retrieved from Truth Tobacco Industry Documents : https://www.industrydocuments.ucsf.edu/docs/hfgb0048

38. Mekemson C, Glantz SA. How the tobacco industry built its relationship with Hollywood. *Tob Control* 2002;11:i81–i91.

39. Pollay RW. Exposure of US youth to cigarette television advertising in the 1960s. *Tob Control* 1994;3: 30–133.

40. FTC. *Staff Report on the Cigarette Advertising Investigation.* (Washington, DC: U.S. Federal Trade Commission, 1981).

41. Cummings KM. Programs and policies to discourage the use of tobacco products. *Oncogene* 2002;21: 7349–7364.

42. Borland R, Cummings KM. *IARC Handbooks of Cancer Prevention, Tobacco Control, Vol 12: Methods for Evaluating tobacco Control Policies.* (Lyon, FR: IARC, 2008).

43. Taylor P. *The Smoke Ring: Tobacco, Money & Multinational Politics.* (New York, NY: New American Library, 1985).

44. Cummings KM, O'Connor RJ. Tobacco Harm minimization. In: Quah KH, ed. *International Encyclopedia of Public Health* (San Diego, CA: Academic Press, 2008, pp. 322–331).

45. Chaloupka FJ, Sweanor D, Warner KE. Differential taxes for differential risks — toward reduced harm from nicotine-yielding products. *N Engl J Med*, 2015;373:594–597.

46. Cummings KM, Ballin S, Sweanor D. The past is not the future in tobacco control. *Prev Med* 2020;140:106183 https://doi.org/10.1016/j.ypmed.2020.106183

47. Cummings KM, Brown A, O'Connor RJ. The cigarette controversy. *Cancer Epidemiol Biomarkers Prev* 2007;16:1070–1076.

48. Proctor RN. Angel H Roffo: The forgotten father of experimental tobacco. *Bull World Health Organ* 2006;84:494–496.

49. Garland J. Smoking and Lung Cancer. *New Engl J Med* 1960;262:417–418.

50. Cummings KM. (2003). A promise is a promise. *Tob Control*, 2003;12:117–118.

51. Hanmer HR. (1939, May 11). *Letter.* Retrieved from Truth Tobacco Industry Documents: https://www.industrydocuments.ucsf.edu/docs/rmmp0140

52. Parmele HB. (1946, July 29). *Letter.* Retrieved from Truth Tobacco Industry Documents: https://www.industrydocuments.ucsf.edu/docs/gpnm0104

53. Teague CE Jr. (1953, February 2). *Survey of Cancer Research With Emphasis Upon Possible Carcinogens From Tobacco.* Retrieved from Truth Tobacco Industry Documents: https://www.industrydocuments.ucsf.edu/docs/lphb0086

54. Bentley HR, Felton DGI, Reid WW. (1958, May). *Report on Visit to U.S.A. and Canada — 17th April–12th May 1958.* Retrieved from Truth Tobacco Industry Documents: https://www.industrydocuments.ucsf.edu/docs/ksfd0040

55. Little AD. (1961, March 15). *L&M — a Perspective Review.* Retrieved from Truth Tobacco Industry Documents: https://www.industrydocuments.ucsf.edu/docs/ytbl0135

56. Wakeham H. (1961, November 15). *Tobacco and Health R&D Approach, Presentation to R&D Committee.* Retrieved from Truth Tobacco Industry Documents: https://www.industrydocuments.ucsf.edu/docs/sjgx0106

57. Rodgman A. (1962, September 12). *Chemical Research. The Smoking and Health Problem — a Critical and Objective Appraisal.* Retrieved from Truth Tobacco Industry Documents: https://www.industrydocuments.ucsf.edu/docs/rmpp0092

58. Pepples E. (1976, February 4). *Industry Response to Cigarette/Health Controversy.* Retrieved from Truth Tobacco Industry Documents: https://www.industrydocuments.ucsf.edu/docs/jnxd0024

59. Bross IDJ, Gibson R. Risks of lung cancer in smokers who switch to filter cigarettes. *Am J Public Health* 1967;58:1396–1402.

60. Harris JE, Thun MJ, Mondul AM, Calle EE. Cigarette tar yields in relation to mortality from lung cancer in the cancer prevention study II prospective cohort, 1982–8. *BMJ* 2004;328:72.

61. Tanner NT, Thomas NA, Ward R, *et al.* Association of cigarette type with lung cancer incidence and mortality: Secondary analysis of the national lung screening trial. *JAMA Intern Med* 2019;179:1710–1712.

62. Thun MJ, Carter BD, Feskanich D, *et al.* 50-year trends in smoking-related mortality in the United States. *N Engl J Med* 2013;368:351–364.

63. National Cancer Institute. *Risks Associated with Smoking Cigarettes with Low Machine- Measured Yields of Tar and Nicotine. Smoking and Tobacco*

Control Monograph No. 13. (Bethesda, MD: U.S. Department of Health and Human Services, National Institutes of Health, National Cancer Institute, 2001).

64. Johnston ME Jr. (1966, June). *Special Report No. 248. Market Potential of a Health Cigarette.* Retrieved from Truth Tobacco Industry Documents: https://www.industrydocuments.ucsf.edu/docs/jfvc0123

65. Wakeham H. (1964, March 24). *Trends in Tar and Nicotine Deliveries Over the Past 5 Years.* Retrieved from Truth Tobacco Industry Documents: https://www.industrydocuments.ucsf.edu/docs/pqjp0124

66. CNN. (1988, November 20). *Brooke Sells Cigarette Lines.* Retrieved from CNN Money: https://money.cnn.com/1998/11/20/deals/brooke/#:~:text=NEW%20YORK%20(CNNfn)%20%2D%20Brooke,states%20and%20five%20U.S.%20territories

67. Barkley M, Michels S. (2003, November 1). *Together Again — Merger Would Bring B&W Back Where it Started.* Retrieved from Greensboro News and Record: https://greensboro.com/together-again-merger-would-bring-b-w-back-where-it-started/article96064674-cd02-5459-9518-b5c6cf5ef233.html

68. Kell J. (2014, July 15). *Reynolds to Pay $27.4 Billion for Lorillard.* Retrieved from Fortune.com: https://fortune.com/2014/07/15/reynolds-to-acquire-lorillard

69. Cummings KM, Proctor RN. (2014). The changing public image of smoking in the United States: 1964–2014. *Cancer Epidemiol Biomarkers Prev* 2014;23:32–36.

70. Cummings KM, Gdanski J, Veatch N, Sebrié EM. Assumption of risk and the role of health warnings labels in the United States. *Nicotine Tob Res* 2020;22:975–983.

71. Parascandola M. (2005). Lessons from the history of tobacco harm reduction: the National Cancer Institute's smoking and health program and the "less hazardous cigarette". *Nicotine Tob Res* 2005;7:779–789.

72. Unknown. (1973, March 14). *Meeting of Committee of Counsel of the Tobacco Institute with regards to Dr. Gio Gori and the Tobacco Working Group.* Retrieved from Truth Tobacco Industry Documents: https://www.industrydocuments.ucsf.edu/docs/ghgn0050

73. Pepples E. (1978, April 4). *CTR Budget.* Retrieved from Truth Tobacco Industry Documents: https://www.industrydocuments.ucsf.edu/docs/hhlj0137

74. Unknown. (1975, December 10). *CTR Meeting.* Retrieved from Truth Tobacco Industry Documents: https://www.industrydocuments.ucsf.edu/docs/xgwn0115

75. Seligman RB. (1978, November 17). *Meeting in New York November 15, 1978 .* Retrieved from Truth Tobacco Industry Documents: https://www.industrydocuments.ucsf.edu/docs/yzpm0217

76. Unknown. (1967, October 24). *BAT: R&D Conference Proceedings — Montreal.* Retrieved from Truth Tobacco Industry Documents: https://www.industrydocuments.ucsf.edu/docs/ntfy0042

77. Douglas CE, Davis RM, Beasley JK. (2006). Epidemiology of the third wave of tobacco litigation in the United States, 1994–2005. *Tob Control* 2006;15:iv9–iv16.

78. Lebow BS. (1997, July 18). *Videotaped Deposition.* Retrieved from Truth Tobacco Industry Documents: https://www.industrydocuments.ucsf.edu/docs/fjvn0016

79. Keller TE, Ju TW, Ong M, Sung HY. The US national tobacco settlement: the effects of advertising and price changes on cigarette consumption. *Appl Econ* 2004;36:1623–1629.

80. Szymanczyk ME. (2000, October 11). *Philip Morris USA Website.* Retrieved from Truth Tobacco Industry Documents: https://www.industrydocuments.ucsf.edu/docs/jnxf0061

81. Teague CE Jr. (1982, December 1). *Nordine Study.* Retrieved from Truth Tobacco Industry Documents: https://www.industrydocuments.ucsf.edu/docs/jtjc0094

82. FDA. (2018, June 29). *The History of FDA's Fight for Consumer Protection and Public Health.* Retrieved from United Stated Food and Drug Administration: https://www.fda.gov/about-fda/history-fdas-fight-consumer-protection-and-public-health

83. FDA. (2017, July 27). FDA announces comprehensive regulatory plan to shift trajectory of tobacco-related disease, death. Retrieved from United States Food and Drug Administration: https://www.fda.gov/news-events/press-announcements/fda-announces-comprehensive-regulatory-plan-shift-trajectory-tobacco-related-disease-death

Chapter 2

Smoking and Cancer: The Early Years

Jonathan M. Samet*

1. Introduction

The causal linkage of tobacco smoking with lung cancer represents a paradigm-shifting point in understanding the etiology of cancer. While cancer had long ago been described in patients and groups with unique exposures, in-depth searching for etiology begins with the lung cancer epidemic of the 20th century. Even as early as the 18th century, clinical observations and case series had pointed to causal agents. For example, in 1761, the London surgeon John Hill described ulcerating cancers of the nose in snuff users. Percivall Pott's 1775 report described cancer of the scrotum in chimney sweeps, now known to be exposed to the potent carcinogens — polycyclic aromatic hydrocarbons — in chimney soot. Subsequently, other occupations were associated with cancer occurrence, as described by Hoffman in his 1915 book, *The Mortality from Cancer Throughout the World.*[1] He explored the epidemiology of cancer, concluding that there had been an increase in occurrence. He also noted an established connection of smoking to cancer of the oral cavity and lip, but other associations were not mentioned and at the time of his book, lung cancer was quite uncommon.

*Colorado School of Public Health, 13001 E 17th Pl, Aurora, CO 80045, USA.
jon.samet@cuanschutz.edu

Several decades before the smoking and lung cancer story began, radon (and later radon progeny specifically) was the first cause of lung cancer to be identified. That conclusion, offered in the early decades of the 20th century, came from the observation of unusually high rates of lung cancer in several groups of eastern European miners exposed to high levels of radon.[2] The causal inference approaches that came later in the 1950s and 1960s were lacking and the issue of confounding by smoking had not become a consideration. In the early miner groups, smoking appears to have been limited and certainly the observations antedate mass-marketed cigarettes.[2] That conclusion has been affirmed in subsequent, more formal epidemiological studies on radon and lung cancer, supported by well-worked out mechanistic research on the dosimetry of alpha particles, and confirmed by multiple authoritative reviews.[2]

The epidemic of smoking-caused cancers addressed here resulted from the tobacco industry's tragic success in marketing its main product — cigarettes — beginning early in the 20th century, which was dubbed the "cigarette century" by Harvard historian Allan Brandt (Figure 1).[3] As noted in Chapter 1, Camel was launched in 1913 as the first mass-marketed brand; the lung cancer epidemic surged by the 1930s; epidemiological studies identified smoking as a cause by the 1950s; and tobacco control was motivated by the landmark finding of the 1964 Surgeon General's report that smoking caused lung cancer (in men).[4]

This chapter has three components, first providing historical background on the evolution of the research and findings that identified smoking as a cause of lung and other cancers. Second, it addresses the advances in research methods that were driven by research on smoking. There have been powerful consequences of determining that smoking causes cancer and other diseases. Third, the chapter describes how the causal findings provided the rationale for implementing tobacco control and motivated responses of the tobacco industry, which attempted to undermine the emerging scientific evidence and to thwart efforts to control the use of tobacco. For further background, there are multiple resources that cover these topics in depth, including the 2014 50th anniversary report of the Surgeon General, *The Cigarette Century* by Allan Brandt, and *Golden Holocaust* by Robert Proctor.[3,5,6]

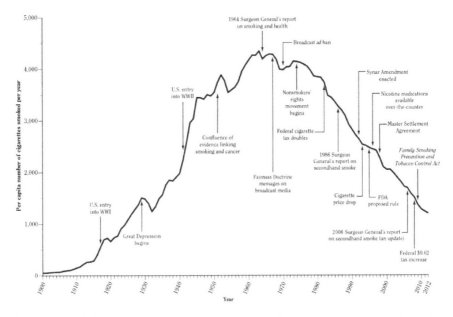

Figure 1: Adult* per capita cigarette consumption and major smoking and health events, United States, 1900–2012.

Note: *Adults ≥18 years of age as reported annually by the Census Bureau.

Sources: Adapted from Warner 1985 with permission from Massachusetts Medical Society, ©1985; US Department of Health and Human Services 1989; Creek *et al*. 1994; US Department of Agriculture 2000; US Census Bureau 2013; US Department of the Treasury 2013.

From: Chapter 2: Fifty Years of Change 1964–2014. The Health Consequences of Smoking — 50 Years of Progress: A Report of the Surgeon General. National Center for Chronic Disease Prevention and Health Promotion (US) Office on Smoking and Health. Atlanta (GA): Centers for Disease Control and Prevention (US), 2014.

2. A Brief Chronology of Research on Smoking and Cancer

2.1. The initial studies on smoking and lung cancer

The 20th century epidemic of lung cancer shifted the approach for identifying causes of cancer from clinical observations and case series to more formal epidemiological studies, buttressed by complementary laboratory research (see Chapter 3). Many of the initial reports on lung cancer related to the observations of clinicians, documenting that they were seeing rising numbers of what had been a rare cancer and describing surgical approaches for treating it. Such reports were published across the 1920s and 1930s, as the tobacco epidemic continued and the numbers of long-term smokers grew, particularly in the United States and United Kingdom (where smoking was highly prevalent). One key report was by Evarts Graham, a thoracic surgeon at Washington University St. Louis, who described the first pneumonectomy for lung cancer in 1933. Another thoracic surgeon, Alton Ochsner, along with colleagues including the pioneering cardiovascular surgeon Michael DeBakey, described a case series of lung cancer patients in 1938 at the Clinical Congress of the American College of Surgeons and commented in a 1939 paper that irritation of the lung from smoking might be a contributing cause.[7]

The more formal epidemiological studies were initiated from the 1930s. Although the terminology for various study designs was yet to be formalized, the principal designs were the case-control study (comparing smoking among people with lung cancer and comparable controls without lung cancer) or the cohort study (following smokers and non-smokers over time and tracking the occurrence of lung cancer in the two groups). By the 1930s, the first epidemiological studies, largely case-control studies, were carried out on smoking and cancer, including lung cancer without definitive findings. Convincing findings on smoking and overall risk for dying were reported by the biostatistician Raymond Pearl at Johns Hopkins in *Science* in 1938.[8] Pearl was carrying out a cohort study of families in East Baltimore and made a comparison of the survival curves for groups he termed "non-smokers", "moderate smokers", and "heavy smokers". The survival curves are striking in showing a substantial difference in life expectancy (~10 years), comparing the heavy smokers with the non-smokers, which is equivalent to that observed at present. Pearl did not explore what causes of death contributed to this significant difference in life expectancy, perhaps missing the opportunity to identify the strong association of smoking with lung cancer.

Initially, attention was given to the possibility that the lung cancer epidemic was artefactual, reflecting increased detection. That explanation was set aside and attention turned to searching for etiological factors. Early case-control studies were carried out in the 1930s–1940s, including two in Germany during the Nazi era. The evidence from these studies, all not surprisingly having methodological limitations when evaluated with contemporary standards, were not consistent in indicting smoking.[9]

2.2. *From 1950 to 1964*

The next wave of studies, all case-control in design, was launched in the late 1940s. Five were published in 1950, of which three have received the most attention: the US studies of Wynder and Graham and of Levin and colleagues, and the preliminary report of the study in London by Doll and Hill.[4,10–12] The three differed in design: The cases for Wynder and Graham came from physicians and the controls from clinics; Levin *et al.* used admission questionnaire data at Roswell Park Memorial Institute; and Doll and Hill used a hospital-based design. By Levin's account, his paper was initially rejected by the *Journal of the American Medical Association* because the editor was uncertain of its scientific value.[13] However, the paper was accepted after the submission by Wynder and Graham of their paper, replicating the findings. Months later, the initial results of the widely cited study of Doll and Hill were reported in the *British Medical Journal.* Within a few years, further case-control studies were carried out and initial, confirmatory results from cohort studies were reported as well, all showing a very strong association of smoking with lung cancer. As the odds ratio statistic had not yet been described, the magnitude of the association was not quantified.

Other facets of the smoking-lung cancer relationship also became clear during the 1950s. Analyses of the case-control and cohort study data described how risk increased with the amount and duration of smoking.[14] By the mid- to late-1950s, the decline in risk following successful cessation of smoking was also documented.[15] With consistent findings from more and more studies, consideration began regarding whether or not the association of smoking with lung cancer was causal. The discussion centered on the interpretation of the observational evidence and the inference that the observed associations reflected causality.

The evidence on smoking and lung cancer was evaluated systematically in several reports and publications across the 1950s, beginning in the early 1950s, including two commentaries by the US Surgeon General that stopped short of a definitive causal conclusion.[16,17] A particularly comprehensive and well-framed review was published in 1959 by Cornfield and colleagues in *The Journal of the National Cancer Institute* that represented a starting point in the systematic evaluation of evidence on smoking and health.[18] This comprehensive assessment found the available evidence to be highly consistent with a causal association and inconsistent with various non-causal explanations that had been proposed.

The 1964 *Report of the Advisory Committee to the US Surgeon General of the Public Health Service* represents the critical next step in the story of smoking and cancer.[4] Using methodology described below, the report's conclusion that smoking caused lung cancer (in men) ended the controversy as to whether smoking caused cancer. The finding launched tobacco control at the national level, and fueled state and local efforts as well.

2.3. *Smoking causes multiple types of cancer*

With the increasing number of epidemiological studies and deepening understanding of smoking as both a local and systemic cause of cancer, an ever-larger body of evidence linked smoking to an increasing number of cancers (Table 1).[5] The 1964 report further commented that pipe smoking appears to be causally related to cancer of the lip and that smoking appears to be associated with cancers of the esophagus and bladder, but causal conclusions could not be reached. Evidence on smoking and stomach cancer was considered incomplete.

Over the ensuing decades, the evidence on smoking and cancer evolved, such that by the 2014 Surgeon General's report, 10 cancers and other malignancies had been causally associated with smoking.[5] Several reports stand out: the 1982 report, which addressed cancer specifically, and the 2004 report, which re-examined the health consequences of active smoking.[19,20] As the flow of evidence began on secondhand smoke (SHS) and lung cancer in the early 1980s, that association was also considered by the Surgeon Generals' and other reports. The 1986 report of the Surgeon General, then Dr. Everett Koop, concluded that "Involuntary smoking is a cause of disease, including lung cancer, in healthy non-smokers."[21]

Table 1: Conclusions from Surgeon General's report on active cigarette smoking and cancer by type.

Disease	First mention and finding(s) in a Surgeon General's report (year)	Highest level conclusion(s) from subsequent Surgeon General's reports before 2004 (year)	Conclusion(s) from the 2004 Surgeon General's report	Additional or updated conclusion(s) from the 2014 Surgeon General's report
Bladder	"Available data suggest an association between cigarette smoking and urinary bladder cancer in the male but are not sufficient to support a judgment on the causal significance of this association" (1964, p. 225).	"Smoking is a cause of bladder cancer; cessation reduces risk by about 50 percent after only a few years, in comparison with continued smoking" (1990, p. 10).	"The evidence is sufficient to infer a causal relationship between smoking and … bladder cancer" (p. 26).	—
				—
Brain (adult)	—	—	"The evidence is suggestive of no causal relationship between smoking cigarettes and brain cancer in men and women" (p. 26).	—
		—		—
Breast	"Thus, active smoking does not appear to appreciably affect breast cancer risk overall. However, several issues were not entirely resolved, including whether starting to smoke at an	—	"The evidence is suggestive of no causal relationship between active smoking and breast cancer" (p. 26).	"The evidence is sufficient to identify mechanisms by which cigarette smoking may cause breast cancer."

(Continued)

Table 1: *(Continued)*

Disease	First mention and finding(s) in a Surgeon General's report (year)	Highest level conclusion(s) from subsequent Surgeon General's reports before 2004 (year)	Conclusion(s) from the 2004 Surgeon General's report	Additional or updated conclusion(s) from the 2014 Surgeon General's report
	early age increases risk, whether certain subgroups defined by genetic polymorphisms are differentially affected by smoking, and whether ETS exposure affects risk" (2001, p. 217).			"The evidence is suggestive but not sufficient to infer a causal relationship between active smoking and breast cancer" (Chapter 6).
	"The totality of the evidence does not support an association between smoking and risk for breast cancer" (2001, p. 224).[a]			
Cervical	"There are conflicting results in studies published to date on the existence of a relationship between smoking and cervical cancer; further research is necessary to define whether an association exists and, if so, whether that association is direct or indirect" (1982, p. 8).	"Smoking has been consistently associated with an increased risk for cervical cancer. The extent to which this association is independent of human papillomavirus infection is uncertain" (2001, p. 224).	"The evidence is sufficient to infer a causal relationship between smoking and cervical cancer" (p. 26).	— —

	"Smoking may be associated with an increased risk for vulvar cancer, but the extent to which the association is independent of human papillomavirus infection is uncertain" (2001, p. 224).			"The evidence is sufficient to infer a causal relationship between smoking and colorectal adenomatous polyps and colorectal cancer" (Chapter 6).
Colorectal	"Women who smoke may have increased risks for…colorectal cancer" (2001, p. 231).	— —	"The evidence is suggestive but not sufficient to infer a causal relationship between smoking and colorectal adenomatous polyps and colorectal cancer" (p. 26).	
Endometrial	"Several studies have reported that endometrial cancer is less frequent among women who smoke cigarettes than among non-smokers (1986). Cigarette smoking exerts an antiestrogenic effect that may explain this inverse association. The public	"Current smoking is associated with a reduced risk for endometrial cancer, but the effect is probably limited to postmenopausal disease. The risk for this cancer among former smokers	"The evidence is sufficient to infer that current smoking reduces the risk of endometrial cancer in postmenopausal women" (p. 26).	—

(Continued)

Table 1: *(Continued)*

Disease	First mention and finding(s) in a Surgeon General's report (year)	Highest level conclusion(s) from subsequent Surgeon General's reports before 2004 (year)	Conclusion(s) from the 2004 Surgeon General's report	Additional or updated conclusion(s) from the 2014 Surgeon General's report
	health significance of this association is limited because of the overall adverse impact of cigarette smoking on morbidity and mortality" (1989, p. 58).	generally appears more similar to that of women who have never smoked" (2001, p. 224).		—
Esophageal	"The evidence on the tobacco-esophageal cancer relationship supports the belief that an association exists. However, the data are not adequate to decide whether the relationship is causal" (1964, p. 218).	"Cigarette smoking is a major cause of esophageal cancer in the United States" (1982, p. 7).	"The evidence is sufficient to infer a causal relationship between smoking and cancers of the esophagus" (p. 26).	
Kidney	"Cigarette smoking is a contributory factor in the development of kidney cancer in the United States. The term 'contributory factor' by no means excludes the possibility of a causal role for smoking in cancers of this site" (1982, p. 7).	"There is a positive association between smoking and kidney cancer, with relative risks ranging from 1 to more than 5. The increased risk of kidney cancer due to cigarette smoking is	"The evidence is sufficient to infer a causal relationship between smoking and renal cell, [and] renal pelvis... cancers" (p. 26).	—

		found for both males and females, and there is a dose-response relationship as measured by the number of cigarettes smoked per day" (1989, p. 56).	—	
Laryngeal	"Evaluation of the evidence leads to the judgment that cigarette smoking is a significant factor in the causation of laryngeal cancer in the male" (1964, p. 212).	"Cigarette smoking is causally associated with cancer of the lung, larynx, oral cavity, and esophagus in women as well as in men…" (1980, p. 126).	—	"The evidence is sufficient to infer a causal relationship between smoking and cancer of the larynx" (p. 25).
Leukemia (acute)	"Leukemia has recently been implicated as a smoking-related disease … but this observation has not been consistent" (1990, p. 176).	"Smoking may be associated with an increased risk for acute myeloid leukemia among women but does not appear to be associated with other lymphoproliferative or hematologic cancers" (2001, p. 231).	—	"The evidence is sufficient to infer a causal relationship between smoking and acute myeloid leukemia" (p. 26).

(Continued)

Table 1:   *(Continued)*

Disease	First mention and finding(s) in a Surgeon General's report (year)	Highest level conclusion(s) from subsequent Surgeon General's reports before 2004 (year)	Conclusion(s) from the 2004 Surgeon General's report	Additional or updated conclusion(s) from the 2014 Surgeon General's report
Liver	"Primary hepatocellular cancer has been associated with smoking in a number of recent studies" (1990, p. 176).	"Women who smoke may have increased risks for liver cancer…" (2001, p. 231).	"The evidence is suggestive but not sufficient to infer a causal relationship between smoking and liver cancer" (p. 26).	"The evidence is sufficient to infer a causal relationship between smoking and hepatocellular carcinoma" (Chapter 6).
Lung	"Cigarette smoking is causally related to lung cancer in men; the magnitude of the effect of cigarette smoking far outweighs all other factors. The data for women, though less extensive, point in the same direction" (1964, p. 196).	"Additional epidemiological, pathological, and experimental data not only confirm the conclusion of the Surgeon General's 1964 Report regarding lung cancer in men but strengthen the causal relationship of smoking to lung cancer in women" (1967, p. 36).	"The evidence is sufficient to infer a causal relationship between smoking and lung cancer" (p. 25).	"The evidence is sufficient to conclude that the risk of developing adenocarcinoma of the lung from cigarette smoking has increased since the 1960s." "The evidence is sufficient to conclude that the increased risk of adenocarcinoma of the lung in smokers results from changes in the design and composition of cigarettes since the 1950s."

		"Cigarette smoking is causally related to lung cancer in both men and women" (1979, p. 1–16). "Cigarette smoking is the major cause of lung cancer in the United States" (1982, p. 5). "Cigarette smoking is the major cause of lung cancer among women. About 90 percent of all lung cancer deaths among U.S. women smokers are attributable to smoking" (2001, p. 13).	"The evidence is not sufficient to specify which design changes are responsible for the increased risk of adenocarcinoma, but there is suggestive evidence that ventilated filters and increased levels of tobacco-specific nitrosamines have played a role." "The evidence shows that the decline of squamous carcinoma follows the trend of declining smoking prevalence" (Chapter 6). — —
Oral cavity and pharyngeal	"The causal relationship of the smoking of pipes to the development of cancer of the lip appears to be established" (1964, p. 204). "Although there are suggestions of relationships between cancer of other specific sites of the oral	"Epidemiological studies indicate that smoking is a significant causal factor in the development of oral cancer. The risk increases with the number of cigarettes smoked per day" (1979, p. 1–17).	"The evidence is sufficient to infer a causal relationship between smoking and cancers of the oral cavity and pharynx" (p. 25).

(Continued)

Table 1: *(Continued)*

Disease	First mention and finding(s) in a Surgeon General's report (year)	Highest level conclusion(s) from subsequent Surgeon General's reports before 2004 (year)	Conclusion(s) from the 2004 Surgeon General's report	Additional or updated conclusion(s) from the 2014 Surgeon General's report
	cavity and the several forms of tobacco use, their causal implications cannot at present be stated" (1964, p. 205).	"Cigarette smoking is a major cause of cancers of the oral cavity in the United States" (1982, p. 6).		
Ovarian	"Smoking does not appear to be associated with risk for ovarian cancer" (2001, p. 224).	—	"The evidence is inadequate to infer the presence or absence of a causal relationship between smoking and ovarian cancer" (p. 26).	—
		—		—
Pancreatic	"Cigarette smoking is a contributory factor in the development of pancreatic cancer in the United States. This relationship is not as strong as that noted for the association between smoking and cancers of the lung, larynx, oral cavity, and esophagus. The term	"Smoking cessation reduces the risk of pancreatic cancer, compared with continued smoking, although this reduction in risk may only be measurable after 10 years of abstinence" (1990, p. 10).	"The evidence is sufficient to infer a causal relationship between smoking and pancreatic cancer" (p. 26).	—
				—

'contributory factor' by no means excludes the possibility of a causal role for smoking in cancers of this site" (1982, p. 7).		"The evidence is suggestive of no causal relationship between smoking and risk for prostate cancer" (p. 26).	"The evidence is suggestive of no causal relationship between smoking and the risk of incident prostate cancer." "The evidence is suggestive of a higher risk of death from prostate cancer in smokers than in non-smokers." "In men who have prostate cancer, the evidence is suggestive of a higher risk of advanced-stage disease and less well-differentiated cancer in smokers than in non-smokers, and — independent of stage and histologic grade — a higher risk of disease progression" (Chapter 6).
Prostate cancer	— —		

(Continued)

Table 1: *(Continued)*

Disease	First mention and finding(s) in a Surgeon General's report (year)	Highest level conclusion(s) from subsequent Surgeon General's reports before 2004 (year)	Conclusion(s) from the 2004 Surgeon General's report	Additional or updated conclusion(s) from the 2014 Surgeon General's report
Stomach	"No relationship has been established between tobacco use and stomach cancer" (1964, p. 229).	"Data on smoking and cancer of the stomach … are unclear" (2001, p. 231).	"The evidence is sufficient to infer a causal relationship between smoking and gastric cancers" (p. 25).	— —

Note: ETS = environmental tobacco smoke. ªRefers to a general conclusion that was reached for breast cancer.

From: Chapter 4: Advances in Knowledge of the Health Consequences of Smoking: From 1964 to 2014. The Health Consequences of Smoking — 50 Years of Progress: A Report of the Surgeon General. National Center for Chronic Disease Prevention and Health Promotion (US) Office on Smoking and Health. Atlanta (GA): Centers for Disease Control and Prevention (US), 2014.

2.4. *From 1964 to present*

Research continues on smoking and cancer, as addressed elsewhere in this book. The scientific questions have shifted as answers are sought to critical questions: What drives susceptibility to smoking? What mechanisms underlie the causation of lung cancer by tobacco smoke? What are predictors of lung cancer risk?[22] The principal research platforms remain case-control and cohort studies, but in combination with biosamples and the -omics and other technologies of 21st century science. The risks of changing tobacco products have also been a focus, beginning with the consequences of adding filters and extending to new non-combustible products (see Chapter 1).

3. Methodological Advances in Cancer Epidemiology from Studying Smoking

The epidemiological studies of smoking and cancer, particularly lung cancer, led to substantial methodological advances. The initial case-control studies were feasible, as cases could be readily identified, but control selection was problematic. The design had previously been in use, but it was refined as it was quickly applied for studying smoking and cancer.[23] Wynder and Graham, for example, interviewed cases from various sources and identified controls through clinics.[10] Doll and Hill selected controls who were comparable to the lung cancer cases from admitted patients in the participating facilities.[24] The case-control study in London by Doll and Hill gave careful attention to the possibility of information bias, contrasting interviews with purported lung cancer cases with interviews with people who had confirmed lung cancer. The hospital-based case-control studies carried out for smoking and lung cancer were soon replicated for other cancers. The case-control model was later moved into a population-based framework using cancer registries. The design unified with the cohort study as case-based sampling, i.e., sampling in different ways from populations that are being followed for disease occurrence, was conceptualized and the grounding of case-control studies in underlying cohorts was recognized.[25]

In 1950, the results of five case-control studies were consistent in showing a strong association of smoking with lung cancer risk. The results were criticized for their "retrospective" nature, a criticism of case-control studies that persisted for decades until finally set aside.[26] Given the attacks on the credibility of the case-control studies, there was a need to have evidence from prospectively collected data, leading to the implementation of pioneering cohort studies: the studies of British Doctors started in 1951, the Dorn study of US Veterans started in 1954, and the Hammond and Horn study of white men in nine states started in 1952.[27–29] Given the state of epidemiology and of data management and analysis at the time, the pace of implementation of the studies and the time to publication are breathtaking.

The study of British Doctors is exemplary. The cohort was established in 1951 and the first results were published in 1954, based on 29 months of follow-up, showing increasing risk for lung cancer risk with amount smoked.[29] The study's successful course reflects its thoughtful design. The population was selected for feasibility, its high likelihood of participation, competency in completing questionnaires, and ease of follow-up. Additionally, at the time, smoking rates among physicians were comparable to those in the general population so that generalizability of findings was not a concern. For the same reasons, the study of British Doctors was the model for the long-running Nurses' Health Studies, which began in 1974.[30]

These early studies were prototypes for the many cohorts that followed addressing cancer and other smoking-caused diseases. These cohort studies considered multiple exposures and multiple outcomes, both cancer and non-cancer. Examples include the American Cancer Society's Cancer Prevention Studies (CPS) I and II, the European Prospective Investigation into Nutrition and Cancer (EPIC), the Million Women Study, and the NIH-AARP Study of Diet and Health.[31–34] These are multi-purpose prospective cohort studies, some now incorporating biosamples that can be used for multiple purposes, e.g., assessing indicators of risk, but their historical roots lie in the initial cohort studies on smoking and lung cancer. The initial Hammond and Horn cohort selected in nine states was carried out by American Cancer Society volunteers and later expanded to 25 states.[35,36] It was the model for the American Cancer Society's CPS I and II studies that were initiated in the 1960s and 1980s, respectively.[37]

There were other methodological advances arising from research on smoking and lung cancer: the 1951 description of the odds ratio by Cornfield for quantifying the strength of association; and Levin's 1953 paper on the attributable risk statistic, used to quantify the burden of lung cancer from smoking.[38,39] These advances have had lasting impact throughout public health and clinical medicine. The odds ratio was perhaps the first parameter for estimating strength of association and Levin's concept of attributable risk underlies contemporary estimates of disease burden.

The epidemic of lung cancer was among the wave of epidemics of non-communicable diseases: cancer, chronic respiratory disease, and cardiovascular disease. Through the first decades of the 20th century, epidemiological research had been focused on infectious diseases, particularly tuberculosis — then a leading cause of death as effective treatments were not available until the 1950s. For infectious diseases, well-defined paradigms existed, i.e., the Henle-Koch postulates, for inferring that an infectious agent caused a particular disease. However, for lung cancer and other chronic diseases there was not comparable specificity of agent with disease, i.e., an infectious agent is by definition necessary, and the evidence on smoking and lung cancer was largely observational as animal models were lacking at the time. Across the 1950s and into the 1960s, there was a robust discussion of how to draw causal conclusions by integration of observational findings with other evidence.[40]

That discussion culminated with the elaboration of guidelines for causal inference, implemented in the 1964 Surgeon General's report and proposed in parallel by Sir Austin Bradford Hill (Table 2).[4,41] These guidelines remain in use.

Table 2: Guidelines for causal inference as outlined by the 1964 Smoking and Health: Report of the Advisory Committee to the Surgeon General and from Hill 1965.

1964 Surgeon General report criteria	Hill criteria
Consistency of association	Strength
Strength of association	Consistency
Specificity of association	Specificity
Temporal relationship of association	Temporality
Coherence of association	Biological gradient
	Coherence
	Experiment

4. The Tobacco Industry Response: Creating Doubt and Thwarting Tobacco Control

Another legacy of the research on smoking and cancer was the development of strategies by the tobacco industry to undermine the emerging findings on causation with a multi-pronged attack intended to create doubt about the evidence.[42,43] These strategies remain in play by the tobacco industry and have been adopted by other entities that produce cancer- and disease-causing agents. Furthermore, the causal conclusions reached concerning smoking and lung cancer initially, and subsequently other cancers and diseases, had powerful consequences for motivating tobacco control, litigation, and regulation. For more than a half century, dating back to the emerging evidence in the 1950s, the tobacco industry acted at levels ranging from local to global to thwart tobacco control and maintain its lethal sales (see Chapter 1).[6]

The orchestrated attack on the scientific evidence related to tobacco can be traced to a 1953 meeting of attorneys for the major companies.[6,42,43] This well-chronicled meeting at the Plaza Hotel in New York brought together the Chief Executive Officers of the major companies, in response to the emerging evidence on the risks of smoking. By then, the epidemiological studies were providing convincing and coherent evidence linking smoking to lung cancer. Furthermore, Wynder and colleagues' research, in which they applied cigarette tar condensates to the shaved skin of mice, showed the development of skin papillomas and histologically proven carcinomas (see Chapter 3).[44]

At the 1953 Plaza Hotel meeting, a strategy emerged that was orchestrated by John Hill of the advertising firm Hill & Knowlton, which had been hired by the industry to create its defensive communications tactics. The strategy included the creation of controversy and "doubt", the founding of the Tobacco Industry Research Committee, later becoming the Council for Tobacco Research, and the initiation of illegal collusion among the tobacco companies.[45]

The strategy of doubt creation that originated with the tobacco industry decades ago persists today and is continually mounted around environmental hazards.

One element of the strategy was to hire consultants and other surrogates to attack the credibility of the evidence, particularly the epidemiological evidence for which there were inevitably potential sources of bias.[6,45] The industry also funded research, some through the Council for Tobacco Research, that was intended to provide evidence to counter the developing consensus that smoking caused lung and other cancers. Repeated points of attack included lack of experimental evidence, given the necessary reliance on observational approaches, and no clear "mechanism" by which smoking caused cancer. The validity of the science of epidemiology itself was repeatedly questioned. One additional strategy was to claim that associations between smoking and lung or other cancers, and later passive smoking, reflected effects of other factors, i.e., confounding factors. With this strategy, the industry and its surrogates could invoke an ever-expanding list of alternatives to tobacco smoking, sometimes making the claim that there might even be still "unknown" confounding factors.

The industry again used this broad strategy, perhaps even more intensely, several decades later as epidemiological studies linked SHS to lung cancer in never smokers.[6,45,46] The tobacco industry used diverse and well-programmed strategies in its efforts to counter the tobacco control implications of the evidence on SHS. The strategies reached broadly and included initiatives to create doubt concerning the scientific evidence on SHS and health, to block regulatory measures to restrict smoking in public places and workplaces, and to advance ineffective strategies for control of SHS in lieu of smoking bans. These strategies were played out at the local, national and international levels and also orchestrated at the international level. The evidence on the industry's actions is voluminous (see Chapter 1), much coming from its own documents (e.g., the Opinion of the US District Court in the US vs. Philip Morris and Robert Proctor's book *Golden Holocaust*).[6,47] Here, the general strategies taken are described, along with specific examples showing the tactics that were used. There was a several-decade long effort to thwart the consequences of the damaging effects of SHS.

Today, the approach of doubt creation continues to evolve and is now amplified through social media. Michaels was among the first to describe comprehensively the approach in his 2008 book, *Doubt is Their Product*, and more recently to capture its continued elaboration in the 2020 follow-on book *The Triumph of Doubt.*[42,48]

5. Summary

Research on smoking and cancer spans almost a century and has continued long after smoking was found to be a cause of multiple types of cancer. Methods developed for investigating the leading edge of the smoking–cancer epidemic remain in use today. Unfortunately, approaches developed by the tobacco industry to counter scientific evidence also remain in play, although to a lesser extent with cigarettes (see Chapter 1), and have spread to other industries that produce injurious products. The next chapter (Chapter 3) will describe how animal models helped to determine that smoking is a cause of cancer. As the tobacco product landscape evolves with the increasing availability of non-combusted (e.g., nicotine vaping, non-tobacco nicotine pouches) potentially "less harmful" products, using the methods described in this and subsequent chapters will determine the public health risk or benefits of these products.

References

1. Hoffman FL. *The Mortality from Cancer Throughout the World*. (Prudential Press, 1915).
2. National Research Council, Committee on Health Risks of Exposure to Radon. *Health Effects of Exposure to Radon: BEIR VI*. (Washington, D.C.: National Academy Press, 1999).
3. Brandt AM. American Council of Learned S. *The Cigarette Century: The Rise, Fall, and Deadly Persistence of the Product that Defined America*. (New York: Basic Books, 2007).
4. U.S. Department of Health, Education, and Welfare. *Smoking and Health. Report of the Advisory Committee to the Surgeon General of the Public Health Service*. (Washington, DC: U.S. Department of Health, Education, and Welfare. Public Health Service, 1964).
5. U.S. Department of Health and Human Services. *The Health Consequences of Smoking — 50 Years of Progress: A Report of the Surgeon General*. (Atlanta, GA: U.S. Department of Health and Human Services, Centers for

Disease Control and Prevention, National Center for Chronic Disease Prevention and Health Promotion, Office on Smoking and Health, 2014).

6. Proctor R. *Golden Holocaust: Origins of the Cigarette Catastrophe and the Case for Abolition.* (Berkeley, CA: University of California Press, 2012).

7. Ochsner M, DeBakey M. Symposium on cancer. Primary pulmonary malignancy. Treatment by total pneumonectomy; analyses of 79 collected cases and presentation of 7 personal cases. *Surg Gynecol Obstet* 1939;68:435–51.

8. Pearl R. Tobacco smoking and longevity. *Science* 1938;87(2253):216–7.

9. Morabia A. Snippets from the past: The evolution of Wade Hampton Frost's epidemiology as viewed from the *American Journal of Hygiene/Epidemiology.* *Am J Epidemol* 2013;178(7):1013–9.

10. Wynder EL, Graham EA. Tobacco smoking as a possible etiologic factor in bronchiogenic carcinoma; a study of 684 proved cases. *J Am Med Assoc* 1950;143(4):329–36.

11. Levin ML, Goldstein H, Gerhardt PR. Cancer and tobacco smoking; a preliminary report. *J Am Med Assoc* 1950;143(4):336–8.

12. Doll R, Hill AB. Smoking and carcinoma of the lung; preliminary report. *Brit Med J* 1950;2(4682):739–48.

13. Armenian HK, Szklo M. *Morton Levin (1904–1995): History in the Making.* (Oxford University Press, 1996).

14. Samet JM. Epidemiology and the tobacco epidemic: How research on tobacco and health shaped epidemiology. *Am J Epidemiol* 2016;183(5):394–402.

15. US Department of Health and Human Services. *Smoking Cessation. A Report of the Surgeon General.* (Atlanta, GA: US Department of Health and Human Services, Centers for Disease Control and Prevention, National Center for Chronic Disease Prevention and Health Promotion, Office on Smoking and Health, 2020).

16. Burney LE. Excessive cigarette smoking: Statement. Public Health Rep. 1957;72(9):786.

17. Burney LE. Smoking and lung cancer: A statement of the Public Health Service. *J Am Med Assoc* 1959;171(13):1829–37.

18. Cornfield J, Haenszel W, Hammond EC, Lilienfeld AM, Shimkin MB, Wynder EL. Smoking and lung cancer: Recent evidence and a discussion of some questions. *J Natl Cancer Inst* 1959;22(1):173–203.

19. US Department of Health and Human Services. The Health Consequences of Smoking: Cancer. A Report of the Surgeon General. 1982.

20. U.S. Department of Health and Human Services. *The Health Consequences of Smoking: A Report of the Surgeon General.* (Atlanta, GA: U.S. Department of Health and Human Services, Centers for Disease Control and Prevention,

National Center for Chronic Disease Prevention and Health Promotion, Office on Smoking and Health, 2004).

21. U.S. Department of Health and Human Services. *The Health Consequences of Involuntary Smoking: A Report of the Surgeon General.* (Washington, D.C.: US Department of Health and Human Services, Public Health Service, Office on Smoking and Health, 1986).

22. Samet JM. Carcinogenesis and lung cancer: Seventy years of progress and more to come. *Carcinogenesis.* 2020; 41(10):1309–17.

23. Morabia A. Snippets from the past: Is Flint, Michigan, the birthplace of the case-control study? *Am J Epidemiol* 2013;178(12):1687–90.

24. Doll R, Hill AB. A study of the aetiology of carcinoma of the lung. *Brit Med J* 1952;2(4797):1271–86.

25. Miettinen O. Estimability and estimation in case-referent studies. *Am J Epidemiol* 1976;103(2):226–35.

26. Berkson J. Smoking and lung cancer. *The Am Statist* 1963;17(4):15–22.

27. Rogot E, Murray JL. Smoking and causes of death among US veterans: 16 years of observation. *Public Health Rep* 1980;95(3):213.

28. Mendes E. The study that helped spur the U.S. Stop-Smoking Movement. 2014; (https://www.cancer.org/latest-news/the-study-that-helped-spur-the-us-stop-smoking-movement.html, accessed September 15, 2020).

29. Doll R, Hill AB. The mortality of doctors in relation to their smoking habits; a preliminary report. *Brit Med Jl* 1954;1(4877):1451–5.

30. Belanger CF, Hennekens CH, Rosner B, Speizer FE. The nurses' health study. *The Am J Nursing* 1978;78(6):1039–40.

31. American Cancer Society. History of the Cancer Prevention Studies (https://www.cancer.org/research/we-conduct-cancer-research/behavioral-and-epidemiology-research-group/history-cancer-prevention-study.html, accessed September 15, 2020).

32. IARC. EPIC Study (https://epic.iarc.fr/, accessed September 15, 2020).

33. University of Oxford. The Million Women Study. 2020 (http://www.millionwomenstudy.org/introduction/, accessed September 15, 2020).

34. National Cancer Institute, Division of Cancer Epidemiology & Genetics. NIH-AARP Diet and Health Study (https://dietandhealth.cancer.gov/, accessed September 15, 2020).

35. Hammond EC, Horn D. The relationship between human smoking habits and death rates: A follow-up study of 187,766 men. *J Am Med Assoc* 1954;155(15):1316–28.

36. Hammond EC, Horn D. Smoking and death rates; report on forty-four months of follow-up of 187,783 men. I. Total mortality. *J Am Med Assoc* 1958;166(10):1159–72.

37. Shopland D, Burns D, Garfinkel L, Samet J. *Monograph 8: Changes in Cigarette Related Disease Risks and Their Implications for Prevention and Control.* (Bethesda, MD: National Institutes of Health, National Cancer Institute, 1997).

38. Cornfield J. A method of estimating comparative rates from clinical data; applications to cancer of the lung, breast, and cervix. *J Natl Cancer Inst* 1951;11(6):1269–75.

39. Levin ML. The occurrence of lung cancer in man. *Acta — Unio Internationalis Contra Cancrum* 1953;9(3):531–41.

40. Samet JM. Epidemiology and the tobacco epidemic: How research on tobacco and health shaped epidemiology. *Am J Epidemiol* 2016;183(5):394–402.

41. Hill AB. The environment and disease: Association or causation? *Proc R Soc Med* 1965;58:295–300.

42. Michaels D. *Doubt is Their Product: How Industry's Assault on Science Threatens your Health.* (Oxford University Press, 2008).

43. Oreskes N, Conway EM. *Merchants of Doubt: How a Handful of Scientists Obscured the Truth on Issues from Tobacco Smoke to Global Warming.* (New York, NY: Bloomsbury Press, 2011).

44. Wynder EL, Graham EA, Croninger AB. Experimental production of carcinoma with cigarette tar. *Cancer Res* 1953;13(12):855–64.

45. Kessler G. Final Opinion Civil Action No. 99-2496 (GK). 2006; (http://www.justice.gov/sites/default/files/civil/legacy/2014/09/11/amended%20opinion_0.pdf, accessed June 8, 2015).

46. Samet JM, Burke TA. Turning science into junk: The tobacco industry and passive smoking. *Am J Public Health* 2001;91(11):1742–4.

47. United States of America v. Philip Morris USA I. United States of America vs. Philip Morris USA, Inc., Civil Action No. 99-2496 (GK). 2006 (http://www.justice.gov/civil/cases/tobacco2/amended%20opinion.pdf, accessed September 10, 2014).

48. Michaels D. *The Triumph of Doubt: Dark Money and the Science of Deception.* (Oxford University Press, 2020).

https://doi.org/10.1142/9789811239533_0003

Chapter 3

Animal Studies of Tobacco and Cancer

Karam El-Bayoumy*

1. Introduction

As described in Chapter 2, cigarette smoking is the single most preventable cause of cancer deaths, being responsible for cancers of the lung, oral cavity, nasopharynx, oropharynx, hypopharynx, nasal cavity, larynx, esophagus, stomach, pancreas, colorectum, liver, kidney, ureter, urinary bladder, uterine cervix, ovary and blood.[1-4] Avoiding tobacco products or quitting the tobacco habit is by far the best strategy for prevention of tobacco-related cancers. Although there are tobacco control measures, resources and widespread cultural changes that allow smokers to quit and non-smokers to avoid smoking in the first place, a smoke-free world remains a major challenge.

Early epidemiological studies in 1950 provided evidence proving the carcinogenicity of tobacco smoke in human lungs.[5,6] So, do we need to pursue studies in animal models if, for over 70 years, we have known that tobacco smoke causes cancer? Yes, realistic and reproducible research approaches are still needed to combat tobacco smoke-related cancers. Animal studies not only complement findings from human epidemiological studies but also play an important role in examining the mechanisms that can account for cancer induction by tobacco smoking. Furthermore,

*The Pennsylvania State University, USA. kee2@psu.edu

animal studies are important in the development of cancer prevention strategies (see Chapter 10) and for the discovery of biomarkers that can assist in the identification of smokers who are at high risk of developing tobacco-related cancers.

The goal of this chapter is to describe some of the challenges of studying cancer induction by tobacco smoke in animal models. The rationale for the continuous need for animal studies is discussed. The strengths and weaknesses of the various animal models reported in the literature are also presented. Moreover, the knowledge gained so far is not the end of this story and practical approaches for future studies are proposed.

2. Why Animal Models?

Why do researchers use animal models? The first and most obvious reason is that it is unethical to perform studies involving human subjects if the study protocol possibly could result in increased and unnecessary risk of harm to participants. Animal testing, following well-defined guidelines (e.g., Public Health Service Policy on the Humane Care and Use of Laboratory Animals), is a viable alternative approach allowing researchers to examine the possible effects of tobacco smoke (see Section 3) on human health. Some early studies used dogs and non-human primates to approximate the effects of human smoking but these approaches are no longer considered ethical. Therefore, considerable efforts have been devoted to research using more time-and cost-efficient rodent models that include testing tobacco smoke by inhalation or tobacco smoke condensate (tar) or its subfractions by topical application. Several points support the continued need for animal models in research on tobacco products.

First, the tobacco industry will undoubtedly continue to offer new products within the strategy of harm reduction.[7] Early approaches including research on "the less harmful cigarette" began about 60 years ago, led by the eminent scientist, the late Ernst L. Wynder, and his team,[7-9] however, it was recognized that there can be no "safe cigarette".[8] One of my mentors (Wynder's close colleague, the late Dietrich Hoffmann) once said that the only safe cigarette is the one you don't smoke. More recent approaches include "heat not burn" products and electronic cigarettes which are advertised as safer alternatives or even cessation aids to tobacco smoking.[10,11] The safety of these products remains to be fully investigated because of the lack of experimental data on their long-term health effects.[12] The potential toxicity and carcinogenicity of these products can be objectively evaluated and compared in animal models (see Section 4).

Second, tissues and blood from laboratory animals exposed to tobacco smoke can be used to identify biomarkers of potential harm, i.e., molecular targets that are involved in the carcinogenesis process. Furthermore, animal studies can provide a platform to estimate the administered dose by measuring the levels of metabolites of various compounds in tobacco smoke such as the nicotine metabolite cotinine, i.e., biomarkers of exposure (see Chapter 7).

Third, animal models can be used to examine a variety of safe and effective agents that may be able to prevent cancer induced by tobacco smoke. Such agents, preferably naturally occurring, could be appealing for risk reduction in smokers and ex-smokers (see Chapter 10).

3. Composition of Cigarette Smoke for Animal Studies

Cigarette smoke is composed of a vapor phase and a particulate phase; major constituents of both phases have been reported.[7] The vapor phase is arbitrarily defined as that portion of the smoke aerosol which passes through a Cambridge glass fiber filter. The particulate phase is that portion which is trapped on the glass fiber filter. Its particle sizes range from 0.1 to <1.0 μm in diameter. This definition does not fully reflect the conditions prevailing in freshly generated cigarette smoke. Some semi-volatile agents, such as phenol for example, appear to some extent in the vapor phase. Some of the substituted phenols, the semi-volatile nitrosamines, and volatile compounds such as hydrogen cyanide and low boiling aldehydes are partially trapped as aerosol inclusions in the particulate matter.[7] The terms "smoke condensate" and "tar" have been used interchangeably.[13–15] In the USA, the term "tar" was used in official reports of tar yield and is equivalent to Total Particulate Matter less nicotine and water.[14,15] Yields of tar and nicotine in the smoke were determined by standardized laboratory methods that required each cigarette to be machine smoked with a 35-mL puff volume, duration over 2 seconds, once per minute.[16,17]

4. Carcinogenicity Studies in Animals

Animal models have been used to study the carcinogenicity of tobacco products since the early 1900s. Mice, rats, rabbits, and guinea pigs were used to examine the effects of tobacco smoke administered by either inhalation or by topical application of the tobacco smoke condensate (tar) onto the mouse skin or the rabbit ears. In general, these earlier studies as summarized by Wynder *et al.*[18] and depicted in Figure 1, utilized different types of tobacco, various methods of tar preparation, different routes of administration, poorly designed inhalation exposure systems, and short durations of animal exposure. In addition, these studies did not provide information on sex and whether animals were inbred (genetically homogenous) or outbred (genetically different) which can influence the

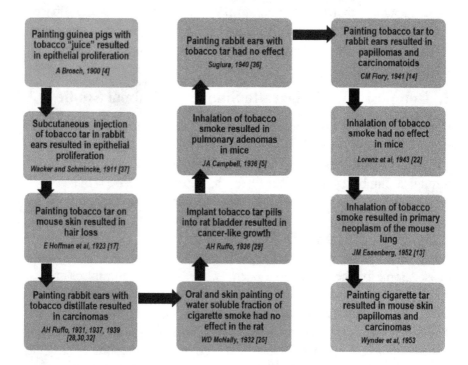

Figure 1:   Early studies of tobacco smoke and cancer in animals: Challenges in the first half of the 20th century.

Note: Section 4 describes the factors that make it challenging to reach definitive conclusions. The number in square brackets represents the citation number in Wynder *et al.*[18]

metabolism of tobacco constituents leading to carcinogenesis. Moreover, in some studies a limited number of animals per group (treated vs. untreated control) were used which made it difficult to statistically evaluate the results. Collectively, the above mentioned factors variably impacted the outcomes making it challenging to consistently reproduce results across various laboratories and definitive conclusions could not be reached. Nevertheless, the results of the studies published in the first half of the 20th century suggested that tobacco smoke may induce cancer in animals.

4.1. *Mice*

In 1953, Wynder *et al.*[18] showed that cigarette tar painting induced papillomas and carcinomas in mouse skin; cigarette tar was obtained with a smoking machine which simulated human smoking habits. The tar was dissolved in acetone and applied to the backs of strain CAF1 mice, at a dose of 40 mg, 3 times/ week. Control mice had their backs painted with pure acetone. While control mice had no skin lesions, 59% of the mice (total: 81 mice per group used in this study) treated with tar-acetone solution developed benign tumors called papillomas and 44% developed histologically confirmed malignant carcinomas.

> *In 1953 mouse studies proved cigarette tar induced papillomas and carcinomas which supported the case that tobacco smoking is harmful.*

These results were not accepted without a fight from the tobacco industry, who questioned the validity of the study. The industry argued that the dose of the tar painted on the mouse skin was far greater than the amount of tar inhaled by the average smoker and that mouse skin tissue was anatomically different from human lung tissue. In spite of their objections, the results of the mouse skin experiment were confirmed in many other laboratories including those of the tobacco industry itself. These animal studies, combined with epidemiological findings, strengthened the case against tobacco smoking.[15]

This mouse skin model allowed researchers to understand the mechanisms and identify the chemicals that can account for tobacco carcinogenesis. The carcinogenic potency of the tar depended on the type of tobacco, composition of the cigarette paper and the presence of various agents that were used as additives. In 1959, Wynder and Hoffmann applied a tedious and detailed analytical protocol which led to the isolation and chemical identification of crystalline benzo[a]pyrene (B[a]P) from the smoke of several thousand cigarettes.[19] B[a]P, a representative example of the class of carcinogens called polycyclic aromatic hydrocarbons (PAHs), is known to induce cancers in various organs, including the lung and oral cavity, in animal models, and is now considered "carcinogenic to humans" by the International Agency for Research on Cancer (IARC).[20–23] In 1971, Hoffmann and Wynder showed[24] that the tumorigenic activity of tobacco tar on mouse skin was reduced by about 50% by removing the PAHs from the tar by tedious analytical methods. These studies also showed that cigarette smoke condensate, when fractionated (separated into its constituents), contains certain compounds that can initiate cancer, while other agents can promote cancer development, or act as co-carcinogens when applied in combination with carcinogenic agents to mouse skin.

Smoke condensates prepared from nicotine-free cigars or pipes have been shown by Croninger *et al.* to induce papillomas and carcinomas on the skin of female Swiss mice.[25] Briefly, the nicotine-free cigars and pipes were prepared by extracting the smoke condensate with sulfuric acid to remove the basic portion which contains nicotine.[25] Topical application to the lips and the oral areas of 100 ICR/Ha Swiss mice with about 26 mg of cigarette smoke condensate in acetone, 5 h/week for 15 months resulted in a significant increase in lung tumors and lymphomas.[26] Many other mouse skin studies involving large groups of animals explored and defined the skin carcinogenicity of tobacco smoke condensates and their fractions.[15]

4.2. *Other animals*

The results of studies that applied cigarette smoke condensate to rat skin were not conclusive.[15] Intrapulmonary injection of cigarette smoke condensate produced lung tumors in female Osborne Mendel pathogen-free rats after thoracotomy.[15] Additional studies revealed that hamster skin was not responsive to cigarette smoke alone. However, the application of condensate induced papillomas and carcinomas in the ears of rabbits.[15]

It is likely that different animals metabolize carcinogens in tobacco smoke condensate differently which may partially account for the varied results.

4.3. *Cigarette smoke inhalation studies*

As a result of the early epidemiological evidence supporting the carcinogenicity of tobacco smoke in the human lung,[5,6] researchers realized they would need to progress beyond animal studies employ-

> *Studies proved that inhalation of cigarette smoke can cause benign and malignant tumors in the mouse and rat lung and hamster larynx.*

ing topical application of tobacco smoke condensate and towards protocols that simulated human smoking inhalation patterns using animals. This required the development of devices designed to expose the animal's whole body or just the nose to cigarette smoke. These machines also allowed researchers to expose animals to either whole tobacco smoke or just the gas phase portion of cigarette smoke.

Inhalation studies used hamsters, rats, mice, dogs, rabbits, non-human primates, ferrets, and guinea pigs. A summary of early inhalation studies was reported in 1967 by Wynder and Hoffmann;[13] subsequently additional reviews were published by others.[14,15,27-31] Based on their genetic make-up, certain strains of animals are highly susceptible to develop lung tumors in the absence of exposure to carcinogenic agents. These spontaneous tumors can make it difficult to conclusively determine the effects of tobacco smoke on lung tumor development. For example, the A/J mouse strain (also known as A strain) belongs to this category (see Section 4.3.3). Furthermore, infections with human and mouse papillomavirus can potentiate the carcinogenicity of tobacco smoke for induction of head and neck and cervical cancers in humans and animal models.[23,32]

A number of devices and standardized approaches have been developed to effectively deliver tobacco smoke to these animals, specifically under conditions that simulate human smoking patterns. However, at the present time, there is clear evidence that smokers' behaviors can influence the levels of exposure to tobacco smoke[33] which are different from those measured by machine smoking under the FTC conditions (see

Section 3). Thus, extensive efforts were focused on altering machine smoking methods and FTC parameters to better reflect smokers' behaviors (puffing patterns, blocking cigarette filter vents as well as the composition and number of cigarettes smoked per day). Although there is a need for improvement, smoking machines remain very useful for screening newly developed tobacco products.[33,34] Using machine smoking, animals are exposed to smoke that is diluted with air and forced into a chamber for a short period followed by an air purge. The smoke in the chamber can be assayed for carbon monoxide and total particulate matter. At various time points during smoke exposure, blood can be drawn from the animals to measure their levels of carboxyhemoglobin, nicotine (or its metabolite cotinine) as well as deposition and retention of particulate matter in various organs, giving some indication of the doses administered.

4.3.1. *Inhalation studies in the hamster*

The advantage of using the Syrian golden hamster in cancer research is its low background incidence of spontaneous pulmonary tumors and its low susceptibility to interfering respiratory infections. In 1973, Dontenwill et al.[35] using more than 4,000 male and female hamsters discovered that nose-only inhalation of tobacco smoke generated from various cigarettes caused carcinoma in the larynx. Each individual dose of smoke was generated over a 7–10-min period from 30 German reference cigarettes; this was repeated once, twice, or 3 times a day, 5 days a week until death of the animals. The severity of the disease in the larynx increased with the duration of treatment and dosage.[35] The higher concentration of smoke particles in the hamster larynx than in the lungs and bronchi may explain why tumors were observed in the larynx but not in the lung. Sham exposed (control) hamsters or those exposed only to the gas phase portion of smoke did not develop such tumors. The hamster model was used extensively in several laboratories and similar results were obtained by other investigators.[36–41] In this model, Dontenwill et al.[35] and Hoffmann et al.[42] examined whether cigarette smoke can act as a promoter of carcinogenesis. Thus, animals were first treated with a single dose of a carcinogen as a tumor initiator by an intratracheal administration (e.g., B[a]P at a dose of 5 mg mixed with ferric oxide or the synthetic carcinogen 7,12-dimethylbenz[a]-anthracene [DMBA] at a dose of 500 µg) followed by cigarette smoke exposure. The results showed that cigarette smoke potentiated the induction of larynx tumors in animals treated with DMBA or B[*a*]P as tumor initiators. In a related study, one of my mentors (Dr. Stephen S. Hecht, a co-editor of this book) demonstrated that a single subcutaneous injection of 4-(methylnitrosamino)-1-(3-pyridyl)-1-butanone (NNK), a known lung carcinogen found in cigarette smoke,[43] at doses ranging from 1 to 10 mg, induced significant incidences of lung tumors in Syrian Golden hamsters, but this was not increased by subsequent cigarette smoke exposure (2× daily for 69 weeks).[44] My own research interest and contributions to the area of tobacco carcinogenesis would not have been possible without the mentorship of Dr. Hecht.

4.3.2. *Inhalation studies in the rat*

Early inhalation studies[15] in the rat using a nose-only exposure protocol were performed by Davis *et al.*,[45,46] Dalbey *et al.*,[47] and Wehner *et al.*[48] In these studies, the daily exposure period was very brief, a small number of animals were used and in certain studies the method for histological classification of the tumors was not provided. Because of the poor experimental design, the rats in these experiments did not consistently show an increase of tumors in several sites including the lung. Studies reported by Coggins also did not show significant increases in tumors in any site including the lung and nasal cavity.[28] However, in a study by Mauderly *et al.*[49] the rat's whole body was exposed to cigarette smoke since this method leads to a higher dose than nose-only exposure. Male and female F344 rats were exposed for 6 h/day, 5 days/week for up to 30 months to smoke generated from 1R3 research cigarettes (commonly used as a standard cigarette in various laboratories) or to clean air as a control. In the high exposure group (250 mg/m^3), the combined incidence of benign bronchioloalveolar adenoma and malignant carcinomas was 14% while the corresponding figures in the low exposure (100 mg/m^3) and control groups were 6% and 0%, respectively. These investigators also observed mutations in codon 12 of the *K-ras* gene (a gene known to potentiate cancer development and highly expressed in human lung cancer). Furthermore, this report showed that both males and females had significant increases of nasal cavity neoplasia. In contrast to earlier studies,[28,45–48] the positive results of this study were due to the higher dose associated with whole body vs. nose-only exposure and the relatively long duration of exposure of the rats to cigarette smoke.

4.3.3. *Inhalation studies in the mouse*

As shown in Figure 1, the first experiment in which strain A mice (known to develop spontaneous lung tumors) were exposed to cigarette smoke was performed by Lorenz et al. as early as 1943;[50] however, there was no increase in tumors above those spontaneously found. Further studies that exposed Albino mice to tobacco smoke were carried out in 1952 by Essenberg et al. and although an increased lung tumor incidence was observed, the results were not conclusive.[51] Studies performed in 1967 by Harris and Negroni[52] as well as by Otto and Elmenhorst[53] and by Wynder et al.,[54] exposed different strains of mice (C57BL, BLH, C57BL6/Mil) either to mainstream tobacco smoke or to the gas phase only. The incidence of lung tumors was not significantly different between exposed and control mice. In 1970, Leuchtenberger and Leuchtenberger[55] exposed a mouse strain (different from those used above) called Snell's mice to either the whole smoke or the gas phase only (15 mL puff volume, 2 second duration, 58 second interval between puffs). No significant increase in pulmonary adenocarcinomas was observed in mice exposed to whole smoke; however, the number of mice with adenocarcinomas in males (10 of 44 treated mice, $p = 0.005$) but not in females (5/44, $p = 0.15$) exposed to the gas phase was significantly higher than controls. In 1986, Henry and Kouri[56] used genetically modified (C57BL/Cum × C3H/AnFCum) F1 mice that were exposed (nose-only) to cigarette smoke from reference 2R1 cigarettes, 5 days/week for 110 weeks, and observed until death. The mice developed alveolar adenocarcinomas but the difference in the incidence in smoke-exposed and control (sham-exposed) mice was not significant.

Both mainstream cigarette smoke and secondhand smoke (a mixture of mainstream smoke exhaled from active smokers and sidestream smoke) which can be involuntarily inhaled by passive smokers, are classified by the IARC as Group 1 human carcinogens. Prior to this classification, in the 1990s, Witschi's group[57] exposed strain A mice, similar to those used earlier by Lorenz et al.,[50] to environmental tobacco smoke (ETS, now known as secondhand smoke), generated from mainstream

(11%) and sidestream (89%) smoke. Mice were exposed to ETS for 5 months and then allowed to recover in air for another 4 months before evaluation of lung tumor response. A significant increase in the number of lung tumors per mouse (tumor multiplicity: about 2.8 tumors/mouse in exposed mice and about 1 tumor/mouse in control mice) was observed. The increase in lung tumor multiplicity in the A/J mice was due to a constituent of the gas phase which is consistent with studies performed by Leuchtenberger and Leuchtenberger in Snell's mice.[55] Of particular importance, these results were reproducible in different laboratories. In fact, this was the first animal model in which cigarette smoke consistently induced tumors in the lung and not in the larynx as was observed in the hamster model.[35] DeFlora *et al.*[58] reviewed the results obtained in their laboratories using 4 different strains of mice (A/J, Swiss Albino, SKH-1 hairless and p53 mutant [UL53-3XA/J] F1) including that used by Witschi *et al.*[57] These mice were exposed (whole body) to ETS. Although the increase in lung tumor multiplicity and incidence was significant, it was weak.

In 2005, Hutt *et al.*[59] exposed a different strain of mice (B6C3F1 that has a low baseline incidence of lung tumors) to high doses of mainstream cigarette smoke. Briefly, female B63F1 mice were exposed via whole body 6 h/day, 5 days/week for 920–930 days, to mainstream cigarette smoke (250 mg/m³), a dose equal to that used in the rat by Mauderly,[49] or sham exposed. The authors reported a significant elevation of adenocarcinoma of the lung of treated mice (20.3% treated vs. 2.8% in control), benign lung adenoma (28.2% vs. 6.7%), total benign pulmonary neoplasms (30.9% vs. 6.7%) and distant metastases (1.52% vs. 0.31%).

4.3.4. *Inhalation studies in other animal models*

To replicate human smoking patterns, scientists were interested in training larger animals to inhale cigarette smoke. Dogs were trained to inhale cigarette smoke through tracheostoma and by nasal inhalation.[15,29] Rabbits and non-human primates have also been used for inhalation studies.[15] These studies did not yield useful results and were time-consuming and expensive to perform; they would not be considered ethical today. Because of the resemblance of the ferret's airways to those of humans, it was suggested in 1985 that it would be a useful model for inhalation toxicology; however, no ferret carcinogenicity studies of cigarette smoke alone have been reported.[60-65] In one study, Kim *et al.*[66] exposed ferrets to the combination of cigarette smoke and NNK, a tobacco-specific carcinogenic component of smoke. The results showed that this combination induced both preneoplastic lesions and gross lung tumors whereas the unexposed animals did not show any histological abnormality in the lung. The authors also showed that the urinary cotinine concentrations of smoke-exposed ferrets were similar to that found in humans smoking one pack of cigarettes per day. Since Kim *et al.*'s previous study[66] did not test NNK alone, the same team[67] demonstrated that injecting ferrets with NNK resulted in the formation of both preneoplastic lesions and lung tumors which are commonly seen in humans. Although no ferret carcinogenicity studies of cigarette smoke alone have been reported, this model was employed to monitor the effects of potential preventive agents on targets involved in the carcinogenesis process.[60-65]

In 2005, our team[68] reported that male Hartley guinea pigs treated with whole-body exposure to cigarette smoke twice per day for 28 days developed various types of preneoplastic lung lesions (bronchial hyperplasia, dysplasia and squamous metaplasia), analogous to those found in human smokers. Regarding the dose of cigarette smoke, from analysis of cotinine in the guinea pig urine on day 28 of this study, the amount of smoke inhaled was comparable to that of a human smoking one pack of cigarettes per day, assuming that the metabolism of nicotine in guinea pigs and humans is similar.[68] The results indicate that ferrets and guinea pigs were exposed to cigarette smoke at doses comparable to those of smokers.

5. Carcinogenicity Studies of Smokeless Tobacco in Animals

A wide variety of smokeless tobacco products are popular worldwide (see Chapter 5). These products induce a variety of cancer types.[69,70] Smokeless tobacco contains various classes of compounds, some of which are known to induce cancer in animals.[71,72] Studies on the effects of smokeless tobacco in animal models are described below.

5.1. *Hamster cheek pouch*

In 1960, Peacock *et al.*[73] performed a study placing a single application of unburned tobacco in a unique organ — the hamster cheek pouch. Follow-up studies employed the same animal model but multiple applications of unburned tobacco were applied. In general, the results of early studies in the hamster cheek pouch were negative. Epithelial lesions induced by tobacco in the hamster cheek pouch have been detected in only one study by Kandarkar and Sirsat in 1977.[74] Interestingly, as described above, the skin of the hamster was not susceptible for tumor induction by tobacco smoke condensate.[15] It has been speculated[73,74] that the lack of saliva in the hamster's cheek pouch made it unsusceptible to lesion induction by smokeless tobacco.[75,76]

5.2. *Rat lip*

In 1981, an experimental model was developed by Hirsch and Thilander to study the effects of snuff on the oral mucosa[77] using 3-month-old male and female outbred Sprague–Dawley rats. Following anesthesia, and via surgical means, these investigators created a test canal in the lower lip. After 14 days of healing, the canal was filled with snuff once in the morning and again at night, 5 days/week. After 9 months of exposure

> *Snuff (smokeless tobacco) induced tumors in the oral cavity of rats; these results support the observations in humans.*

to snuff, rats developed lesions of the oral mucosa. In a follow-up study using the same model, Hirsch and Johansson[78] showed that exposure of the test canal of rats to snuff for 10–16 h/day, 5 days/week for their life-span (9–22 months) resulted in lesions mainly restricted to the epithelium and the underlying connective tissue of the surgically created test canal.

In 1986, the tumorigenic activity toward the oral cavity of snuff was evaluated by Hecht *et al.*[79] using two different experimental protocols employing male inbred F344 rats. In the first protocol, 10 week old rats were treated by chronic application to the oral cavity for 131 weeks with either water (control group) or water-extract of snuff. No tumors were observed in either of these groups. In the second protocol, using the same approach developed by Hirsch and Thilander[77] the surgically created test canal in the lower lip of the rats was treated 5 times/week for 116 weeks with either snuff, water-extracted snuff, or snuff enriched with its own water-extract. A group of rats had the same surgery without anything being applied to serve as controls; oral tumors were not observed in this group. The incidences of oral cavity tumors developed in the rats treated with snuff, water-extracted snuff, or snuff-enriched with its own water-extract were 9.4%, 9.5%, and 1.5%, respectively. These results were similar to those reported by Hirsch and Johansson,[78] supporting the epidemiological findings which indicate that snuff dipping causes oral cancer in humans.[69,70,80]

6. Have We Made Any Real Progress and What Comes Next?

Throughout the 20th century, addiction to cigarette smoking resulted in immeasurable suffering from various chronic diseases. Researchers have been able to clearly establish that tobacco consumption in various forms causes cancer in appropriate animal models and in humans. Furthermore, the carcinogenicity of secondhand tobacco smoke has been well established.[81] Over several decades, the knowledge gained and efforts to educate the public resulted in the decline of smoking rates to their current lowest levels in 50 years. Clearly, science-based information and public education can change human behavior for the better. That being said, in 2018 there were still more than 34 million adult smokers in the USA and in 2019 about 10 million youth (12–17 years old) were identified to be at risk for cigarette smoking.[82] The World Health Organization (WHO) Global Report on trends in Prevalence of Tobacco Use, 2000–2025[83] projected that the number of tobacco smokers in the world will remain around 1.1 billion until at least the year 2025. Globally, at least 43.8 million adolescents aged 13–15 used some form of tobacco. These facts demonstrate that the tobacco epidemic is far from over.

There is no doubt that the tobacco industry will continue to manufacture newer and more enticing tobacco products, making it essential for scientists to continue to perform vital research while educating the general public on the risks of tobacco products. Recently popular and addictive contemporary products like e-cigarettes should be investigated using animal models that simulate human behavior. Several animal models are described in this chapter; however, no single animal model can perfectly replicate human smoking patterns and thus careful selection of appropriate models to study these new tobacco related products should be based on the specific question being raised. One of my mentors (the late E. L. Wynder) early in my career advised me to always ask the right question that will inform the selection of the appropriate experimental model. He also said: know what not to do!

6.1. *Strengths and limitations of animal models*

There are a number of factors which should be considered prior to the selection of the animal model that best provides answers to the question being raised. For example, whole body exposure to cigarette smoke can lead to deposition of particles on the animal's pelt which leads to oral exposure when the animal grooms itself. In addition, extensive handling and restraining of

> *Research animals are valuable for studying the toxicity and carcinogenicity of new tobacco products.*

animals for nose-only exposure can lead to stress and body weight loss which also compromises the interpretation of the results.

The collective outcomes of the studies performed in the hamster model demonstrating that inhalation of tobacco smoke induced cancer in the larynx are convincing. However, the lack of tumor induction in the hamster lung remains a limitation of this model. The hamster model tends to be prohibitively expensive and furthermore weight loss can compromise the interpretation of the results.

The lung tumor model using the strain A/J mouse is rather simple and inexpensive and the results are reproducible, but it has several drawbacks. The A/J mouse strain is highly susceptible to lung tumor induction by agents other than cigarette smoke[84] and the observed increase in mainly benign lung tumors induced by smoke, while statistically significant, is generally small. This relatively weak response makes the model unsuitable to statistically evaluate the impact of modifiers on the development of lung tumors. For a solid statistical experimental design, a relatively large number of mice would be needed to achieve an unequivocal conclusion and such a study could be prohibitively expensive. Additional concerns are the lack of body weight gain of treated mice as well as the current incomplete understanding regarding the need for a recovery period following smoke inhalation to induce tumors.

There are several attractive features of the B63F1 mouse strain model reported by Hutt *et al.*[59] demonstrating the powerful carcinogenicity in the lung of tobacco smoke administered by whole body exposure. The histological features and the genetic and epigenetic alterations observed in the mouse lung following whole body exposure are similar to those found in human lung cancer. However, the long duration of this study (~930 days) as well as the need for specialized equipment and resources constitute potentially major obstacles. It would be very expensive to compare multiple different tobacco products for their potential carcinogenicity or to test several promising cancer preventive agents in this model. Similar limitations apply to whole body exposure of rats to tobacco smoke.

6.2. *Human smoking inhalation patterns differ from those of animals*

Mouse skin painting studies using tobacco smoke condensate (tar) provided mechanistic insights related to cancer induction. This model was useful

> *Humans are deep inhalers of cigarette smoke, but rodents are shallow breathers.*

in the identification of some of the active carcinogenic components in tobacco smoke condensate. However, smoke inhalation models are more realistic. As described above, several animal models of inhaled tobacco smoke have been employed, each having unique strengths and weaknesses. Animals are usually forced involuntarily to inhale the smoke but they do everything possible to avoid it and they will change to a shallow breathing pattern that affects the dose delivered to the various parts of their respiratory system. Rodents are obligatory nose-breathers and because both rodents and dogs have more convoluted and intricate nasal turbinate patterns than humans, the dynamics of particle deposition in the upper respiratory tract might be different.[15] As a result, these approaches to respiratory system exposure to tobacco smoke can never fully represent the exposure patterns of human smokers since humans deeply inhale cigarette smoke to satisfy their nicotine addiction (see Section 4.3). Nevertheless, animal studies remain important for elucidating mechanisms that can account for cancer induction by tobacco products (see Section 2) and evaluating new products.

6.3. *Animal Inhalation Studies and Biomarkers of Risk and Exposure to Tobacco Smoke*

Using sensitive analytical methods, the levels of tobacco carcinogen-induced DNA damage can be measured and are considered potential biomarkers of cancer risk. There are also other types of biomarkers which reflect the extent of tobacco smoke exposure (see Chapter 7).

In addition to the numerous carcinogens identified in tobacco smoke, it is also a rich source of free radicals that are thought to play an important role in the induction of oxidative damage that contributes to carcinogenesis and the depletion of protective blood antioxidant levels.[85] Oxidative damage to DNA, proteins, and lipids can be measured in smokers. Additional studies used proteomics and metabolomics approaches to discover potential biomarkers of tobacco smoke exposure. In our laboratory, a proteomic profiling of human plasma identified a protein (APOE) as being associated with smoking and a marker for lung squamous metaplasia.[86] The effects of cigarette smoke on metabolomics profiles in the blood of smokers have been examined.[87] Several metabolites were identified that provided important insights toward a better understanding of the mechanisms that can account for tobacco-related carcinogenesis. Further studies examined the effects of tobacco smoke and e-cigarettes on the gut and the oral microbiome.[88] The results, based on the effects of smoking on potentially beneficial or harmful bacteria, suggest that e-cigarettes may be a safer alternative to tobacco smoking. Well-designed inhalation studies in laboratory animals exposed to tobacco smoke can provide insights on the role of tobacco products and factors such as diet and cancer preventive agents on the levels of various biomarkers. A comparison of biomarkers identified in animal inhalation studies with those of active smokers may lead to identification of factors that contribute to the carcinogenicity of tobacco smoke.

7. Summary

In the first half of the 20th century, scientists examined the potential carcinogenic effects of tobacco smoke administered in different forms and via different routes (injection, painting, inhalation) to various laboratory animals (guinea pigs, rabbits, rats, mice). The results of these studies were not conclusive because of the lack of appropriate resources and poorly designed experimental protocols; however, they did suggest that tobacco smoke could induce cancer in animals. In the second half of the 20th century, scientists improved their experimental designs employing better smoke delivery devices, well-defined dose response studies and thorough histological examinations of tumors. Collectively, these studies further supported the carcinogenicity of tobacco smoke in laboratory animals (see Section 4).

Topical application (painting) of cigarette smoke condensate (tar) induced both benign and malignant tumors in mouse skin and in rabbit ears. Topical application of the tar to the oral mucosa of mice resulted in increased incidences of lung tumors and lymphoma. Intra-pulmonary injection of the tar produced lung tumors in the rat. Studies revealed that the tar can act as a tumor initiator as well as a co-carcinogen or tumor promoter. Taken together, the evidence that mainstream cigarette smoke condensate causes cancer in laboratory animals is convincing. Cigarette smoke has also been tested in animals by inhalation in attempts to simulate human smoking patterns. Exposing hamsters to whole tobacco smoke resulted in the development of carcinoma in the larynx. Rats exposed to whole tobacco smoke developed benign and malignant lung tumors. Exposure of mice to environmental tobacco smoke or whole tobacco smoke induced both benign and malignant lung tumors.

Among cancer researchers, it is recognized that animal models do not fully recapitulate human exposure to tobacco smoke and even the specific types of tumors developed in animals do not fully represent human cancer. Based on the question being raised and the available resources, the selection of the appropriate animal model to study tobacco carcinogenesis is critical. Animal models consistently provide important mechanistic insights on the carcinogenicity of individual carcinogens identified in tobacco smoke.[89–91] Undoubtedly they will remain valuable resources when evaluating the risks of newly developed tobacco-related products. Furthermore, animal models can be used to discover biomarkers of exposure and harm of tobacco smoke and to examine approaches to cancer prevention.

References

1. Siegel RL, Miller KD, Jemal A. Cancer statistics, 2020. *CA Cancer J Clin* 2020;70(1):7–30. doi: 10.3322/caac.21590.
2. International Agency for Research on Cancer. Personal habits and indoor combustions. In *IARC Monographs on the Evaluation of Carcinogenic Risks to Humans, vol 100e*. (Lyon FR: IARC, 2012).
3. Vineis P, Alavanja M, Buffler P, *et al*. Tobacco and cancer: recent epidemiological evidence. *J Natl Cancer Inst* 2004;96(2):99–106. doi: 10.1093/jnci/djh014.
4. Thun M, Day-Lally C, Myers D, *et al*. Changes in cigarette-related disease risks and their implication for prevention and control: Smoking and Tobacco Control Monograph 8, Chapter 4. (Bethesda, MD: U.S. Department of Health and Human Services, Pubic Health Service, National Institute of Health, 1997).
5. Wynder EL, Graham EA. Landmark article May 27, 1950: Tobacco Smoking as a possible etiologic factor in bronchiogenic carcinoma. A study of six hundred and eighty-four proved cases. By Ernest L. Wynder and Evarts A. Graham. *JAMA* 1985;253(20):2986–94. doi: 10.1001/jama.253.20.2986.
6. Doll R, Hill AB. Smoking and carcinoma of the lung; preliminary report. *Br Med J* 1950;2(4682):739–48. doi: 10.1136/bmj.2.4682.739.
7. Hoffmann D, Hoffmann I, El-Bayoumy K. The less harmful cigarette: A controversial issue. a tribute to Ernst L. Wynder. *Chem Res Toxicol* 2001;14(7):767–90.
8. Hoffmann D, Hoffmann I. The changing cigarette, 1950–1995. *J Toxicol Environ Health* 1997;50(4):307–64.
9. Wynder EL, Hoffmann D. Some practical aspects of the smoking-cancer problem. *N Engl J Med* 1960;262:540–5. doi: 10.1056/nejm196003172621102.

10. Carroll Chapman SL, Wu LT. E-cigarette prevalence and correlates of use among adolescents versus adults: a review and comparison. *J Psychiatr Res* 2014;54:43–54. doi: 10.1016/j.jpsychires.2014.03.005.

11. Pearson JL, Richardson A, Niaura RS, Vallone DM, Abrams DB. e-Cigarette awareness, use, and harm perceptions in US adults. *Am J Public Health* 2012;102(9):1758–66. doi: 10.2105/ajph.2011.300526.

12. Oriakhi M. Vaping: An emerging health hazard. *Cureus* 2020;12(3):e7421. doi: 10.7759/cureus.7421.

13. Wynder E, Hoffmann D. *Tobacco and tobacco smoke: Studies in experimental carcinogenesis*. (New York: Academic Press, 1967).

14. International Agency for Research on Cancer. Tobacco smoking. In *IARC Monographs on the Evaluation of Carcinogenic Risks to Humans, vol 38*. (Lyon FR: IARC, 1983).

15. International Agency for Research on Cancer. Tobacco smoke and involuntary smoking. In *IARC Monographs on the Evaluation of Carcinogenic Risks to Humans, vol 83*. (Lyon FR: IARC, 2004).

16. Bradford JA, Harlan WR, Hanmer HR. Nature of cigaret smoke: Technic of experimental smoking. *Industr Eng Chem* 1936;28(7):836–9.

17. Pillsbury H, Bright C, O'Connor K, Irish F. Tar and nicotine in cigarette smoke. *J Assoc Off Anal Chem* 1969:458–62.

18. Wynder EL, Graham EA, Croninger AB. Experimental production of carcinoma with cigarette tar. *Cancer Res* 1953;13(12):855–64.

19. Wynder EL, Hoffmann D. A study of tobacco carcinogenesis. VII. The role of higher polycyclic hydrocarbons. *Cancer* 1959;12:1079–86. doi: 10.1002/1097-0142 (195911/12)12:6<1079::aid-cncr2820120604>3.0.co;2-i.

20. Conney AH. Induction of microsomal enzymes by foreign chemicals and carcinogenesis by polycyclic aromatic hydrocarbons: G. H. A. Clowes Memorial Lecture. *Cancer Res* 1982;42(12):4875–917.

21. El-Bayoumy K, Chen KM, Zhang SM, *et al.* Carcinogenesis of the oral cavity: Environmental causes and potential prevention by black raspberry. *Chem Res Toxicol* 2017;30(1):126–44. doi: 10.1021/acs.chemrestox.6b00306.

22. International Agency for Research on Cancer. Some Non-Heterocyclic Polycyclic Aromatic Hydrocarbons and Some Related Exposures. In *IARC Monographs on the Evaluation of Carcinogenic Risks to Humans, vol 92* (Lyon, FR: IARC, 2010).

23. El-Bayoumy K, Christensen ND, Hu J, *et al.* An integrated approach for preventing oral cavity and oropharyngeal cancers: two etiologies with distinct and shared mechanisms of carcinogenesis. *Cancer Prev Res (Phila)* 2020;13(8):649–660. doi: 10.1158/1940-6207.capr-20-0096.

24. Hoffmann D, Wynder EL. A study of tobacco carcinogenesis. XI. Tumor initiators, tumor accelerators, and tumor promoting activity of condensate fractions. *Cancer* 1971;27(4):848–64. doi: 10.1002/1097-0142(197104)27:4<848::aid-cncr2820270415>3.0.co;2-4.

25. Croninger AB, Graham EA, Wynder EL. Experimental production of carcinoma with tobacco products. V. Carcinoma induction in mice with cigar, pipe, and all-tobacco cigarette tar. *Cancer Res* 1958;18(11):1263–71.

26. Dipaolo JA, Levin ML. Tumor incidence in mice after oral painting with cigarette smoke condensate. *J Natl Cancer Inst* 1965;34:595–600.

27. El-Bayoumy K, Muscat JE, Hoffmann D. Chapter 10: Nutrition and Tobacco-Related Cancers, *Nutritional Oncology*, 2nd Ed., Heber D, pp. 199–217. (Burlington: Academic Press, 2006).

28. Coggins CR. A review of chronic inhalation studies with mainstream cigarette smoke in rats and mice. *Toxicol Pathol* 1998;26(3):307–14; discussion 315. doi: 10.1177/019262339802600301.

29. Coggins CR. A review of chronic inhalation studies with mainstream cigarette smoke, in hamsters, dogs, and nonhuman primates. *Toxicol Pathol* 2001;29(5):550–7. doi: 10.1080/019262301317226357.

30. Coggins CR. A minireview of chronic animal inhalation studies with mainstream cigarette smoke. *Inhal Toxicol* 2002;14(10):991–1002. doi: 10.1080/08958370290084746.

31. Witschi H. A/J mouse as a model for lung tumorigenesis caused by tobacco smoke: strengths and weaknesses. *Exp Lung Res* 2005;31(1):3–18. doi: 10.1080/01902140490494959.

32. Wei T, Buehler D, Ward-Shaw E, Lambert PF. An infection-based murine model for papillomavirus-associated head and neck cancer. mBio 2020;11(3) doi: 10.1128/mBio.00908-20.

33. Marian C, O'Connor RJ, Djordjevic MV, Rees VW, Hatsukami DK, Shields PG. Reconciling human smoking behavior and machine smoking patterns: implications for understanding smoking behavior and the impact on laboratory studies. *Cancer Epidemiol Biomarkers Prev* 2009;18(12):3305–20. doi: 10.1158/1055-9965.epi-09-1014.

34. International Organization for Standardization. ISO 3308:2012. Routine analytical cigarette-smoking machine-definitions and standard conditions. London, UK, 2012.

35. Dontenwill W, Chevalier HJ, Harke HP, Lafrenz U, Reckzeh G, Schneider B. Investigations on the effects of chronic cigarette-smoke inhalation in Syrian golden hamsters. *J Natl Cancer Inst* 1973;51(6):1781–832. doi: 10.1093/jnci/51.6.1781.

36. Bernfeld P, Homburger F, Russfield AB. Strain differences in the response of inbred Syrian hamsters to cigarette smoke inhalation. *J Natl Cancer Inst* 1974;53(4):1141–57. doi: 10.1093/jnci/53.4.1141.

37. Bernfeld P, Homburger F, Soto E, Pai KJ. Cigarette smoke inhalation studies in inbred Syrian golden hamsters. *J Natl Cancer Inst* 1979;63(3):675–89. doi: 10.1093/jnci/63.3.675.

38. Wehner A, Busch R, Olson R. In *Experimental lung cancer: Carcinogenesis and bioassays international symposium held at the Battelle Seattle Research Center*, Karbe E, JF P, eds., 360–8. (Seattle WA.: Springer, 1974).

39. Wehner AP, Busch RH, Olson RJ, Craig DK. Chronic inhalation of asbestos and cigarette smoke by hamsters. *Environ Res* 1975;10(3):368–83. doi: 10.1016/0013-9351(75)90032-8.

40. Wehner AP, Busch RH, Olson RJ, Craig DK. Chronic inhalation of nickel oxide and cigarette smoke by hamsters. *Am Ind Hyg Assoc J* 1975;36(11):801–10. doi: 10.1080/0002889758507346.

41. Wehner AP, Olson RJ, Busch RH. Increased life span and decreased weight in hamsters exposed to cigarette smoke. *Arch Environ Health* 1976;31(3):146–53. doi: 10.1080/00039896.1976.10667209.

42. Hoffmann D, Rivenson A, Hecht SS, Hilfrich J, Kobayashi N, Wynder EL. Model studies in tobacco carcinogenesis with the Syrian golden hamster. *Prog Exp Tumor Res* 1979;24:370–90. doi: 10.1159/000402112.

43. Hecht SS. Biochemistry, biology, and carcinogenicity of tobacco-specific *N*-nitrosamines. *Chem Res Toxicol* 1998;11(6):559–603. doi: 10.1021/tx980005y.

44. Hecht SS, Adams JD, Numoto S, Hoffmann D. Induction of respiratory tract tumors in Syrian golden hamsters by a single dose of 4-(methylnitrosamino)-1-(3-pyridyl)-1-butanone (NNK) and the effect of smoke inhalation. *Carcinogenesis* 1983;4(10):1287–90. doi: 10.1093/carcin/4.10.1287.

45. Davis BR, Whitehead JK, Gill ME, Lee PN, Butterworth AD, Roe FJ. Response of rat lung to inhaled tobacco smoke with or without prior exposure to 3,4-benzpyrene (BP) given by intratracheal instillation. *Br J Cancer* 1975;31(4):469–84. doi: 10.1038/bjc.1975.87.

46. Davis BR, Whitehead JK, Gill ME, Lee PN, Butterworth AD, Roe FJ. Response of rat lung to inhaled vapour phase constituents (VP) of tobacco smoke alone or in conjunction with smoke condensate or fractions of smoke condensate given by intratracheal instillation. *Br J Cancer* 1975;31(4):462–8. doi: 10.1038/bjc.1975.86.

47. Dalbey WE, Nettesheim P, Griesemer R, Caton JE, Guerin MR. Chronic inhalation of cigarette smoke by F344 rats. *J Natl Cancer Inst* 1980;64(2):383–90. doi: 10.1093/jnci/64.2.383.

48. Wehner AP, Dagle GE, Milliman EM, *et al.* Inhalation bioassay of cigarette smoke in rats. *Toxicol Appl Pharmacol* 1981;61(1):1–17. doi: 10.1016/0041-008x(81)90002-8.

49. Mauderly JL, Gigliotti AP, Barr EB, *et al.* Chronic inhalation exposure to mainstream cigarette smoke increases lung and nasal tumor incidence in rats. *Toxicol Sci* 2004;81(2):280–92. doi: 10.1093/toxsci/kfh203.

50. Lorenz E, Stewart H, Daniel J, Nelson C. The effects of breathing tobacco smoke on strain A mice. *Cancer Res* 1943;3:123.

51. Essenberg JM. Cigarette smoke and the incidence of primary neoplasm of the lung in the albino mouse. *Science* 1952;116(3021):561–2. doi: 10.1126/science.116.3021.561.

52. Harris RJ, Negroni G. Production of lung carcinomas in C57BL mice exposed to a cigarette smoke and air mixture. *Br Med J* 1967;4(5580): 637–41. doi: 10.1136/bmj.4.5580.637.

53. Otto H, Elmenhorst H. Experimental studies on tumour induction with the gas phase of cigarette smoke (in German). *Z Krebsforsch* 1967;70:45–47.

54. Wynder EL, Taguchi KT, Baden V, Hoffmann D. Tobacco carcinogenesis. IX. Effect of cigarette smoke on respiratory tract of mice after passive inhalation. *Cancer* 1968;21(1):134–53. doi: 10.1002/1097-0142(196801)21: 1<134::aid-cncr2820210122>3.0.co;2-p.

55. Leuchtenberger C, Leuchtenberger R. Differential cytological and cytochemical responses of various cultures from mouse tissues to repeated exposures to puffs from the gas phase of charcoal-filtered fresh cigarette smoke. *Exp Cell Res* 1970;62(1):161–72. doi: 10.1016/0014-4827(79) 90517-2.

56. Henry CJ, Kouri RE. Chronic inhalation studies in mice. II. Effects of long-term exposure to 2R1 cigarette smoke on (C57BL/Cum x C3H/AnfCum)F1 mice. *J Natl Cancer Inst* 1986;77(1):203–12.

57. Witschi H, Espiritu I, Peake JL, Wu K, Maronpot RR, Pinkerton KE. The carcinogenicity of environmental tobacco smoke. *Carcinogenesis* 1997;18(3):575–86. doi: 10.1093/carcin/18.3.575.

58. De Flora S, Izzotti A, D'Agostini F, *et al.* Induction and modulation of lung tumors: genomic and transcriptional alterations in cigarette smoke-exposed mice. *Exp Lung Res* 2005;31(1):19–35. doi: 10.1080/01902140490 494986.

59. Hutt JA, Vuillemenot BR, Barr EB, *et al.* Life-span inhalation exposure to mainstream cigarette smoke induces lung cancer in B6C3F1 mice through genetic and epigenetic pathways. *Carcinogenesis* 2005;26(11):1999–2009. doi: 10.1093/carcin/bgi150.

60. Liu C, Russell RM, Wang XD. Low dose beta-carotene supplementation of ferrets attenuates smoke-induced lung phosphorylation of JNK, p38 MAPK, and p53 proteins. *J Nutr* 2004;134(10):2705–10. doi: 10.1093/jn/134.10.2705.

61. Liu C, Russell RM, Wang XD. Alpha-tocopherol and ascorbic acid decrease the production of beta-apo-carotenals and increase the formation of retinoids from beta-carotene in the lung tissues of cigarette smoke-exposed ferrets in vitro. *J Nutr* 2004;134(2):426–30. doi: 10.1093/jn/134.2.426.

62. Liu C, Lian F, Smith DE, Russell RM, Wang XD. Lycopene supplementation inhibits lung squamous metaplasia and induces apoptosis via up-regulating insulin-like growth factor-binding protein 3 in cigarette smoke-exposed ferrets. *Cancer Res* 2003;63(12):3138–44.

63. Liu C, Russell RM, Wang XD. Exposing ferrets to cigarette smoke and a pharmacological dose of beta-carotene supplementation enhance in vitro retinoic acid catabolism in lungs via induction of cytochrome P450 enzymes. *J Nutr* 2003;133(1):173–9. doi: 10.1093/jn/133.1.173.

64. Liu C, Wang XD, Bronson RT, Smith DE, Krinsky NI, Russell RM. Effects of physiological versus pharmacological beta-carotene supplementation on cell proliferation and histopathological changes in the lungs of cigarette smoke-exposed ferrets. *Carcinogenesis* 2000;21(12):2245–53. doi: 10.1093/carcin/21.12.2245.

65. Wang XD, Liu C, Bronson RT, Smith DE, Krinsky NI, Russell M. Retinoid signaling and activator protein-1 expression in ferrets given beta-carotene supplements and exposed to tobacco smoke. *J Natl Cancer Inst* 1999;91(1):60–6. doi: 10.1093/jnci/91.1.60.

66. Kim Y, Liu XS, Liu C, Smith DE, Russell RM, Wang XD. Induction of pulmonary neoplasia in the smoke-exposed ferret by 4-(methylnitrosamino)-1-(3-pyridyl)-1-butanone (NNK): a model for human lung cancer. *Cancer Lett* 2006;234(2):209–19. doi: 10.1016/j.canlet.2005.03.052.

67. Aizawa K, Liu C, Veeramachaneni S, Hu KQ, Smith DE, Wang XD. Development of ferret as a human lung cancer model by injecting 4-(*N*-methyl-*N*-nitrosamino)-1-(3-pyridyl)-1-butanone (NNK). *Lung Cancer* 2013;82(3):390–6. doi: 10.1016/j.lungcan.2013.09.012.

68. Fiala ES, Sohn OS, Wang CX, *et al.* Induction of preneoplastic lung lesions in guinea pigs by cigarette smoke inhalation and their exacerbation by high dietary levels of vitamins C and E. *Carcinogenesis* 2005;26(3):605–12. doi: 10.1093/carcin/bgh341.

69. Wyss AB, Hashibe M, Lee YA, *et al.* Smokeless tobacco use and the risk of head and neck cancer: pooled analysis of US studies in the INHANCE

Consortium. *Am J Epidemiol* 2016;184(10):703–716. doi: 10.1093/aje/kww075.

70. Winn DM, Blot WJ, Shy CM, Pickle LW, Toledo A, Fraumeni JF, Jr. Snuff dipping and oral cancer among women in the southern United States. *N Engl J Med* 1981;304(13):745–9. doi: 10.1056/nejm198103263041301.

71. Hoffmann D, Djordjevic MV. Chemical composition and carcinogenicity of smokeless tobacco. *Adv Dent Res* 1997;11(3):322–9. doi: 10.1177/08959374970110030301.

72. Stepanov I, Villalta PW, Knezevich A, Jensen J, Hatsukami D, Hecht SS. Analysis of 23 polycyclic aromatic hydrocarbons in smokeless tobacco by gas chromatography-mass spectrometry. *Chem Res Toxicol* 2010;23(1):66–73. doi: 10.1021/tx900281u.

73. Peacock EE, Jr., Greenberg BG, Brawley BW. The effect of snuff and tobacco on the production of oral carcinoma: an experimental and epidemiological study. *Ann Surg* 1960;151(4):542–50. doi: 10.1097/00000658-196004000-00014.

74. Kandarkar SV, Sirsat SM. Changes in vitamin A conditioned hamster cheek pouch epithelium on exposure to commercial shell lime (calcium hydroxide) and tobacco. I-Optical histopathology. *J Oral Pathol* 1977;6(4):191–202. doi: 10.1111/j.1600-0714.1977.tb01641.x.

75. Kolas S. Investigation of normal human saliva for possible anticarinogenic action and chemical carcinogenesis in mucous membranes. *Oral Surg Oral Med Oral Pathol* 1955;8(11):1192–203. doi: 10.1016/0030-4220(55)90383-2.

76. Levy BM. Experimental oral carcinogenesis. *J Dent Res* 1963;2:321–7. doi: 10.1177/00220345630420013601.

77. Hirsch JM, Thilander H. Snuff-induced lesions of the oral mucosa — an experimental model in the rat. *J Oral Pathol* 1981;10(5):342–53. doi: 10.1111/j.1600-0714.1981.tb01286.x.

78. Hirsch JM, Johansson SL. Effect of long-term application of snuff on the oral mucosa: an experimental study in the rat. *J Oral Pathol* 1983;12(3):187–98. doi: 10.1111/j.1600-0714.1983.tb00332.x.

79. Hecht SS, Rivenson A, Braley J, DiBello J, Adams JD, Hoffmann D. Induction of oral cavity tumors in F344 rats by tobacco-specific nitrosamines and snuff. *Cancer Res* 1986;46(8):4162–6.

80. International Agency for Research on Cancer. Tobacco habits other than smoking; betel-quid and areca-nut chewing; and some related nitrosamines. In *IARC Monographs on the Evaluation of Carcinogenic Risks to Humans, vol 37*. (Lyon, FR: IARC, 1985).

81. Mohtashamipur E, Mohtashamipur A, Germann PG, Ernst H, Norpoth K, Mohr U. Comparative carcinogenicity of cigarette mainstream and side-stream smoke condensates on the mouse skin. *J Cancer Res Clin Oncol* 1990;116(6):604–8. doi: 10.1007/bf01637081.

82. Crosby K. How the Food and Drug Administration convinced teens to rethink their relationship with cigarettes. *Am J Prev Med* 2019;56(2 Suppl 1):S1–4. doi: 10.1016/j.amepre.2018.10.013.

83. WHO. *WHO global report on trends in prevalence of tobacco use 2000–2025*, third edition. (Geneva: World Health Organization, 2019).

84. Stoner GD. Lung tumors in strain A mice as a bioassay for carcinogenicity of environmental chemicals. *Exp Lung Res* 1991;17(2):405–23. doi: 10.3109/01902149109064428.

85. Mayne ST. Antioxidant nutrients and chronic disease: use of biomarkers of exposure and oxidative stress status in epidemiologic research. *J Nutr* 2003;133 Suppl 3:933s–940s. doi: 10.1093/jn/133.3.933S.

86. Rice SJ, Liu X, Miller B, *et al.* Proteomic profiling of human plasma identifies apolipoprotein E as being associated with smoking and a marker for squamous metaplasia of the lung. *Proteomics* 2015;15(18):3267–77. doi: 10.1002/pmic.201500029.

87. Hsu PC, Lan RS, Brasky TM, *et al.* Metabolomic profiles of current cigarette smokers. *Mol Carcinog* 2017;56(2):594–606. doi: 10.1002/mc.22519.

88. Stewart CJ, Auchtung TA, Ajami NJ, *et al.* Effects of tobacco smoke and electronic cigarette vapor exposure on the oral and gut microbiota in humans: A pilot study. *PeerJ* 2018;6:e4693. doi: 10.7717/peerj.4693.

89. Wynder EL, Hoffmann D. Smoking and lung cancer: scientific challenges and opportunities. *Cancer Res.* 1994;54(20):5284–95.

90. Penning TM. *Chemical Carcinogenesis.* Humana Press, 2011.

91. Hecht SS, Szabo E. Fifty years of tobacco carcinogenesis research: from mechanisms to early detection and prevention of lung cancer. *Cancer Prev Res (Phila).* 2014;7(1):1–8. doi: 10.1158/1940-6207.capr-13-0371.

https://doi.org/10.1142/9789811239533_0004

Chapter 4

Carcinogens and Toxicants in Combusted Tobacco Products and Related Cancer Risks

Irina Stepanov*

1. Introduction

The phrase "people smoke for the nicotine but they die from the tar", coined in 1976 by Michael Russell,[1] is often quoted to underscore the key role of nicotine in driving tobacco-associated diseases and to emphasize the opportunity for harm reduction. There are some important revisions that could be made to improve the accuracy of this statement. To begin with, "tar" is an arbitrarily defined fraction of cigarette smoke, calculated by subtracting nicotine and water content from the particulate matter trapped on Cambridge filter pads when cigarettes are smoked by machines (more on this later). In addition, it is not only "tar" but also the highly toxic and carcinogenic chemicals in the gas phase of the smoke that contribute to the harmfulness of cigarette smoke. And the evidence that exposure to secondhand smoke causes deadly diseases in non-smokers, including lung cancer, is convincing. Lastly, people who use certain smokeless tobacco products, also for nicotine, die not from the "tar" but from oral and esophageal cancer caused by potent

---

*University of Minnesota, USA. stepa011@umn.edu

carcinogens that are present in tobacco itself (see Chapter 5). Despite these shortcomings, the phrase is still accurate in referring to the process of combustion, and the inhalation of the resulting mixture of thousands of chemicals, as key features that make cigarettes and other combusted tobacco products the deadliest form of nicotine intake. After all, combusted tobacco products are "the only legal consumer products that kill when used as intended".

2. Types of Combusted Tobacco Products

The most popular product in the combusted tobacco category — cigarettes — are smoked by more than 1 billion people in the world and are responsible for the majority of tobacco-attributable disease and death in the US and worldwide. Cigarettes have a deceivingly simple appearance (Figure 1): a paper "tube" with tobacco filler inside (containing processed tobacco leaves and additives), with or without a filter tip attached to it. However, cigarettes are highly sophisticated products, carefully engineered to efficiently deliver nicotine to smokers. Other combusted tobacco product types, such as cigars of various sizes, cigarillos, and pipes (Figure 1) are also used by burning tobacco and inhaling the resulting smoke. The use of such products is less prevalent than cigarette smoking, but not negligible. For example, an estimated 9.3 million adults in the US currently smoke cigars and an estimated 190,000 high school students smoke pipes.[2] In addition to such traditional combusted tobacco

Figure 1:   Types of combusted tobacco products.
Source: FDA CTP website.

products, popular in the Western world, other products types, such as kreteks (made with a blend of tobacco, cloves, and flavors) and bidis (tobacco wrapped in tendu or temburni leaf) are used in some countries in Asia and imported to other parts of the world. While prevalence of such distinctive cigarettes is relatively low on the global scale, studies conducted in places where they are predominantly used suggest that their risks are similar to those from smoking regular tobacco cigarettes, including various cancers and a range of pulmonary and cardiovascular diseases.

3. A Closer Look at the Components and Ingredients of Combusted Tobacco Products

Tobacco is the common key component of all combusted tobacco products. There are numerous species of tobacco plant, although the predominant species used in the manufacturing of commercial tobacco products are *Nicotiana tabacum, Nicotiana rustica*, and *Nicotiana glauca*. Tobacco fillers of combusted products and smokeless products such as moist snuff and snus are typically made with various types of *N. tabacum*. Smokeless tobacco products popular in Southeast Asia are often made with *N. rustica*, while *N. glauca* is used in preparation of toombak in Africa.[3-5]

The US-manufactured cigarettes are made with a blend of various tobacco types, such as Burley, Maryland, Virginia-type, and Oriental tobacco. Each tobacco type in the blend makes a unique contribution to the chemical composition, flavor and other characteristics of cigarette smoke, and is processed by a certain technique. For example, Burley and Maryland tobaccos are air-cured, Virginia-type bright tobaccos are flue-cured, and Oriental tobacco is sun-cured. Each tobacco type is cured by a specific curing method because of the differences in the chemical profile of green tobacco leaves across the tobacco types. The goal of the curing process is to increase the levels of "favorable" and minimize the "unfavorable" chemical compounds. The resulting physico-chemical properties of the processed tobacco determine its burn rate, nicotine content and flavor of the resulting smoke, as well as cigarette smoldering rate between puffs.[6] For example, Burley tobacco is typically lighter in weight and higher in nicotine, but lower in sugar content compared to Virginia tobacco. These tobacco characteristics result in quick burning and harsh, difficult to inhale smoke if cigarettes are made exclusively from Burley tobacco. On the other hand, cigarettes made from Virginia-type tobacco may burn slower and give a smoother, but lower-nicotine smoke with less complex flavor. For these reasons, blending of various tobacco types is another approach to balance out the chemical composition of the tobacco filler that is used in the manufacturing of some cigarettes. As mentioned earlier, American-blended cigarettes contain Burley, Maryland, Virginia-type, and often Oriental tobacco (for its aromatic properties), in various proportions. In addition, expanded, puffed and freeze-dried tobaccos are often being used in blended cigarettes, which allows reduction of the amount of tobacco required to fill a cigarette.[7] Reconstituted tobacco is also used in cigarette blends for similar reasons. Such tobacco is made of tobacco by-products (e.g., leaf ribs, stems, and tobacco "dust") which are processed into a pulp and mixed with adhesives, fibers, humectants, and flavorings.[6,7] Reconstituted tobacco is less expensive and has a faster burn rate than the filler made with tobacco leaves.

In addition to various tobacco types, cigarette filler more often than not contains a range of non-tobacco ingredients, or additives. Additives are used for the general purpose of further "improving" the smoking experience by making cigarette smoke less harsh and more palatable and appealing. However, individual contributions of additives are diverse and complex. For example, various sugar-containing ingredients such as brown sugar, honey, corn syrup, and molasses are commonly added to tobacco filler.[8] Such ingredients undergo caramelization and other transformations during cigarette combustion, and play an important role in palatability-related smoke characteristics such as flavor, taste, and harshness. In addition, as we will discuss later in this chapter, these processes can lead to the formation of a variety of toxic and carcinogenic chemical compounds. Ammonia and diammonium phosphate represent another type of key additives that have a range of effects on cigarette smoke properties.[6] These additives increase the amount of unprotonated (biologically available) nicotine in the smoke, enhance the "mouth feel" sensation, and their reactions with sugars and acids in tobacco and smoke contribute to the formation of smoke flavor.[6,9,10] Some other ingredients are added to directly modify the flavor, for example menthol or cocoa.[6,11] However, such ingredients may contribute to bronchodilation and the subsequent enhanced absorption of smoke in the respiratory tract.[11] A special category of additives is humectants, which are added to retain moisture and assure plasticity of tobacco filler, but also to prevent harshness of smoke that would be produced by dry tobacco. Such humectants are mainly glycerol and propylene glycol, and can account for up to 5% of the weight of cigarette tobacco.[12] Both compounds can produce toxic decomposition by-products, such as acrolein and propylene oxide, during smoking.[12] Importantly, these complex effects of additives do not happen in isolation, but are closely intertwined with the complex chemistry of the tobacco blend which is most likely carefully engineered by cigarette manufacturers to enhance nicotine delivery and the palatability of cigarettes.

Other basic components of most cigarettes are paper wrapping and a filter. The obvious role of paper wrapping is to contain the tobacco filler. However, features like paper thickness, porosity and the presence of the ignition propensity bands (in "fire safe" cigarettes) can affect the rate at which a cigarette burns.[6] Most modern cigarettes feature filters which are commonly made of cellulose acetate fibers, but may include other components such as paper or charcoal. The purported role of filters is to trap or remove some of the cigarette smoke particles and chemicals. However, as in the case with additives, the impact of filters on smoke properties is complex and is likely to result in more harm than benefit. This may be especially true if filters contain ventilation holes (more on this later in this chapter).[13,14] Cigars, cigarillos, and pipe tobacco do not typically include the paper wrapping or filters; instead, such products may be wrapped in tobacco leaf or used in loose form. However, all these products involve the combustion of tobacco and share the inventory of chemical constituents that are present in their smoke.

4. Overall Chemical Makeup of Tobacco Smoke

The evidence that there is a dose-response association between smoking and lung cancer, which has been accumulating from epidemiological studies since the 1950s, prompted research into the chemical composition of tobacco and cigarette smoke. The data were accumulating at an exponential rate: in 1959, Johnstone and Plimmer reported about 600 compounds in cigarette smoke[15]; in 1968 this number increased to 1,000[16]; in 1988 it was 3,794[17]; and by 1996, Green and Rodgman reported 4,800 compounds in tobacco smoke.[12] The most recent comprehensive assessment concludes that there are 9,390 unique chemical compounds in tobacco and cigarette smoke combined, and 6,010 of these are found in tobacco smoke.[18] The quest for even more complete characterization of tobacco smoke chemistry is not over, and new important chemical constituents may be identified in the future.

There are two primary ways by which various chemical constituents end up in cigarette smoke (Figure 2). One is desorption of compounds present in tobacco filler material. This occurs in the parts of the tobacco rod that are close to the burning tip of the cigarette, at temperatures that are below those necessary to initiate the combustion process, but high enough to "evaporate" intact compounds from the surface of tobacco filler (Figure 2). The desorbed constituents are then carried by the flow of smoke that passes through the tobacco rod towards the mouth-end of the cigarette. Constituents that are originally present in the tobacco filler and are transferred by desorption into the smoke include nicotine and other tobacco alkaloids, tobacco-specific nitrosamines, metals, and some other organic and inorganic compounds.

The second mechanism by which chemical constituents appear in the smoke is their formation during the tobacco combustion process. This can occur either through decomposition of compounds originally present in tobacco filler or paper, or via pyrosynthesis from reactive radicals and other molecules present in the smoke. Of the 6,010 compounds in cigarette smoke, only 2,215 are also present in tobacco[18] and the rest are formed during the combustion process. Such constituents are typically volatile and semi-volatile complex molecules such as polycyclic aromatic hydrocarbons (PAHs), aromatic amines, furans, carbonyls, as well as simple gases such as nitrogen oxides, ammonia, and sulfur oxides. For highly ventilated cigarettes, it is also possible that certain chemical constituents are incorporated into cigarette smoke from the ambient air when it is drawn through the filter ventilation holes or the porous paper. Such mechanism could be particularly important if smoking occurs in a highly contaminated environment, such as polluted urban air or indoor smoking spaces.

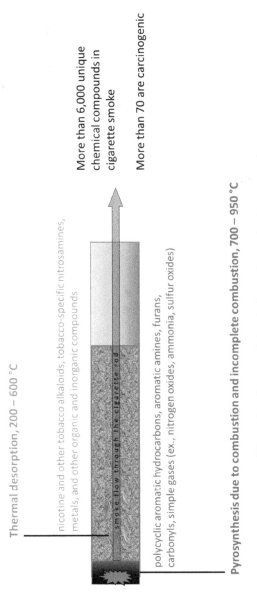

Figure 2:   Sources of chemical constituents in cigarette smoke.

Independent of the source (e.g., desorption or pyrosynthesis), chemical constituents in tobacco smoke are distributed between particulate matter and gas phase, depending on their volatility and other physico-chemical properties. It is important to note that these components of cigarette smoke are defined somewhat arbitrarily. The particulate matter — the mixture of solid particles and liquid droplets — is the portion of the smoke that is trapped on glass-fiber Cambridge filters when cigarettes are smoked by smoking machines for chemical analysis purposes. The Cambridge filters are highly efficient in trapping the particulate matter; for example, unpublished experiments in our laboratory showed that more than 99% of nicotine, which primarily resides in solid particles and liquid droplets in the smoke, is retained by the filters. In addition to nicotine, the particulate matter contains other tobacco alkaloids, various hydrocarbons, phenols, terpenes, organic acids, aromatic amines, and other non-volatile or semi-volatile compounds.[17,19] However, particulate matter accounts for only a fraction of the total weight of the smoke. Smoke "tar", which is widely used in the scientific literature and by the tobacco control community as a reference to the carcinogenic fraction of cigarette smoke, accounts for an even smaller portion of the total smoke mass. Tar is calculated by subtracting the mass of nicotine and water (both originally present in particulate matter) from the total mass of particulate matter. Therefore, tar is an abstract value, rather than a defined smoke fraction, and this term should not be used as a reference to particles present in cigarette smoke. Furthermore, as mentioned earlier in this chapter, carcinogenic and toxic constituents in cigarette smoke are not confined to tar or particulate matter. Significant amounts of such constituents are present in the gas phase of tobacco smoke, which is defined as the remaining portion of smoke that passes through Cambridge filters. The gas phase contains carbon oxides, nitrogen and its oxides, aldehydes, volatile acids and aromatic hydrocarbons, furans, pyridines, pyrazines, and other gases and volatile compounds. A number of compounds of the gas phase are present at very high levels compared to the majority of those found in the particulate matter.[12] As a result, despite containing fewer chemical constituents than the particulate matter, the gas phase accounts for the majority of the total smoke mass. The chemicals present in both the particulate and the gas phase of tobacco smoke are responsible for the detrimental health outcomes associated with smoking.

5. Carcinogens in Tobacco Smoke and Their Role in Cancer Risk

At least 70 carcinogenic constituents have been reported to be present in tobacco smoke, belonging to several classes of chemicals (Table 1). Extensive research has been conducted on the majority of these carcinogens, including animal experiments and epidemiological and clinical studies in humans, providing strong supportive evidence for their role in

Table 1: Classes of chemical carcinogens in tobacco smoke and examples of specific compounds, their IARC classifications and representative ranges.

Chemical class	Examples of specific carcinogens	IARC classification	Range of amounts in cigarette smoke (ng/cigarette)[31]	
			ISO/FTC[a]	Health Canada[a]
Polycyclic aromatic hydrocarbons	BaP	1	1.02–13.9	6.58–29.9
Tobacco-specific *N*-nitrosamines	NNN	1	5.0–195.3	20.6–410.6
	NNK	1	12.4–107.8	39.1–263.0
Aromatic amines	4-Aminobiphenyl	1	0.5–3.3	1.6–7.02
	2-Naphthylamine	1	2.2–17.2	7.8–31.7
Aldehydes	Formaldehyde	1	1,600–52,100	29,300–130,300
	Acetaldehyde	2B	32,000–643,000	930,000–1,540,000
Phenols	Catechol	2B	5,100–62,200	44,200–167,300
Volatile hydrocarbons	Benzene	1	6,100–45,700	49,700–98,300
	1,3-Butadiene	2A	6,400–51,600	77,000–118,300
Other organic carcinogens	Acrylonitrile	2B	900–11,700	12,100–34,300
Metals and other inorganic compounds	Cadmium	1	1.6–101	43.5–197.1
	Lead	2A	3.9–31.4	25.7–70.9

[a]Machine-smoking regimens: ISO/FTC, low-intensity smoking regimen developed by the International Organization for Standardization (ISO) and later adapted in the US as the Federal Trade Commission (FTC); Health Canada, higher-intensity regimen established by Health Canada. More on the implications of machine-smoking regimens can be found later in this chapter.

smoking-associated cancers. The strength of such evidence is sufficient for 15 of these constituents to be classified by the International Agency for Research on Cancer (IARC) as human carcinogens (Group 1), and the rest are classified as probably (Group 2A) or possibly (Group 2B) carcinogenic to humans.[20] Each of these carcinogens is implicated in one or more particular types of cancer, including cancers of the lung, oral cavity, liver, pancreas, bladder, and other cancers, as outlined below. However, the role of individual carcinogens in the development of a specific type of cancer is not likely to be exclusive, and is rather a result of concomitant exposure to multiple carcinogens and other harmful agents in tobacco smoke (Figure 3).

5.1. Combustion-related carcinogens

The first carcinogen identified in cigarette smoke was benzo[*a*]pyrene (BaP),[21] which is one of many PAHs formed during tobacco combustion. BaP is classified as a human carcinogen by the IARC and is widely accepted as a major contributor to lung cancer in smokers.[22,23]

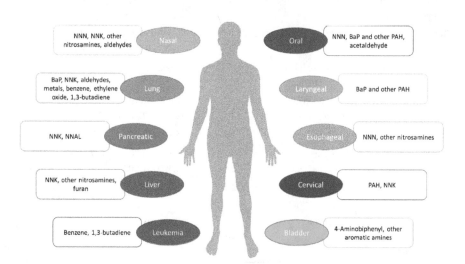

Figure 3:   Examples of tobacco smoke carcinogens implicated as the causative agents for cancers associated with smoking.[20,27] According to the US Surgeon General, smoking is also causally linked to cancers of oropharynx, stomach, kidney and ureter, and colorectal cancer.[20]

Diol-epoxide metabolites of BaP can damage DNA and cause mutations in the TP53 tumor suppressor gene, and such damage and mutations have been detected in human lung.[24-26] Many other PAH are potent carcinogens and are likely to contribute to tobacco smoke carcinogenesis.[23,25,27,28] For example, the carcinogenic activity of dibenz[*a,h*]anthracene and 5-methylchrysene in mouse lung is higher than that of BaP.[29] An important characteristic of PAH is that these compounds are primarily topical carcinogens, acting at the place of contact with tissues. For example, the presence of PAH in the "tar" applied to mouse skin in Wynder's landmark experiments was likely a key causative factor in the development of carcinomas.[30] Therefore, BaP and other carcinogenic PAH are likely to be involved in cancers of the oral cavity and other tissues of upper aerodigestive tract that come in direct contact with cigarette smoke.[25,27]

The majority of other combustion-related carcinogens that are present in tobacco smoke are likely contributors to the risk of aerodigestive tract cancers in smokers, either due to their direct pulmonary carcinogenicity or by inducing oxidative and inflammatory processes that can exacerbate the carcinogenic effects of other smoke constituents. For example, many aldehydes are respiratory irritants and carcinogens. Acetaldehyde and formaldehyde are respiratory tumorigens in laboratory animals[32,33]; acrolein causes cilia-toxicity in the lung and is proposed to be a lung carcinogen[34,35]; and crotonaldehyde forms DNA adducts in the human lung.[36] Respiratory irritation and other toxic and carcinogenic effects caused by aldehydes and other harmful constituents in tobacco smoke can trigger inflammatory processes in the lung. Inflammation involves infiltration of lymphocytes, macrophages, and neutrophils into tissues under stress, and induces lipid peroxidation, these processes resulting in the generation of a spectrum of reactive oxygen and nitrogen species capable of causing extensive damage to DNA and proteins, and resulting in toxic and mutagenic events.[37,38] In addition, cigarette smoke is a rich source of other important pro-oxidants, such as reactive oxygen and nitrogen species, catechols and other compounds which can induce redox cycling, oxidative damage and lead to an inflammatory state.[28,39] Chronic inflammation and oxidative stress are important interlinked contributing factors in the pathogenesis of cigarette smoke-associated diseases, including lung cancer.[40-43]

While cancers of the lung and other upper aerodigestive tract are most prominently associated with smoking, other organs are also targets for carcinogenicity of some combustion-related tobacco smoke constituents. For example, BaP-derived DNA adducts have been detected in smokers' cervical tissues.[44] A substantial body of data supports the role of aromatic amines as the main cause of bladder cancer in smokers, and 4-aminobiphenyl and 2-naphthylamine are known human bladder carcinogens.[45,46] Furan is an effective hepatocarcinogen, and benzene and 1,3-butadiene are the likely contributors to leukemia in smokers.[33,47–49]

5.2. *Tobacco-derived carcinogens*

Among other carcinogens present in tobacco smoke, the IARC Group 1 carcinogens N'-nitrosonornicotine (NNN) and 4-(methylnitrosamino)-1-(3-pyridyl)-1-butanone (NNK) are of particular importance. These compounds are transferred from tobacco filler to smoke during combustion, and exhibit a deadly combination of abundance and organ-specific carcinogenic potency.[50,51] NNN, NNK, and other tobacco-specific N-nitrosamines (TSNA) are formed via nitrosation of tobacco alkaloids during tobacco processing, and therefore are specific to tobacco products.[51–53] Most of the TSNA content in the smoke is due to the transfer of these constituents from tobacco when a cigarette is smoked; however, small amounts may also be formed via pyrosynthesis.[54–56]

The first TSNA reported to be present in tobacco smoke was NNN. The report was published in 1973,[57] almost a decade after the first publication on pulmonary carcinogenicity of NNN in mice.[58] Respiratory carcinogenicity of NNN was intriguing, potentially identifying a new causative agent for lung cancer in smokers. However, later studies showed that respiratory carcinogenicity of NNN varies across laboratory animal models: for example, it was also observed in hamsters,[59,60] but not in rats. Instead, new studies of NNN exposure in F344 rats revealed that NNN is a potent esophageal and oral carcinogen in this model, causing tumors in 100% of animals treated with doses comparable to the lifetime NNN exposure in smokers.[61]

The formation of NNK, another potent carcinogenic TSNA was reported in 1978.[62] Unlike NNN, the lung-specific carcinogenicity of NNK is remarkable: it causes lung tumors in all species studied, independent of the route of administration, and is generally a more potent carcinogen than NNN.[51] Both NNN and NNK require metabolic activation and formation of DNA adducts to exert their carcinogenicity.[51,63] The mechanisms of NNK and NNN carcinogenicity are discussed in more detail in Chapter 7.

Evidence from extensive mechanistic, clinical, and epidemiological studies supports the applicability of the NNN and NNK animal carcinogenicity findings to human cancer risk. First, the doses at which laboratory animals develop tumors are comparable to smokers' exposures, as mentioned earlier for the oral and esophageal carcinogenicity of NNN in rats. Similarly, treatment of rats with NNK caused significant incidence of lung tumors at a total dose of 6 mg NNK/kg of body weight, comparable to an estimated 1.1 mg NNK/kg body weight after 40 years of smoking.[27,51,64] Secondly, the ability of human target tissues to metabolize NNN and NNK and form DNA adducts was demonstrated in vitro and by analyzing biospecimens collected from smokers.[65–67] Lung organ-specificity of NNK in humans is supported by the findings from epidemiological studies in cigar smokers who develop lung cancer even though they do not inhale the smoke.[68] Lastly, in prospective epidemiological studies with smokers, levels of NNK metabolite 4-(methylnitrosamino)-1-(3-pyridyl)-1-butanol (NNAL) in plasma and urine were associated with lung cancer risk, while levels of urinary total NNN were associated with esophageal cancer risk, after adjustment for smoking history and other confounders.[69–71] The latter findings are remarkably consistent with the findings of organ-specificity of NNN and NNK in F344 rats and provide uniquely strong support for the role of these constituents in respective cancers in smokers. In addition, it is also likely that these carcinogens play important roles in the development of other smoking-associated cancers, such as cancers of the pancreas, liver, and cervix.[72,73] Rats treated with NNK also develop tumors in liver and pancreas, and both NNK and NNN can cause nasal tumors.[74,75]

Metals and metalloids comprise another class of carcinogens that are present in tobacco filler and transferred to the smoke during combustion. These elements are absorbed into the tobacco plant from the soil and their levels in tobacco leaves depend on agricultural practices and proximity to natural or industrial sources of soil and air contamination.[76,77] Most carcinogenic metals and metalloids cause cancer of the lung, including arsenic, beryllium, cadmium, chromium (VI), nickel and their compounds.[78]

However, other organs are also targets for metal and metalloid carcinogenicity. For example, arsenic and its compounds cause cancer of the urinary bladder and skin, and potentially the liver. Exposure to arsenic, cadmium, and their compounds was also positively associated with cancers of the kidney and prostate. Also, positive associations have been reported for exposures to chromium (VI) and nickel compounds and cancers of the nasal cavity and sinuses. All these elements are classified as carcinogenic to humans.[78]

Other carcinogenic constituents that have not yet been characterized are likely to be present in cigarette smoke and may be discovered in the future.

6. The Central Role of Nicotine

While nicotine is not known to cause cancer, it is a toxic tobacco chemical; for example, it may contribute to acute cardiovascular events in tobacco users, can cause birth defects upon in utero exposure, and lead to memory deficits and negative behavioral outcomes in exposed adolescents.[79,80] However, the major impact of nicotine is centered on its addictive properties. Being the major known addictive constituent in tobacco and cigarette smoke, nicotine is primarily responsible for continued smoking and use of other tobacco product types. See Chapter 12 to learn more about nicotine addiction and its treatment. The levels/yields of nicotine in a tobacco product determine how intensely the product is used. Furthermore, people differ in how they metabolize nicotine, which also affects how much and how intensely they smoke (more on this in Chapter 8). Therefore, by generating and sustaining addiction and driving the intensity of product use, nicotine plays a central role in exposure to the harmful chemicals present in cigarette smoke and in the detrimental health outcomes due to such exposure, including cancer.

7. Measurement of Chemical Constituents in Tobacco Smoke

Levels of various chemical constituents in tobacco smoke are typically measured by using smoking machines that imitate human smokers by periodically puffing certain volumes of smoke from a lit cigarette. The smoke is then collected either on Cambridge filter pads (particulate matter) or in impingers or gas bags (gas phase), and the collected material is extracted, processed, and analyzed. Standardized approaches to cigarette puffing are critical for the ability to compare and cross-reference the results of such machine-based measurements across different laboratories and various cigarette brands. Historically, the puffing regimen established by the International Organization for Standardization (ISO) was most commonly used for cigarette smoke analyses. The regimen, which was later adapted in the US as the Federal Trade Commission (FTC) method, draws 35 mL of smoke every 60 s, and each puff lasting 2 s (Table 2).[81] Other, more intense smoking regimens have been developed later, in response to concerns that the measurements based on the ISO/FTC method underestimate exposures in smokers.[82] For example, smokers of cigarettes with ventilated filters adjust their nicotine intake by puffing such cigarettes more intensely and blocking filter ventilation holes to reduce smoke dilution with air.[83] This ultimately increases smokers' exposures to other constituents present in cigarette smoke. Therefore it is not surprising that, despite the lower yields of some harmful emissions measured by the ISO/FTC method, ventilated cigarettes did not reduce smokers' exposure to tobacco carcinogens and did not lower the risk of smoking-induced diseases.[84] Two updated, more intense regimens introduced by the Massachusetts Department of Health and by Health Canada not only prescribed drawing larger and more frequent puffs but also blocking filter ventilation holes (Table 2).[85–87]

It should be noted that none of the standard smoking machine regimens, even the more intense ones, account for the complexities and the

Table 2: Key standard smoking regimens used for generating cigarette smoke by machines.

Smoking parameter	Puff volume (mL)	Puff duration (s)	Inter-puff interval (s)	Filter vent blocking
ISO/FTC[81]	35	2	60	No
Massachusetts Department of Health[85]	45	2	30	50%
Health Canada[86]	55	2	30	100%

variability of human smoking behaviors, and therefore machine-based chemical analyses are not representative of exposures in smokers.[82,88–91] Nevertheless, such measurements are important because they allow for brand comparisons and can provide important insights into the potential impact of cigarette characteristics on carcinogen and toxicant yields in the smoke. The importance of such measurements is illustrated through the efforts over the past several years by the World Health Organization's Tobacco Laboratory Network (WHO TobLabNet) to develop standard operating procedures for the analysis of key tobacco toxicants and carcinogens.[92] Such standardized analytical methods are critical tools for global tobacco control. There are 10 established and validated WHO TobLabNet SOPs, including the method for machine-smoking of cigarettes (by intense regimen, similar to the Health Canada method) as well as methods for analysis of nicotine, CO, TSNA, BaP, aldehydes, and a range of volatile organic compounds in cigarette smoke.

8. Levels of Carcinogens in Combusted Tobacco Products and the Impact of Product Characteristics

The levels of various carcinogenic constituents in cigarette smoke vary substantially, with some being present at just a few nanograms and others at hundreds of microgram levels (one microgram equals one thousand nanograms) (Table 1). It is important to note, however, that some carcinogens present in cigarette smoke have very high potency, meaning that they can cause cancer at very low doses of exposure. Such highly potent carcinogens (e.g., TSNA, PAH, aromatic amines) are typically present at lower levels (up to 200 ng/cigarette) and are predominantly concentrated in the particulate matter of tobacco smoke. Weaker carcinogens, such as acetaldehyde, formaldehyde, catechol, and others are mostly volatile components of the gas phase and are present at much higher levels. This distribution of the relative potency and abundance across the two fractions of tobacco smoke suggests that both fractions may contribute somewhat equally to the cancer risk in smokers. The total amount of carcinogens in tobacco smoke may reach a few milligram per cigarette, which is comparable to the amount of nicotine.

In addition to the wide distribution of concentrations across carcinogenic constituent classes, there is also a substantial degree of variability in the levels of the same constituents across various cigarette brands. Representative ranges for the key carcinogenic constituents in cigarette smoke are listed in Table 1, showing 7- to over 60-fold difference, depending on carcinogen, between the lowest and the highest values reported for a set of cigarette brands smoked by ISO/FTC regimen. Differences in tobacco blends, additives, and physical cigarette characteristics (such as dimensions and paper and filter properties) are responsible for such variability. As described earlier in this chapter, the content of nicotine and naturally occurring sugars vary across different tobacco types; this is also true for many other chemical compounds that naturally occur in the tobacco plant and decompose or lead to the formation of carcinogenic and inflammatory agents during tobacco combustion. For example, higher amounts of flue-cured tobacco in a cigarette blend can lead to higher formaldehyde and CO deliveries, while Maryland tobacco generates lower yields of PAH and phenols than other tobacco types. Higher amounts of expanded tobacco may lead to increases in CO and nitrogen oxides, but decreases in the yields of particulate matter. The presence of reconstituted tobacco leads to lower levels of CO, hydrogen cyanide and PAH than cigarettes made without reconstituted tobacco.

Variable amounts of added sugars and humectants can affect the levels of aldehydes and other volatile toxicants and carcinogens in tobacco smoke. During cigarette combustion, sugar pyrolysis can result in the formation of a variety of products, including aldehydes, furans, benzene, acrylamide, PAH, and other harmful constituents (Figure 4).

The role of tobacco type in the levels of TSNA in cigarette smoke has been of particular importance, because tobacco processing and blending approaches could dramatically decrease the smoke yields of these potent carcinogens. For example, using tobaccos with lower nitrate and nitrite content could reduce the levels of TSNA formed during the curing. For Virginia-type tobacco, flue-curing at reduced temperatures could also lead to reductions in TSNA formation.[93,94] In fact, in 1999 RJ Reynolds and later Philip Morris stated their intentions to start using low-TSNA tobacco in cigarette manufacturing, apparently by shifting to the use of heat exchangers (instead of direct-fire burners) in the flue-curing process.[95]

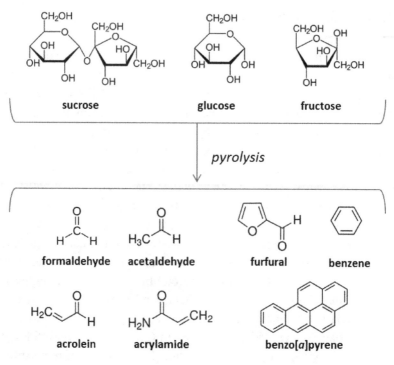

Figure 4:   Some of the products of sugar pyrolysis.

However, since flue-cured tobacco accounts for only a fraction of the American cigarette blend, TSNA reduction in only this type of tobacco would not have a significant impact on overall TSNA exposure levels. For example, TSNA levels are significantly higher in Burley than in Virginia-type tobacco, regardless of the curing method.[96] Indeed, comparison of historical levels of these carcinogens in the tobacco filler of popular US cigarette brands shows no substantial changes over the past 40 years (Figure 5). This lack of change despite the known approaches to reduce TSNA levels in tobacco is quite remarkable, given the carcinogenic potency of some TSNA such as NNN and NNK.

As stated earlier, filter ventilation is another key determinant of the measured yields of smoke constituents. The amount of filter ventilation can range from about 10% in some full flavored varieties to 80% in very low delivery brands.[97] A study across 172 cigarette varieties from various countries, including the US, showed that filter ventilation accounted for

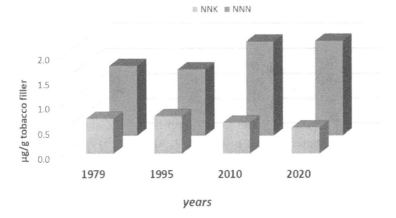

Figure 5: Levels of NNK and NNK in tobacco filler of a US filtered cigarette over a 40-year period.

Sources: Data for 1979, 1995 and 2010 are from a previous publication.[95] Data for 2020 are from analyses of several varieties of a popular US brand carried out in Dr. Stepanov's laboratory (*unpublished data*).

85–95% of variability in tar, nicotine, and CO yields.[98] Indeed, constituent level variation across cigarette brands smoked using the Health Canada intense regimen (with blocked filter vents), as shown in Table 1, is much smaller than that for the ISO/FTC regimen. The largest variation under intense smoking conditions is seen for NNN: from 20.6 to 410.6 ng/cigarette, or 20-fold (as compared to a 40-fold range variation for this constituent under the low-intensity regimen). Nevertheless, the variation is still substantial, indicating that other cigarette characteristics, as discussed above, play a major role.

9. Bottom Line

Tobacco smoke is a complex mixture of thousands of chemical constituents. Some of these constituents are potent carcinogens, and although it is difficult to fully attribute a particular type of smoking-induced cancer to a specific carcinogen, research evidence strongly supports such causative relationship (Figure 3). An additional, historical perspective can be added in the case of NNK. Changes in tobacco blending practices led to an increase in the levels of this carcinogen in cigarette smoke over the period

from 1959 to 1997, which coincided with the subsequent shift to adenocarcinoma as the most common lung cancer type in the US.[12] This is
consistent with the carcinogenic potency of NNK, which primarily produces adenocarcinomas in animal models.[51] In addition to such carcinogens that target specific organs by specific mechanisms, many
combustion-derived smoke constituents act as strong toxicants, irritants,
and tumor promoters, facilitating and amplifying the avalanche of carcinogenic and pro-carcinogenic processes. Uptake of this complex chemical
mixture makes smoking the deadliest form of tobacco use.

References

1. Russell MA. Low-tar medium-nicotine cigarettes: A new approach to safer
   smoking. *Br Med J* 1976;1(6023):1430–3.
2. Wang TW, Gentzke A, Sharapova S, Cullen KA, Ambrose BK, Jamal A.
   Tobacco product use among middle and high school students — United
   States, 2011–2017. *MMWR Morb Mortal Wkly Rep* 2018;67(22):629–33.
3. Lewis RS, Nicholson JS. Aspects of the evolution of Nicotiana tabacum L.
   and the status of the United States Nicotiana Germplasm Collection. *Gen Res
   Crop Evol* 2007;54:727–40.
4. Bhide SV, Kulkarni JR, Padma PR, *et al.* Studies on the tobacco specific
   nitrosamines and other carcinogenic agents in smokeless tobacco products.
   In *Tobacco and Health: The Indian Scene*, Sanghvi LD, Notani P, eds.,
   121–131. (Bombay, India: UICC Workshop, Tata Memorial Centre, 1989).
5. Stanfill SB, Stepanov I. Chapter 3: A Global View of Smokeless Tobacco
   Products. U.S. Department of Health and Human Services, National Cancer
   Institute, ed. Smokeless Tobacco and Public Health: A Global Perspective.
   NIH Publication No. 14-7983.2014.
6. Talhout R, Richter PA, Stepanov I, Watson CV, Watson CH. Cigarette design
   features: Effects on emission levels, user perception, and behavior. *Tobacco
   Reg Sci* 2018;4(1):592–604.
7. Hoffmann D, Hoffmann I. The changing cigarette, 1950–1995. *J Toxicol
   Environ Health* 1997;50:307–64.
8. Talhout R, Opperhuizen A, van Amsterdam JG. Sugars as tobacco ingredient:
   Effects on mainstream smoke composition. *Food Chem Toxicol*
   2006;44(11):1789–98.

9. Henningfield J, Pankow J, Garrett B. Ammonia and other chemical base tobacco additives and cigarette nicotine delivery: Issues and research needs. *Nicotine Tobacco Res* 2004;6(2):199–205.

10. McNeill A, Munafo MR. Reducing harm from tobacco use. *J Psychopharmacol* 2013;27(1):13–8.

11. Ferris Wayne G, Connolly GN. Application, function, and effects of menthol in cigarettes: A survey of tobacco industry documents. *Nicotine Tobacco Res* 2004;6 Suppl 1:S43–54.

12. Hoffmann D, Hoffmann I, El Bayoumy K. The less harmful cigarette: A controversial issue. A tribute to Ernst L. Wynder. *Chem Res Toxicol* 2001;14(7):767–90.

13. Song MA, Benowitz NL, Berman M, *et al*. Cigarette filter ventilation and its relationship to increasing rates of lung adenocarcinoma. *J Natl Cancer Inst* 2017;109(12):djx075.

14. Carroll DM, Stepanov I, O'Connor R, *et al*. Impact of cigarette filter ventilation on U.S. smokers' perceptions and biomarkers of exposure and potential harm. *Cancer Epidemiol Biomarkers Prev* 2021;30(1):38–44.

15. Johnstone RAW, Plimmer JR. The chemical constituents of tobacco and tobacco smoke. *Chem Rev* 1959;59:885–936.

16. Stedman RL. The chemical composition of tobacco and tobacco smoke. *Chem Rev* 1968;68:153–207.

17. Roberts NL. Natural tobacco flavor. *Rec Adv Tobacco Sci* 1988;37:49–81.

18. Rodgman A, Perfetti TA. *The Chemical Components of Tobacco and Tobacco Smoke*. 2nd edn. (Boca Raton: CRC Press, 2013).

19. Hoffmann D, Djordjevic MV, Brunnemann KD. Changes in cigarette design and composition over time and how they influence the yields of smoke constituents. *Journal of Smoking-related Disease*. 1995;6:9–23.

20. U.S. Department of Health and Human Services. *The Health Consequences of Smoking — 50 Years of Progress. A Report of the Surgeon General*. (Atlanta, GA: U.S. Dept. of Health and Human Services, Centers for Disease Control and Prevention, National Center for Chronic Disease Prevention and Health Promotion, Office on Smoking and Health, 2014).

21. Cooper RL, Lindsey AJ, Waller RE. The presence of 3,4-benzopyrene in cigarette smoke. *Chem Ind* 1954;46:1418.

22. Ding YS, Ashley DL, Watson CH. Determination of 10 carcinogenic polycyclic aromatic hydrocarbons in mainstream cigarette smoke. *J Agri Food Chem* 2007;55:5966–73.

23. International Agency for Research on Cancer. Some non-heterocyclic polycyclic aromatic hydrocarbons and some related exposures. In *IARC Monographs on the Evaluation of Carcinogenic Risks to Humans, vol 92.* (Lyon, FR: IARC, 2010).

24. Denissenko MF, Pao A, Tang M, Pfeifer GP. Preferential formation of benzo[a]pyrene adducts at lung cancer mutational hot spots in P53. *Science* 1996;274:430–2.

25. Pfeifer GP, Denissenko MF, Olivier M, Tretyakova N, Hecht SS, Hainaut P. Tobacco smoke carcinogens, DNA damage and p53 mutations in smoking-associated cancers. *Oncogene* 2002;21:7435–51.

26. Boysen G, Hecht SS. Analysis of DNA and protein adducts of benzo[a] pyrene in human tissues using structure-specific methods. *Mutation Res.* 2003;543:17–30.

27. Hecht SS. Tobacco carcinogens, their biomarkers, and tobacco-induced cancer. *Nature Rev Cancer* 2003;3:733–44.

28. Hecht SS. Tobacco smoke carcinogens and lung cancer. *J Natl Cancer Inst* 1999;91:1194–210.

29. Ross JA, Nelson GB, Wilson KH, *et al.* Adenomas induced by polycyclic aromatic hydrocarbons in strain A/J mouse lung correlate with time-integrated DNA adduct levels. *Cancer Res* 1995;55:1039–44.

30. Wynder EL, Graham EA, Croninger AB. Experimental production of carcinoma with cigarette tar. *Cancer Res* 1953;13(12):855–64.

31. Counts ME, Morton MJ, Laffoon SW, Cox RH, Lipowicz PJ. Smoke composition and predicting relationships for international commercial cigarettes smoked with three machine-smoking conditions. *Reg Toxicol Pharmacol* 2005;41(3):185–227.

32. International Agency for Research on Cancer. Re-evaluation of some organic chemicals, hydrazine and hydrogen peroxide. In *IARC Monographs on the Evaluation of the Carcinogenic Risk of Chemicals to Humans, vol 71.* (Lyon, FR: IARC, 1999).

33. International Agency for Research on Cancer. A review of human carcinogens: Chemical agents and related occupations. In *IARC Monographs on the Evaluation of Carcinogenic Risks to Humans, vol 100F.* (Lyon, FR: IARC, 2012).

34. International Agency for Research on Cancer. Dry cleaning, some chlorinated solvents and other industrial chemicals. In *IARC Monographs on the Evaluation of Carcinogenic Risks to Humans, vol 63.* (Lyon, FR: IARC, 1995).

35. Feng Z, Hu W, Hu Y, Tang M-S. Acrolein is a major cigarette-related lung cancer agent. Preferential binding at p53 mutational hotspots and inhibition of DNA repair. *Proc Natl Acad Sci USA* 2006;103:15404–9.

36. Zhang S, Villalta PW, Wang M, Hecht SS. Analysis of crotonaldehyde- and acetaldehyde-derived $1,N^2$-propanodeoxyguanosine adducts in DNA from human tissues using liquid chromatography-electrsopray ionization-tandem mass spectrometry. *Chem Res Toxicol* 2006;19:1386–92.

37. Nair U, Bartsch H, Nair J. Lipid peroxidation-induced DNA damage in cancer-prone inflammatory diseases: A review of published adduct types and levels in humans. *Free Rad Biol Med* 2007;43:1109–20.

38. Bartsch H, Nair J. Accumulation of lipid peroxidation-derived lesions: Potential lead markers for chemoprevention of inflammation driven malignancies. *Mutation Res* 2005;591:34–44.

39. Pryor WA, Hales BJ, Premovic PI, Church DF. The radicals in cigarette tar: Their nature and suggested physiological implications. *Science* 1983;220:425–7.

40. Church DF, Pryor WA. Free radical chemistry of cigarette smoke and its toxicological implications. *Environ Health Perspect* 1985;64:111–26.

41. Bhalla DK, Hirata F, Rishi A, Gairola CG. Cigarette smoke, inflammation, and lung injury: A mechanistic perspective. *J Toxicol Environ Health B* 2009;12:45–64.

42. Lonkar P, Dedon PC. Reactive species and DNA damage in chronic inflammation: Reconciling chemical mechanisms and biological fates. *Int J Cancer* 2011;128(9):1999–2009.

43. Weinberg RA. *The Biology of Cancer*. (New York: Garland Science, 2007).

44. Melikian AA, Sun P, Prokopczyk B, *et al.* Identification of benzo[a]pyrene metabolites in cervical mucus and DNA adducts in cervical tissues in humans by gas chromatography-mass spectrometry. *Cancer Lett* 1999;146(2):127–34.

45. Probst-Hensch NM, Bell DA, Watson MA, *et al.* N-Acetyltransferase 2 phenotype but not NAT1*10 genotype affects aminobiphenyl-hemoglobin adduct levels. *Cancer Epidemiol Biomarkers Prev* 2000;9:619–23.

46. Castelao JE, Yuan JM, Skipper PL, *et al.* Gender- and smoking-related bladder cancer risk. *J Natl Cancer Inst* 2001;93(7):538–45.

47. Soeteman-Hernandez LG, Bos PM, Talhout R. Tobacco smoke-related health effects induced by 1,3-butadiene and strategies for risk reduction. *Toxicol Sci* 2013;136(2):566–80.

48. Korte JE, Hertz-Picciotto I, Schulz MR, Ball LM, Duell EJ. The contribution of benzene to smoking induced leukemia. *Environ Health Perspect* 2000; 108(4):333–9.

49. International Agency for Research on Cancer. Benzene. In *IARC Monographs on the Evaluation of Carcinogenic Risks to Humans, vol 120.* (Lyon, FR: IARC, 2018).

50. International Agency for Research on Cancer. Smokeless tobacco and tobacco-specific nitrosamines. In *IARC Monographs on the Evaluation of Carcinogenic Risks to Humans, vol 89.* (Lyon, FR: IARC, 2007).

51. Hecht SS. Biochemistry, biology, and carcinogenicity of tobacco-specific N-nitrosamines. *Chem Res Toxicol* 1998;11:559–603.

52. Hoffmann D, Hecht SS, Ornaf RM, Wynder EL, Tso TC. Nitrosonornicotine: Presence in tobacco, formation and carcinogenicity. In *Environmental N-Nitroso Compounds: Analysis and Formation*, Walker EA, Bogovski P, Griciute L, eds. 1st edn., 307–20. (Lyon, France: IARC, 1976).

53. Hecht SS, Chen CB, Dong M, Ornaf RM, Hoffmann D, Tso TC. Studies on non-volatile nitrosamines in tobacco. *Beitr Tabakforsch Int* 1977;9:1–6.

54. Hoffmann D, Dong M, Hecht SS. Origin in tobacco smoke of N′-nitrosonornicotine, a tobacco-specific carcinogen: Brief Communication. *J Natl Cancer Inst* 1977;58:1841–4.

55. Adams JD, Lee SJ, Vinchkoski N. On the formation of the tobacco-specific carcinogen 4-(methylnitrosamino)-1-(3-pyridyl)-1-butanone during smoking. *Cancer Lett* 1983;17:339–46.

56. Fischer S, Spiegelhalder B, Eisenbarth J, Preussmann R. Investigations on the origin of tobacco-specific nitrosamines in mainstream smoke of cigarettes. *Carcinogenesis* 1990;11:723–30.

57. Klus H, Kuhn H. Determination of nornicotine nitrosamine in the smoke condensate of nornicotine-rich cigarettes. *Fachliche Mitteilungen der Oesterreichischen* 1973;14:251–7.

58. Boyland E, Roe FJC, Gorrod JW. Induction of pulmonary tumours in mice by nitrosonornicotine, a possible constituent of tobacco smoke. *Nature.* 1964;202:1126.

59. Hilfrich J, Hecht SS, Hoffmann D. Effects of N′-nitrosonornicotine and N′-nitrosoanabasine in Syrian golden hamsters. *Cancer Lett* 1977; 2:169–76.

60. Hoffmann D, Castonguay A, Rivenson A, Hecht SS. Comparative carcinogenicity and metabolism of 4-(methylnitrosamino)-1-(3-pyridyl)-1-butanone and N′-nitrosonornicotine in Syrian golden hamsters. *Cancer Res* 1981;41:2386–93.

61. Balbo S, James-Yi S, Johnson CS, *et al.* (S)-N′-Nitrosonornicotine, a constituent of smokeless tobacco, is a powerful oral cavity carcinogen in rats. *Carcinogenesis* 2013;34:2178–83.

62. Hecht SS, Chen CB, Ornaf RM, Jacobs E, Adams JD, Hoffmann D. Reaction of nicotine and sodium nitrite: Formation of nitrosamines and fragmentation of the pyrrolidine ring. *J Org Chem* 1978;43:72–6.

63. Wang M, Cheng G, Sturla SJ, *et al.* Identification of adducts formed by pyridyloxobutylation of deoxyguanosine and DNA by 4-(acetoxymethylnitrosamino)-1-(3-pyridyl)-1-butanone, a chemically activated form of tobacco-specific carcinogens. *Chem Res Toxicol* 2003;16:616–26.

64. Belinsky SA, Foley JF, White CM, Anderson MW, Maronpot RR. Dose-response relationship between O^6-methylguanine formation in Clara cells and induction of pulmonary neoplasia in the rat by 4-(methylnitrosamino)-1-(3-pyridyl)-1-butanone. *Cancer Res* 1990;50:3772–80.

65. Castonguay A, Stoner GD, Schut HAJ, Hecht SS. Metabolism of tobacco-specific N-nitrosamines by cultured human tissues. *Proc Natl Acad Sci USA* 1983;80:6694–97.

66. Foiles PG, Akerkar SA, Carmella SG, *et al.* Mass spectrometric analysis of tobacco-specific nitrosamine-DNA adducts in smokers and nonsmokers. *Chem Res Toxicol* 1991;4:364–8.

67. Stepanov I, Muzic J, Le CT, *et al.* Analysis of 4-hydroxy-1-(3-pyridyl)-1-butanone (HPB)-releasing DNA adducts in human exfoliated oral mucosa cells by liquid chromatography-electrospray ionization-tandem mass spectrometry. *Chem Res Toxicol* 2013;26:37–45.

68. Shapiro JA, Jacobs EJ, Thun MJ. Cigar smoking in men and risk of death from tobacco-related cancers. *J Natl Cancer Inst* 2000;92(4):333–7.

69. Hecht SS, Murphy SE, Stepanov I, Nelson HH, Yuan JM. Tobacco smoke biomarkers and cancer risk among male smokers in the Shanghai Cohort Study. *Cancer Lett* 2012;334:34–8.

70. Stepanov I, Sebero E, Wang R, Gao YT, Hecht SS, Yuan JM. Tobacco-specific N-nitrosamine exposures and cancer risk in the Shanghai Cohort Study: Remarkable coherence with rat tumor sites. *Int J Cancer* 2014; 134(10):2278–83.

71. Church TR, Anderson KE, Caporaso NE, *et al.* A prospectively measured serum biomarker for a tobacco-specific carcinogen and lung cancer in smokers. *Cancer Epidemiol Biomarkers Prev* 2009;19:260–6.

72. Prokopczyk B, Hoffmann D, Bologna M, *et al.* Identification of tobacco-derived compounds in human pancreatic juice. *Chem Res Toxicol* 2002; 15:677–85.

73. Prokopczyk B, Trushin N, Leszczynska J, Waggoner SE, El Bayoumy K. Human cervical tissue metabolizes the tobacco-specific nitrosamine, 4-(methylnitrosamino)-1-(3-pyridyl)-1-butanone, via alpha-hydroxylation and carbonyl reduction pathways. *Carcinogenesis* 2001;22(1):107–14.

74. Hecht SS, Chen CB, Ohmori T, Hoffmann D. Comparative carcinogenicity in F344 rats of the tobacco specific nitrosamines, N′-nitrosonornicotine and 4-(N-methyl-N-nitrosamino)-1-(3-pyridyl)-1-butanone. *Cancer Res* 1980;40:298–302.

75. Rivenson A, Hoffmann D, Prokopczyk B, Amin S, Hecht SS. Induction of lung and exocrine pancreas tumors in F344 rats by tobacco-specific and Areca-derived N-nitrosamines. *Cancer Res* 1988;48:6912–7.

76. Adamu CA, Bell RE, Mulchi CL, Chanev RL. Residual metal levels in soils and leaf accumulations in tobacco a decade following farmland application of municipal sludge. *Environ Pollut.* 1989;56(2):113–26.

77. Mulchi CL, Adamu CA, Bell PF, Chaney RL. Residual heavy metal concentrations in sludge amended coastal plain soils — II. Predicting metal concentrations in tobacco from soil test information. *Commun Soil Sci Plant Anal* 1992;23(9–10):1053–69.

78. International Agency for Research on Cancer. A review of human carcinogens: Arsenic, metals, fibres, and dusts. In *IARC Monographs on the Evaluation of Carcinogenic Risks to Humans, vol 100C.* (Lyon, FR: IARC, 2012).

79. Benowitz NL, Burbank AD. Cardiovascular toxicity of nicotine: Implications for electronic cigarette use. *Trends Cardiovasc Med* 2016;26(6):515–23.

80. England LJ, Aagaard K, Bloch M, *et al.* Developmental toxicity of nicotine: A transdisciplinary synthesis and implications for emerging tobacco products. *Neurosci Biobehav Rev* 2017;72:176–89.

81. International Organization for Standardization. ISO Standard 3308. *Routine Analytical Cigarette-smoking Machine — Definitions and Standard Conditions*, 4th edn., 2000.

82. Djordjevic MV, Stellman SD, Zang E. Doses of nicotine and lung carcinogens delivered to cigarette smokers. *J Natl Cancer Inst* 2000;92(2):106–11.

83. Strasser AA, Ashare RL, Kozlowski LT, Pickworth WB. The effect of filter vent blocking and smoking topography on carbon monoxide levels in smokers. *Pharmacol Biochem Behav* 2005;82(2):320–9.

84. Hecht SS, Murphy SE, Carmella SG, *et al.* Similar uptake of lung carcinogens by smokers of regular, light, and ultra-light cigarettes. *Cancer Epidemiol Biomarkers Prev* 2005;14:693–8.

85. Borgerding MF, Bodnar JA, Wingate DE. The 1999 Massachusetts Benchmark Study — Final report. A Research Study Conducted after

Consultation with the Massachusetts Department of Public Health http://legacy.library.ucsf.edu/tid/spt10j00 (accessed 10/26/2021).

86. Canada Government Tobacco Act: Tobacco Reporting Regulations. Part 3: Emissions from designated tobacco products. SOR/2000-273. Registration June 26, 2000.

87. Massachusetts General Laws. Chapter 94, Sect. 307B, 105 Code of Massachusetts Regulations 660.000 et seq. 1997.

88. Byrd GD, Davis RA, Caldwell WS, Robinson JH, deBethizy JD. A further study of the FTC yield and nicotine absorption in smokers. *Psychopharmacology* 1998;139:291–9.

89. Gori GB, Lynch CJ. Analytical cigarette yields as predictors of smoke bioavailability. *Reg Toxicol Pharmacol* 1985;5:314–26.

90. Jarvis MJ, Boreham R, Primatesta P, Feyerabend C, Bryant A. Nicotine yield from machine-smoked cigarettes and nicotine intakes in smokers: Evidence from a representative population survey. *J Natl Cancer Inst.* 2001; 93(2):134–8.

91. Stratton K, Shetty P, Wallace R, Bondurant S. *Clearing the Smoke: Assessing the Science Base for Tobacco Harm Reduction*. Institute of Medicine. (Washington, DC: National Academy Press, 2001).

92. World Health Organization. Information sheet on WHO TobLabNet methods for measuring priority contents and emissions in tobacco and related products. (Geneva: WHO, 2020) https://www.who.int/publications/i/item/WHO-HEP-HPR-2020.1

93. Morin A, Porter A, Ratavicius A, Joly J. Evolution of tobacco-specific nitrosamines and microbial populations during flue-curing of tobacco under direct and indirect heating. *Beitr Tabakforsch Int* 2004;21:40–6.

94. Peele DM, Riddick MG, Edwards ME. Formation of tobacco-specific nitrosamines in flue-cured tobacco. *Recent Adv Tobacco Sci* 2001;27:3–12.

95. Stepanov I, Knezevich A, Zhang L, Watson CH, Hatsukami DK, Hecht SS. Carcinogenic tobacco-specific N-nitrosamines in US cigarettes: Three decades of remarkable neglect by the tobacco industry. *Tobacco Control* 2012;21:44–8.

96. Chamberlain WJ, Chortyk OT. Effects of curing and fertilization on nitrosamine formation in bright and burley tobacco. *Beitr Tabakforsch Int* 1992;15:87–92.

97. Centers for Disease Control and Prevention. Filter ventilation levels in selected U.S. cigarettes, 1997. *MMWR Morb Mortal Wkly Rep* 1997;46(44):1043–7.

98. O'Connor RJ, Hammond D, McNeill A, *et al.* How do different cigarette design features influence the standard tar yields of popular cigarette brands sold in different countries? *Tobacco Control* 2008;17 Suppl 1:i1–5.

https://doi.org/10.1142/9789811239533_0005

Chapter 5

Carcinogens and Toxicants in Smokeless Tobacco Products*

S. Jane Henley[†,§], Taylor Ellington[†], Stephen Stanfill[†],
Kathi Mills[†] and Michael J. Thun[‡]

1. Introduction

In countries around the world, people not only smoke tobacco but also suck, chew, dip, and snort it.[1] An estimated 350 million people worldwide use smokeless tobacco products.[2] The largest number (250 million) live in South-East Asia, yet a diverse array of smokeless tobacco products is used in at least 133 countries.[2] Despite the widespread use of these products, many of which have been used for centuries, smokeless tobacco was not formally recognized to cause cancer in humans until 1986,[3] 20 years after cigarette smoking was designated the major cause of lung cancer in men.[4]

This chapter will review the major scientific discoveries and lines of evidence that established the carcinogenicity of smokeless tobacco products. It will also consider (1) the wide variety of smokeless tobacco products produced and consumed in different regions of the world; (2) a brief history of the use of smokeless products in the United States, including

---

*The findings and conclusions in this report are those of the authors and do not necessarily represent the official position of the Centers for Disease Control and Prevention.

[†]Centers for Disease Control and Prevention, Atlanta, GA, USA.

[‡]Epidemiology Research Program, American Cancer Society, Atlanta, GA, USA.

[§]skh3@cdc.gov

the industry's recruitment of professional baseball players to market these products; (3) the constituents of smokeless tobacco products and how levels of two of the most important constituents — nicotine and tobacco-specific nitrosamines (TSNAs) — are controlled by the methods used to grow, cure, and process tobacco; (4) the discovery of TSNA in smokeless tobacco and its evolving role as a biomarker and potential target for regulation; and (5) the scientific evidence on which smokeless tobacco was classified as carcinogenic to humans. Where possible, the chapter will also include personal stories from individuals who were either harmed by smokeless tobacco products or whose scientific research has informed control measures to reduce their harm.

2. Types of Smokeless Tobacco

Cultures around the world have long produced non-combusted tobacco products for nasal or oral use.[5] A common feature of these, as defined by the International Agency for Research on Cancer (IARC), is that *smokeless tobacco* refers to tobacco products that are not burned or heated during use.[6] These products vary with respect to their ingredients, methods of curing and processing, and mode of delivery. Their nearly ubiquitous use by people around the world attests to the determination and ingenuity of humans to extract nicotine from tobacco.

Another thing smokeless tobacco products have in common is that they are made with a few *Nicotiana* species that are members of the alkaloid-containing *Solanaceae* family that also includes poisonous nightshade.[7] Commercially produced products in Western countries are generally made from *Nicotiana tabacum* (cultivated tobacco), whereas those made in South America, Africa, and Asia often contain *Nicotiana rustica* (Aztec or wild tobacco). At least one product (Toombak), used in the Sudan, is made from *Nicotiana glauca* (tree tobacco).

Tobacco plants, leaves, and stems are harvested, then dried, or, cured by air, sun, flue, or fire. The curing method has important consequences for the level of nicotine, the types and levels of *carcinogens* (something that causes cancer), and the flavor. To enhance the flavor and aroma of the product, tobacco is often mixed with sweeteners such as molasses or brown sugar; flavors such as wintergreen, licorice, cinnamon, or menthol; spices such as clove, cardamom, or mint; and plant materials such as areca nut (also known as betel nut), betel leaf, tonka bean, or cocoa. Humectants like glycerol, glycerin, and propylene glycol may be added for moisture control. For some products, the tobacco is fermented after drying, which can facilitate the production of cancer-causing chemicals and introduce bacteria and fungi. After drying and processing, smokeless tobacco is shaped into a variety of forms: strips, twists, powders, tars, pastes, dentifrices (tooth cleaner), sticks, gums, sachets, lozenges, and pellets. A few products are described below and pictured in Figure 1.

The two main types of smokeless tobacco products used for centuries in North America are chewing tobacco and snuff.[3] The tobacco in chewed products (chew) is usually air-cured and sold as loose leaf, plug, twist, or

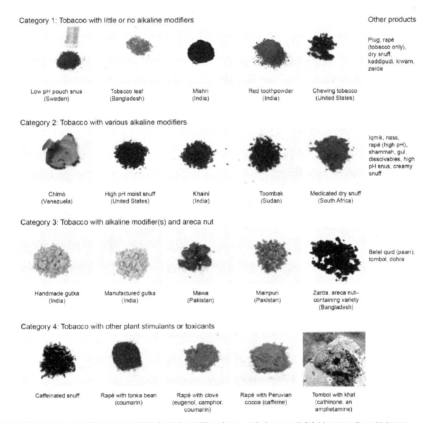

Category 1: Tobacco with little or no alkaline modifiers

| | | | | | Other products |

Low pH pouch snus (Sweden) · Tobacco leaf (Bangladesh) · Mishri (India) · Red toothpowder (India) · Chewing tobacco (United States)

Plug, rapé (tobacco only), dry snuff, kaddipudi, kiwam, zarda

Category 2: Tobacco with various alkaline modifiers

Chimó (Venezuela) · High pH moist snuff (United States) · Khaini (India) · Toombak (Sudan) · Medicated dry snuff (South Africa)

Iqmik, nass, rapé (high pH), shammah, gul, dissolvables, high pH snus, creamy snuff

Category 3: Tobacco with alkaline modifier(s) and areca nut

Handmade gutka (India) · Manufactured gutka (India) · Mawa (Pakistan) · Mainpuri (Pakistan) · Zarda, areca nut–containing variety (Bangladesh)

Betel quid (paan), tombol, dohra

Category 4: Tobacco with other plant stimulants or toxicants

Caffeinated snuff · Rapé with tonka bean (coumarin) · Rapé with clove (eugenol, camphor, coumarin) · Rapé with Peruvian cocoa (caffeine) · Tombol with khat (cathinone, an amphetamine)

Notes: Tombol (Category 4) shown on betel leaf prior to addition of noura (alkaline agent), fofal (areca nut), and tobacco. This figure groups products with similar constituents for further investigation and research and highlights constituents of concern. This categorization, which is based on product knowledge at the time of publishing, does not reflect the safety or the addictive properties of a product or product type. The composition of products of a given type can vary such that seemingly similar products may fit into different categories. Detailed product information is given in Appendix A.

Sources: All images except tombol with khat courtesy of Clifford Watson, Centers for Disease Control and Prevention. Image of tombol with khat courtesy of Dr. Mazen Abood Bin Thabit, University of Aden.

Figure 1:   Diverse constituents found in smokeless tobacco products worldwide

Source: Smokeless tobacco and public health: A global perspective (Figure 3.4).[1]

roll. Snuff is fire cured, fermented, and marketed as either dry (Scotch) or moist (dip). Dry snuff is processed into a fine tobacco powder, whereas moist snuff is processed into a damp, finely cut product. Moist snuff currently is the predominant form of snuff sold in the United States.[6] Both chewing tobacco and moist snuff are used orally by placing a wad or pinch of product in the mouth and sucking or chewing to release nicotine. Dry snuff can also be used orally but is more often used nasally by placing a pinch in the nostril and inhaling. Because oral use of chewing tobacco and unpackaged snuff requires the user to spit out saliva mixed with tobacco, these products are also referred to as *spit tobacco*. Beginning in 2001, tobacco companies introduced several spit-free dissolvable products in the United States. They are made of finely ground tobacco mixed with additives and flavorings; shaped into pellets, lozenges, sticks, and strips; and often packaged like candy or mints.[8]

Low pH snus is a moist Swedish snuff made with air-dried tobacco mixed with sodium carbonate and flavoring that can be used without spitting. Snus differs from other smokeless products in that it has been modified specifically to have low levels of TSNA.[9] It is the only product shown in Figure 1 that the US Food and Drug Administration (FDA) allows to be marketed with a "modified risk" claim.[10] This means that the product has a lower relative risk of disease (mouth cancer, heart disease, lung cancer, stroke, emphysema, and chronic bronchitis) compared to cigarettes, but it does not mean that the product is safe or "FDA approved". The FDA maintains that "All tobacco products are potentially harmful and addictive, and those who do not use tobacco products should continue to refrain from their use".

Mishri is a toasted, powdered tobacco produced in Southeast Asia that is rubbed on the teeth and gums as a dentifrice (cleaner). In Venezuela, chimó is made by crushing and boiling tobacco leaves into a sticky black paste which is mixed with sodium bicarbonate, ash, sugar, and other flavorings. In India, khaini is made from a pinch of coarsely cut and crushed tobacco leaves and slaked lime paste vigorously rubbed together between the palm and thumb and placed in the mouth. Toombak, a moist tobacco product from Sudan, is made from sun-dried, fermented tobacco leaves blended with sodium bicarbonate; compared to other smokeless tobacco products, toombak has one of the highest concentrations of TSNA. Gutka (pan masala with tobacco) is a sweet mixture of sun-dried chopped or powdered tobacco, crushed areca nut (itself a carcinogen), spices, and slaked lime (an alkaline enhancer). Gutka, khaini, and mishri are common products in South Asia, including India, and among Indian immigrants. Rapé is a dry nasal snuff used in Brazil (but is not common); it is made from dried tobacco leaf mixed with flavorings such as tonka bean, clove, and cinnamon, ground into a fine powder, and mixed with wood ash. Nass is common in Pakistan and is a mixture of tobacco, slaked lime, ash from tree bark, oil, flavorings, and water rolled into balls and placed in the mouth.[1] Tambaku (tobacco) paan is often served after dinner as a treat or mouth freshener: a betel leaf is spread with slaked lime and katha powder, rolled into a cone, filled with powdered tobacco and assorted ingredients (such as aromatic spices and chopped betel nut), then folded into a triangle quid, which is placed between the gum and cheek and sucked. In western Alaska, Yup'ik Eskimos use Iq'mik, a homemade mixture of dried tobacco leaves and punk ash, derived from burning punk fungus collected from birch trees.[11] Betel nut and other products that contain tobacco mixed with other plants, such as areca nut, tonka bean, camphor, and cloves, are considered smokeless tobacco, but vaping products that heat the tobacco are excluded according to the IARC definition.[6]

The type of tobacco leaf, the way it is processed, and the additives to a smokeless tobacco product can contribute to its cancer-causing and dependence-producing effects. Therefore, knowing what is in the product is important for understanding how the product is linked to cancer.

3. A Brief History of Smokeless Tobacco Use in the United States

Like smoked tobacco, chewing tobacco and snuff were used for centuries by Native Americans before the arrival of Europeans. Chewing tobacco gained popularity among white men during the first half of the nineteenth century, displacing pipe smoking and the use of dry snuff. Chewing tobacco remained the most common form of tobacco usage among US men until World War I, when manufactured cigarettes were distributed free to soldiers.[12] The public perception that the practice of spitting saliva and tobacco juice was unhygienic led to anti-spitting laws and the placement of cuspidors (also known as spittoons) in public places. Cuspidors were not removed from US federal buildings until 1945.[6]

Chewing tobacco and moist snuff became a prominent feature of professional baseball, the quintessential American sport.[13] The tobacco industry marketed smokeless tobacco aggressively in baseball, recruiting celebrity players, distributing free samples to players and fans, and sponsoring athletic events.[14] Despite advertising being prohibited on television, televised baseball games covertly advertised cigarette smoking since billboards promoting cigarettes were often clearly visible to viewers.[15] Tobacco industry expenditures for smokeless tobacco advertising and promotion rose from $80 million in 1985 to $658.5 million in 2018 (unadjusted for inflation).[16]

Having seen the negative health effects of oral tobacco use, Greg Connolly, a public health dentist in the Massachusetts Department of Health, led efforts against smokeless tobacco.[17] He led Massachusetts to be the first state to require health warning labels on smokeless tobacco products and championed the federal Comprehensive Smokeless Tobacco Health Education Act of 1986. To understand better why people who use smokeless tobacco have trouble quitting, Connolly surveyed 282 baseball players during spring training camps in 1987.[14] Many players who used snuff or chewing tobacco said it was "something to do" or a habit, and 28% said they couldn't stop or were "hooked". The researchers suggested that a successful cessation program would include a staged model of change including information about the adverse health consequences related to use and the benefits of quitting, instruction in effective quitting techniques (for example, substituting chewing gum or sunflower seeds; building skills to handle situations associated with smokeless tobacco use, and encouragement to seek support for behavioral changes), and policies to ensure a tobacco-free work environment.

A tragic consequence of the industry's recruitment of professional baseball players to market smokeless products is that renowned players and trainers have developed oral or other cancers after decades of chewing tobacco. Publicity about the fate of these athletes has stimulated public concern about smokeless tobacco products and, ironically, contributed to a movement to ban or restrict the use of spit tobacco in baseball.[18]

However, smokeless tobacco products continue to be used by school children in the United States. According to the 2020 National Youth Tobacco Survey, smokeless tobacco is used by approximately 630,000 middle and high school students. According to the 2019 National Health

Interview Survey, smokeless tobacco is used by approximately 5.9 million adults.[19,20] Smokeless tobacco use in the United States tends to be more common among people who are male, white race, did not graduate from college, or live in the Midwest or South.[19] During 2000–2015, a decline in US chewing tobacco consumption was offset by an increase in moist snuff consumption: chewing tobacco consumption decreased from 45.6 to 20.2 billion pounds while moist snuff consumption increased from 66.2 to 117.4 billion pounds.[21]

4. Constituents of Smokeless Tobacco Products

Unburned tobacco contains more than 4,000 chemicals including TSNAs, nicotine, polycyclic aromatic hydrocarbons (PAHs), volatile aldehydes (such as formaldehyde), and toxic metals. More than 30 of the chemical constituents in smokeless tobacco products are classified by IARC as carcinogenic to humans (Group 1) or as probably or possibly carcinogenic (Group 2A/2B) (Table 1).

Table 1:   Substances identified in smokeless tobacco products and their categorization as carcinogens.

Substance	Representative carcinogens	IARC group
Tobacco-specific nitrosamines	N'-nitrosonornicotine (NNN)	1
	4-(methylnitrosamino)-1-(3-pyridyl)-1-butanone (NNK)	1
Volatile N-nitrosamines	N-Nitrosodiethanolamine (NDELA)	2B
	N-Nitrosodimethylamine (NDMA)	2A
	N-Nitrosomorpholine (NMOR)	2B
	N-Nitrosopiperidine (NPIP)	2B
	N-Nitrosopyrrolidine (NPYR)	2B
Nitrosamino acids	N-Nitrososarcosine (NSAR)	2B
Polycyclic aromatic hydrocarbons	Benz[a]anthracene (BaA)	2B
	Benzo[a]pyrene (BaP)	1

(*Continued*)

Table 1:   (*Continued*)

Substance	Representative carcinogens	IARC group
	Benzo[*b*]fluoranthene (BbF)	2B
	Benzo[*j*]fluoranthene (BjF)	2B
	Benzo[*k*]fluoranthene (BkF)	2B
	Dibenz[*a,h*]anthracene (DBahA)	2A
	Dibenzo[*a,i*]pyrene (DBaiP)	2B
	Indeno[*1,2,3-cd*]pyrene (IcdP)	2B
	5-Methylchrysene (5MC)	2B
	Naphthalene (NAP)	2B
Aldehydes	Acetaldehyde	2B
	Formaldehyde	1
Metals/metalloids	Arsenic	1
	Beryllium	1
	Cadmium	1
	Cobalt	2B
	Chromium VI	1
	Lead/Inorganic lead compounds	2B/2A
	Nickel compounds	1
	Polonium-210	1
Inorganic compounds	Nitrate (under conditions resulting in endogenous nitrosation)	2A
	Nitrite (under conditions resulting in endogenous nitrosation)	2A
Plant material	Areca nut	1
	Betel quid (with or without tobacco)	1
Fermentation-related compound	Ethyl carbamate (urethane)	2A
Mycotoxins	Aflatoxins (mixtures of)	1
	Aflatoxin M1	1 (updated from 2B to 1 in 2012)
	Ochratoxin A	2B

Source: Smokeless tobacco and public health: A global perspective (Table 3.2).[1]

PAHs, such as benzo[*a*]pyrene, are formed when organic matter doesn't burn completely. In smokeless tobacco, PAHs are often formed during the fire-curing process. Carcinogenic metals or metalloids found in smokeless tobacco products include arsenic, beryllium, cadmium, chromium, cobalt, lead, nickel, and the radioactive metal polonium-210. Other harmful metals include mercury and uranium. Most toxic metals in smokeless tobacco are thought to be absorbed from the soil into the tobacco leaf as it grows or are deposited from the soil onto the tobacco leaf during growth or harvesting.

Nicotine and the TSNAs are the most important chemicals in terms of addictiveness or carcinogenicity and are strongly influenced by the methods used to grow, cure, and process the tobacco plant. All smokeless tobacco products contain nicotine as the major constituent that sustains use and creates addiction.[6,22,23] Other lesser alkaloids synthesized by the tobacco plant include nornicotine, myosmine, anabasine, anatabine, and isonicoteine, although these are present in much smaller amounts. Alkalinating agents such as slaked lime, wood ash, calcium carbonate, magnesium carbonate, or sodium bicarbonate are added during the manufacture of these products to increase the concentration and bioavailability of nicotine. The addition of alkylating agents increases the pH level and raises the concentration of free (unprotonated) nicotine, the form of nicotine that is most readily released from products and absorbed across mucous membranes.

Particularly important are several TSNAs that are present at much higher concentrations in conventional smokeless products than in tobacco smoke. TSNAs are pro-carcinogenic compounds that are present at low levels in freshly harvested tobacco leaves but accumulate during curing, processing (particularly fermentation and aging), and long-term storage. TSNA formation is a multi-step process, and conditions at each step can impact the amount of TSNA formed. Tobacco absorbs nitrate during cultivation and tobacco alkaloids, such as nicotine and nornicotine, are synthesized in the plant. When tobacco is dried during curing, tobacco cells burst, and nitrate and tobacco alkaloids are released. If nitrate-reducing bacteria are present under appropriate conditions, they convert nitrate to nitrite and expel it from the cell. The nitrate-to-nitrite conversion process allows the bacteria to continue respiration when oxygen is absent. Extracellular nitrite that is acidified to form nitrous acid can react with tobacco alkaloids to form TSNAs. The reaction can also occur at neutral pH, although not as rapidly. Because the concentrations of TSNAs in tobacco are determined by factors such as the nitrate content in fertilizer and the mode of curing and processing, levels can be manipulated by controlling these factors.

Several different laboratory methods can be used to examine the inorganic, organic, and biological constituents of smokeless tobacco products.[24] Inorganic chemists study the metals and metalloids present in various products using liquid chromatography–inductively coupled plasma mass spectrometers (ICP-MS) and visualize materials deposited on tobacco using scanning electron microscopy.[25,26]

Organic agents studied include nicotine and other tobacco alkaloids, TSNAs, PAHs, volatile organic compounds (VOCs), and flavoring agents.[27,28] Simple pH measurements allow calculations of free nicotine.[29] The organic constituents of smokeless tobacco products can be separated and identified using gas chromatography–mass spectrometry (GC-MS) or liquid chromatography–mass spectrometry (LC-MS).[28] A mass spectrometer uses a stream of high-energy electrons (or other means) to break a molecule into fragments; the resulting fragmentation pattern, called a mass spectrum, is generally unique for most compounds and may also help identify a compound's elemental composition. For GC-MS, mass spectral libraries are available that can search an unknown compound against thousands of mass spectra and can usually identify most compounds. This instrument is helpful when scientists aren't sure what ingredients were added to the tobacco product or were present in the tobacco. Different tobacco species and plant materials that are mixed with tobacco such as areca nut have been identified with infrared spectroscopy.[28]

The quest to identify the microbial species that contribute most to TSNA formation has spanned several decades. Scientists use molecular microbiology tools to study the bacteria, fungi, and viruses in the smokeless tobacco microbiome. They also use DNA sequencing and imputed metagenomics to identify bacterial families with nitrate-reducing genes that could lead to carcinogenic TSNAs.[30] They found moist snuff contained mostly Firmicutes; dry snuff contained Proteobacteria, Firmicutes, and a bit of Actinobacteria; and Sudanese toombak contained

Actinobacteria, Firmicutes, including a few genera of bacteria with nitrate-reducing genes.[30,31] The genes that encode respiratory nitrate reductases and specific ion transporters are "switched on" or expressed in bacteria when exposed to nitrate and low-oxygen conditions, such as may exist for long periods of time while tobacco is fermented and aged.[30] It should be noted that bacterial genera, such as *Corynebacterium* and *Staphylococcus*, can contain nitrate reductases and ion transporters.[30–32] Although these species were found in this toombak product, other bacteria populations with similar genes may contribute to extracellular nitrite in other tobacco products. Undoubtedly, as the number of products analyzed increases, the list of nitrate-reducing organisms will grow. One of the most effective ways to minimize TSNA levels is to use heat treatment (pasteurization) to kill microorganisms in tobacco products, which results in TSNA levels 10,000 times lower in snus than in some toombak products.[8,33]

In addition to generating nitrite leading to the formation of TSNAs, microbes in tobacco also contribute to the formation of endotoxins and other pro-inflammatory molecules.[31] Chronic inflammation is linked with increased risk of cancer.[34] Researchers also reason that the tobacco mosaic virus, of the *Virgaviridae* family, may contribute to chronic oral inflammation.[31] Reducing the viral load of tobacco could make it somewhat less harmful.

Identifying the constituents of smokeless tobacco products helps determine the levels of addiction, toxicity, and carcinogenicity that may result from their use.

5. Research Links Smokeless Tobacco to Cancer

Although TSNAs are now recognized as the most abundant and potent carcinogens in smokeless tobacco, their presence was not known until the 1970s. In 1972, Stephen Hecht, one of the editors of this book, was finishing a postdoctoral position as a chemist at the US Department of Agriculture in Wynwood, Pennsylvania (S Hecht, personal communication, June 11, 2020). Jobs were scarce at the time, especially for chemists, and when Hecht heard about a position at the fledgling American Health Foundation in New York City, he jumped at the chance. The American Health Foundation was founded as a revolutionary, interdisciplinary research center for disease prevention by the eminent tobacco epidemiologist Ernst Wynder.[35]

In 1950, with his mentor Evarts Graham, Wynder published "Tobacco smoking as a possible etiologic factor in bronchiogenic carcinoma: a study of six hundred and eighty-four proved cases".[36] Wynder was one of the first scientists to describe the harms of smoking and investigate the mechanisms of carcinogenesis, collaborating on this pioneering mechanistic work with Graham and, later, with renowned tobacco chemist Dietrich Hoffmann.[35] In 1968, Wynder and Hoffmann published an article in *Science* called "Experimental tobacco carcinogenesis", stating "The objective of the laboratory studies is, rather, to contribute to an understanding of the factors and mechanisms leading to the disease and thereby to eliminate these decisive factors".[37] Stephen Hecht began his career in this laboratory.

One of Hecht's first projects was to analyze the TSNA N'-nitrosonornicotine (NNN) in tobacco smoke. IARC classified NNN as a probable carcinogen in 1977[38] and as a Group 1 carcinogen (meaning it is considered to cause cancer in humans) in 2007.[6] When Hecht started his work, studies were beginning to show that NNN caused cancer in rats and mice. One day a technical assistant in Hecht's laboratory named Ralph Ornaf suggested, "Let's also analyze *unburned* tobacco for NNN". Hecht says he still remembers the day Ornaf came running into his office shouting, "You should see the size of the NNN peak!" (S Hecht, personal communication, June 11, 2020). Their hypothesis was confirmed: unburned tobacco contained a potential carcinogen, indicating that the tobacco itself, not just its combustion, could be toxic.

In 1974, Hoffmann, Hecht, Ornaf, and Wynder published "N'-nitrosonornicotine in tobacco" in *Science*. It was the first paper to describe carcinogens in smokeless tobacco.[39] And so began the search for similar nitrosamines and other carcinogens in smokeless tobacco. In 1978, Hecht discovered a nitrosamine derived from nicotine, nitrosamine 4-(N-methyl-N-nitrosamino)-1-(3-pyridyl)-1-butanone (nicotine-derived nitrosamino ketone, NNK).[40] Ultimately, Hecht and Hoffmann identified seven TSNAs in unburned tobacco.[41]

Hecht moved to Minnesota in 1996 and began work with Dorothy Hatsukami, co-editor of this book, and shifted his research emphasis to biomarkers of tobacco product exposure. Because people use tobacco and metabolize its carcinogens differently, exposure to carcinogens can be measured by looking at biomarkers in the body in samples of urine, blood, hair, and nails.[42] Recent technological advances also allow researchers to detect DNA damage in human tissues and cells that can be linked to carcinogen exposure.[43] Hecht had previously quantified 4-(methyl-nitrosamino)-1-(3-pyridyl)-1-butanone (NNAL), a metabolite of NNK, in the urine of cigarette smokers.[44] With Hatsukami, Hecht found that total NNAL was as high among people who used smokeless tobacco products as those who used cigarettes, suggesting that switching to smokeless tobacco was not a "safe" substitute for smoking.[45]

In 2000, Hecht recruited Irina Stepanov (author of Chapter 4), a young chemist with a lifelong interest in nitrosamines (I. Stepanov, personal communication, July 22, 2020). While Stepanov's undergraduate work involved nitrosamines in meat products, she turned to tobacco products in her graduate work. Her first assignment in Hecht's lab was to develop a biomarker for NNN. She showed that NNN and its pyridine-*N*-glucuronide, as well as NAT, NAB, and their pyridine-*N*-glucuronides, were present in the urine of people who used smokeless tobacco or cigarettes.[46] This discovery opened the field to link carcinogens to specific cancers; for example, NNN and esophageal cancer.[42] Stepanov became fascinated with the diversity of tobacco products.[47,48] She suspected that the broad range of carcinogens present in the products, even within a single brand, suggested the potential for reducing these carcinogens to a minimum level. Furthermore, Hatsukami in collaboration with Stepanov and Hecht found that levels of carcinogens in smokeless tobacco are directly related to levels of exposures to these carcinogens in humans.[49] Altogether, this work provided key evidence for the FDA to propose that all finished smokeless tobacco products comply with a limit for NNN (to 1 microgram per gram of dry weight tobacco) and requirements on the sale and distribution of these products[50] (see Chapter 14).

Lab and convenience sample clinical studies often look at a select group of people but it is also important to monitor *population*-level exposures. The National Health and Nutrition Examination Survey (NHANES) combines interviews and physical examinations to assess the health and nutritional status of US adults and children. A nationally representative sample of about 10,000 people are examined in each 2-year cycle. Results from NHANES can be used to inform decisions to improve safety of consumer products; for example, finding unacceptably high levels of lead in blood samples led to the removal of lead from gasoline and from food and soft drink cans.[51] Using blood and urine samples from the 1992 to 2012 NHANES surveys, FDA and CDC researchers looked for biomarkers of tobacco exposure including serum cotinine, NNAL, blood lead, blood cadmium, blood mercury, and urinary arsenic. They found that people who used smokeless tobacco had higher concentrations of cotinine and much higher concentrations of NNAL than people who smoked cigarettes, and higher concentrations of lead (but not cadmium, mercury, or arsenic) than people who did not use tobacco.[52] In a more recent study called the Population Assessment of Tobacco and Health (PATH), people who used smokeless tobacco had higher concentrations of biomarkers of exposure to nicotine, TSNAs, and PAHs than people who never used tobacco, and these concentrations went up with frequency of use.[53]

Identifying the carcinogens and toxicants in smokeless tobacco products and developing methods to quantify and monitor their levels in both products and people were important first steps to reduce the products' contamination and carcinogenic potential. However, *knowing* is one thing and *doing* is another. So, in "Call to establish constituent standards for smokeless tobacco products", Stepanov and Hatsukami examined evidence for potential standards for nicotine, NNN, NNK, benzo[*a*]pyrene, cadmium, arsenic, acetaldehyde, crotonaldehyde, and formaldehyde in smokeless tobacco products.[54] They built their case by outlining the levels of these nine toxicants in different products, showing how these levels were linked to human biomarkers, and demonstrating that these biomarkers were associated with subsequent cancer risk. They maintained that reasonable and achievable standards could be set, and met, immediately for NNN, NNK, and benzo[*a*]pyrene, and that limits based on "lower achievable level" could be introduced for cadmium, arsenic, acetaldehyde, crotonaldehyde, and formaldehyde.

It is important to note that these standards would reduce, but not eliminate, the risks associated with smokeless tobacco use, and would be considered just one tool in the tobacco control and prevention toolkit. This comprehensive approach includes screening for tobacco dependence, promoting tobacco cessation, increasing the price of tobacco products, implementing tobacco-free laws, and conducting educational mass media campaigns.[55] These strategies are effective in reducing use of smokeless tobacco products.[56]

6. Key Characteristics of Carcinogens in Smokeless Tobacco Products

How tobacco causes cancer is described briefly here, and in more detail later in Chapter 7. The process of converting a normal cell into a transformed cell into a malignant tumor takes multiple steps.[57] People used to characterize carcinogens as "initiators" or "promoters" of this process,[58] but some agents seem to cause cancer in different ways at different times, and so cannot simply be labeled as an initiator or a promoter. In meetings convened by the IARC, researchers made a list of the top 10 ways an agent can contribute to the carcinogenic process[59]:

(1) act as an electrophile either directly or after metabolic activation,
(2) be genotoxic,
(3) alter DNA repair or cause genomic instability,
(4) induce epigenetic alterations,
(5) induce oxidative stress,
(6) induce chronic inflammation,
(7) be immunosuppressive,
(8) modulate receptor-mediated effects,
(9) cause immortalization,
(10) alter cell proliferation, cell death, or nutrient supply.

In this story, the process of carcinogenesis begins with the initiation of smokeless tobacco use, which quickly leads to nicotine addiction and sustained use (Figure 2).

When people use smokeless tobacco, they expose their mouth and digestive system to irritants and ingest a lethal stew. Some constituents in this stew exhibit one or more of the 10 key characteristics that distinguish them as carcinogens. Building on the work of scientists around the world, including those noted above, Table 2 describes carcinogenic constituents

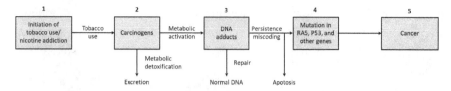

Figure 2:   The process of carcinogenesis begins with the initiation of smokeless tobacco use, which quickly leads to nicotine addiction and sustained use.

Source: Smokeless tobacco and public health: A global perspective (Figure 4.1).[1]

Table 2:   Smokeless tobacco products: Constituents, key characteristics/biologic mechanisms, and biomarkers of human exposure.

Product constituent	Key characteristic(s)/ Biologic mechanism related to cancer	Biomarker of human exposure (may not be specific to smokeless tobacco use)
Tobacco-specific nitrosamines[a] NNN NNK (NNAL metabolite) NAB NAT	Increase DNA adduct levels, cause oxidative DNA damage, cause gene mutations, disrupt mechanisms for cell growth control; systemic carcinogens	TSNAs and metabolites (NNAL) in urine TSNA–Hb adducts in red blood cells TSNA–DNA adducts in oral cells TSNAs in saliva
Volatile nitrosamines[b] (NDELA, NDMA, NMOR, NPIP, NPYR)	Form DNA adducts	information not available
Polycyclic aromatic hydrocarbons (PAH)[c] (Benz[*a*]anthracene, Benzo[*a*] pyrene, Benzofluoranthene, Chrysene, Dibenzo[*a,h*] anthracene, Ideno[*1,2,3-cd*] pyrene, Naphthalene)	Form DNA adducts	PAH biomarkers in urine
Aldehydes[d] (Formaldehyde, Crotonaldehyde, Acetaldehyde)	Form DNA adducts, cause inflammation, increase cell proliferation	Aldehyde–DNA adducts in white blood cells
Metals[e] (Arsenic, Beryllium, Cadmium, Chromium, Lead, Nickel, Polonium)	Cause inflammation and sensitization	Metal levels in urine, saliva, blood, and hair
Ethyl carbamate (urethane)	Form DNA adducts	information not available

Table 2: *(Continued)*

Product constituent	Key characteristic(s)/ Biologic mechanism related to cancer	Biomarker of human exposure (may not be specific to smokeless tobacco use)
Nicotine	Precursor to TSNAs	Nicotine and metabolites (cotinine) in urine
Arecoline	Inhibits cellular growth, depletes cellular glutathione	Arecoline in urine and blood
Areca-nut-specific nitrosamines (MNPN)	Form reactive oxygen species	MNPN in saliva
Alkaline agents (such as sodium bicarbonate)	Increase the absorption of carcinogens and contribute to chronic inflammation and tumor promotion	Sodium levels in urine
Flavorings (such as menthol)		
Bacteria, fungi, viruses		

Notes: [a]NNN, NNK (NNAL metabolite), NAB, NAT. [b]NDELA, NDMA, NMOR, NPIP, NPYR. [c]Benz[*a*]anthracene, benzo[*a*]pyrene [BaP], benzofluoranthene, chrysene, dibenzo[*a,h*]anthracene, ideno[1,2,3-cd]pyrene, naphthalene. [d]Formaldehyde, crotonaldehyde, acetaldehyde. [e]Arsenic, beryllium, cadmium, chromium, lead, nickel, polonium. NNN = N'-nitrosonornicotine; NNK = 4-(methylnitrosamino)-1-(3-pyridyl)-1-butanone; NNAL = 4-(methylnitrosamino)-1-(3-pyridyl)-1-butanol; NAB = N'-nitrosoanabasine; NAT = N'-nitrosoanatabine; NDELA = N-nitrosodiethanolamine; NDMA = N-nitrosodimethylamine; NMOR = N-nitrosomorpholine; NPIP = N-nitrosopiperidine; NPYR = N-nitrosopyrrolidine; NSAR = N-nitrosarcosine; MNPA = 3-methylnitrosamino propionaldehyde; MNBA = methylnitroso-N-butylamine; MNPN = 3-methylnitrosamino propionitrile; PAHs = polycyclic aromatic hydrocarbons; BAP = benzo[*a*]pyrene.
Source: Smokeless tobacco and public health: A global perspective (Table 4.1).[1]

commonly found in smokeless tobacco, their key carcinogenic character-istics and biologic mechanisms, and biomarkers of human exposure.

7. Scientific Basis on Which Smokeless Tobacco Is Classified as Carcinogenic to Humans

Since the 18th century, periodic case reports have described nasal or oral cancers developing after prolonged use of smokeless tobacco. In 1761, a London physician named John Hill described five cases of "polypusses, a swelling in the nostril that was hard, black and adherent with the symptoms of an open cancer" and concluded these nasal cancers were the consequence of snuff use.[6] In one unusual case, a letter to the *New England Journal of Medicine* in 1960 described a 3 cm × 4 cm squamous cell carcinoma that developed in the left ear of a 58-year-old farmer in Minnesota who had applied snuff to his ear regularly since his teen years.[60] The editors report however that this is not common practice in Minnesota!

Dental surveys conducted in many countries have documented oral precancerous lesions at sites where the chewing tobacco or oral snuff are placed.[6] One US study of 1109 professional baseball players found that almost half of those who reported using moist snuff or chewing tobacco in the past week had *oral leukoplakia* — hyperplasia of the squamous epithelium that look like thick white or gray patches on the roof of mouth, cheeks, gum, or tongue.[61] Oral leukoplakia is considered pre-carcinogenic, as some lesions progress to cancer.

In the late 1970s, Debbie Winn was a doctoral student in the epidemiology department at the University of North Carolina at Chapel Hill searching for a dissertation topic (D Winn, personal communication, June 16, 2020). About that time, NCI epidemiologists William Blot and Joseph Fraumeni had published *Atlas of Cancer Mortality for US Counties*[62] and embarked on a series of ecologic studies to discover potential reasons for cancer hot spots, such as the association between lung cancer and shipyards — and, perhaps, the asbestos used in those ships.[63] Blot and Fraumeni planned to follow these ecologic studies with case-control studies to test any resulting hypotheses. One compelling hot spot was the disproportionately higher death rate from cancers of the oral cavity and pharynx among women in Southern states compared to the rest of the United States.[64] This group of cancers includes those that develop on the lip, along the cheek and gum, on the tongue, in the upper part of the throat, or in a salivary gland.[65]

Researchers had long determined that tobacco smoking and alcohol use increased the risk of these cancers, accounting for about three of four oral cancers in men.[64] They were now trying to figure out what else might be a risk factor, especially among people who didn't smoke or drink — studying characteristics such as ill-fitting dentures and snuff dipping.[66] The majority of men smoked or had smoked, which made it difficult to separate the effects of smokeless tobacco from smoking. In North Carolina, relatively few women smoked cigarettes, but 30% used dry snuff orally, placing a pinch of the powder between their gum and cheek.[67]

Noting an unusually high death rate and a unique exposure, Winn had her dissertation topic. She wrote a proposal, developed survey instruments, and assembled a case-control study, recruiting 255 women diagnosed with an oral or pharynx cancer and 502 matched controls from North Carolina.[68] Using analyses that controlled for confounding by smoking, Winn and her colleagues found that white women who used snuff had a 4-fold increased risk of developing oral cancer compared to those who did not use snuff. For women who used snuff for 50 or more years (which is possible if you start when you're 10 years old), the risk of developing a cancer in the gum or cheek was 47-fold. According to Winn's calculations, among these women, snuff use accounted for nine out of 10 cancers of the gum or cheek. The results were published in the *New England Journal of Medicine* and it is now considered the seminal study linking oral snuff use to oral cancer.

The evidence that smokeless tobacco causes cancer stacked up quickly. In January 1986, the National Institutes of Health invited experts to a consensus conference on the health implications of smokeless tobacco use.[69] Their conclusions were similar to those in the Report to the Surgeon General on the health consequences of using smokeless tobacco released in March of that year[3]: The use of smokeless tobacco increased the risk of oral cancer, led to the development of the non-cancerous oral conditions gingival recession and oral leukoplakia, and led to nicotine addiction and dependence. The NCI cosponsored the First International Conference on Smokeless Tobacco in 1991, including presentations about epidemiology, clinical and pathological effects, carcinogenesis, nicotine addiction, prevention, cessation, and control policies.[9] In 1985, IARC evaluated the carcinogenicity of betel quid and areca nut chewing and concluded there was sufficient evidence that the habit of chewing betel quid with tobacco was carcinogenic, particularly for oral cancers.[70] In a 2004 update, IARC concluded that betel quid *without* tobacco caused oral cancers (indicating that areca nut was carcinogenic) and betel quid with tobacco also caused pharyngeal and esophageal cancers, and classified areca nut and betel quid as Group 1 carcinogens.[71] IARC later evaluated the carcinogenicity of other smokeless tobacco products, including the types discussed earlier in this chapter, and classified smokeless tobacco as a Group 1 carcinogen and concluded the evidence was sufficient that smokeless tobacco caused cancers of the oral cavity and pancreas.[6] In 2012, IARC added cancer of the esophagus to the list.[72]

Some evidence suggests smokeless tobacco use is associated with increased risk of cancers of the lung, stomach, prostate, and cervix.[73,74] In addition, evidence suggests that use of some smokeless tobacco products may be associated with increased risk of periodontal conditions (gum recession, dental caries, leukoplakia, erythroplakia, and erythroleukoplakia), fatal ischemic heart disease, fatal stroke, type 2 diabetes, and adverse reproductive outcomes (stillbirth, pre-term birth, and low birth weight).[6,72,75] Even the low-nitrosamine snus seems to increase fatal prostate cancer[76] and fatal cardiovascular health outcomes.[77] As with cancer, the risks of other health outcomes vary substantially by smokeless tobacco product characteristics, ingredients, and manner of use, as well as potential interactions with other tobacco use, such as cigarette smoking.

Recently, using different methods and datasets, two teams independently assessed the global burden of cancer attributed to smokeless tobacco use.[2,78] Using the comparative risk assessment method, Siddiqi *et al.* estimated that using smokeless tobacco led to 62,283 deaths in 2010 due to cancers of the mouth, pharynx, and esophagus.[78] Using the population attributable fraction method, Sinha *et al.* estimated that 101,004 cancers (including 46,917 cancers of the mouth, pharynx, esophagus, and larynx) were attributable to smokeless tobacco use.[2] Both studies illustrate the considerable, yet preventable, cancer burden due to smokeless tobacco use.

As a global effort to reduce the harms of tobacco use, the World Health Organization recommends implementing the MPOWER policy package, consisting of six evidence-based components: M: monitor tobacco use and prevention policies; P: protect people from tobacco smoke; O: offer help to quit tobacco use; W: warn about the dangers of tobacco; E: enforce bans on tobacco advertising, promotion, and sponsorship; R: raise taxes on tobacco.[79] Many of these components can be applied to smokeless tobacco prevention and control.

8. Conclusion

The story of smokeless tobacco is an ancient one. Local flora, cultural influences, and personal tastes influenced its form and use over the millennia. By the 1970s, US tobacco companies were using marketing tactics to drive consumer demand for smokeless tobacco products. In the mid-1970s, scientists published the first evidence that smokeless tobacco contains carcinogens. Further research has linked more than 30 chemicals in smokeless tobacco products to cancer and has shown that all smokeless tobacco products contain nicotine, which can lead to addiction and tobacco dependence (see Chapter 12). Identifying the carcinogens and toxicants in smokeless tobacco products and developing methods to monitor population-level exposures led to a proposal to regulate the levels of nicotine and several carcinogens in these products. This is one part of a global effort to reduce the harms of smokeless tobacco use. Other components of this effort include regulating the sale of tobacco products, supporting individual cessation efforts, and promoting tobacco-free environments.

References

1. Hatsukami DK ZM, Gupta P, Parascandola M, Asma S, ed. Smokeless tobacco and public health: A global perspective. (Bethesda, MD: U.S. Department of Health and Human Services, Centers for Disease Control and Prevention and National Institutes of Health, National Cancer Institute, 2014).
2. Sinha DN, Suliankatchi RA, Gupta PC, *et al.* Global burden of all-cause and cause-specific mortality due to smokeless tobacco use: Systematic review and meta-analysis. *Tobacco Control* 2018;27(1):35. doi: 10.1136/tobaccocontrol-2016-053302.
3. U.S. Department of Health and Human Services. *The Health Consequences of Using Smokeless Tobacco, A Report of the Advisory Committee to the Surgeon General.* (Bethesda, MD: U.S. Department of Health and Human Services, Public Health Service, Centers for Disease Control and Prevention, Office on Smoking and Health, 1986).
4. U.S. Department of Health, Education, and Welfare. *Smoking and Health. Report of the Advisory Committee to the Surgeon General of the Public*

Health Service. (Washington, DC: U.S. Department of Health, Education, and Welfare. Public Health Service, 1964).

5. Musk AW, de Klerk NH. History of tobacco and health. *Respirology* 2003;8(3):286–90. doi: 10.1046/j.1440-1843.2003.00483.x.

6. International Agency for Research on Cancer. Smokeless Tobacco and Some Tobacco-specific *N*-Nitrosamines. In: *IARC Monographs on the Evaluation of Carcinogenic Risks to Humans, vol. 89* (Lyon, FR: IARC, 2007).

7. Koob GF, Arends MA, Le Moal M. Chapter 7 — Nicotine. In: *Drugs, Addiction, and the Brain*, Koob GF, Arends MA, Le Moal M, eds., 221–59. (San Diego: Academic Press, 2014).

8. Stanfill SB, Stepanov I. Chapter 3: A global view of smokeless tobacco products. In: *Smokeless Tobacco and Public Health: A Global Perspective*, Hatsukami DK ZM, Gupta P, Parascandola M, Asma S, eds. (Bethesda, MD: U.S. Department of Health and Human Services, Centers for Disease Control and Prevention and National Institutes of Health, National Cancer Institute, 2014).

9. National Cancer Institute. Smokeless tobacco or health. An international perspective. Smoking and tobacco control monograph no. 2. Publication no. 92-3461. (Bethesda, MD: U.S. Department of Health and Human Services, National Institutes of Health, National Cancer Institute, 1992).

10. U. S. Food and Drug Administration. FDA grants first-ever modified risk orders to eight smokeless tobacco products [news release] (https://www.fda.gov/news-events/press-announcements/fda-grants-first-ever-modified-risk-orders-eight-smokeless-tobacco-products).

11. Renner CC, Enoch C, Patten CA, *et al*. Iqmik: A form of smokeless tobacco used among alaska natives. *Am J Health Behav* 2005;29(6):588–94. doi: 10.5993/AJHB.29.6.13.

12. Thun MJ, Henley SJ, Calle EE. Tobacco use and cancer: An epidemiologic perspective for geneticists. *Oncogene* 2002;21(48):7307–25. doi: 10.1038/sj.onc.1205807.

13. Agaku IT, Singh T, Jones SE, *et al*. Combustible and smokeless tobacco use among high school athletes — United States, 2001–2013. *MMWR Morb Mortal Wkly Rep* 2015;64(34):935–9. doi: 10.15585/mmwr.mm6434a2.

14. Connolly GN, Orleans CT, Kogan M. Use of smokeless tobacco in major-league baseball. *N Engl J Med* 1988;318(19):1281–5. doi: 10.1056/nejm198805123181918.

15. Institute of Medicine (US) Committee on Preventing Nicotine Addiction in Children and Youths. *Growing up Tobacco Free: Preventing Nicotine Addiction in Children and Youths*. (Washington, DC: National Academies Press, 1994).

16. U.S. Federal Trade Commission. Smokeless Tobacco Report for 2018. Federal Trade Commission. (https://www.ftc.gov/system/files/documents/ reports/federal-trade-commission-cigarette-report-2018-smokeless-tobacco-report-2018/p114508smokelesstobaccoreport2018.pdf).

17. Folkenberg J. Oral cancer on the rise. *FDA Consum* 1989;23(10):24–25.

18. Campaign for Tobacco-Free Kids. Tobacco-free MLB stadiums. (https:// tobaccofreebaseball.org/tobacco-free-stadiums/).

19. Gentzke AS, Wang TW, Jamal A, *et al*. Tobacco Product Use Among Middle and High School Students — United States, 2020. *MMWR Morb Mortal Wkly Rep* 2020;69:1881–8. doi: http://dx.doi.org/10.15585/mmwr. mm6950a1.

20. Cornelius ME, Wang TW, Jamal A, Loretan CG, Neff LJ. Tobacco product use among adults — United States, 2019. *MMWR Morb Mortal Wkly Rep* 2020;69:1736–42. doi: http://dx.doi.org/10.15585/mmwr.mm6946a4.

21. Wang TW, Kenemer B, Tynan MA, Singh T, King B. Consumption of combustible and smokeless tobacco — United States, 2000–2015. *MMWR Morb Mortal Wkly Rep* 2016;65(48):1357–63. doi: 10.15585/mmwr.mm6548a1.

22. Henningfield JE, Fant RV, Tomar SL. Smokeless tobacco: An addicting drug. *Adv Dent Res* 1997;11(3):330–5. doi: 10.1177/08959374970110030401.

23. Hatsukami DK, Severson HH. Oral spit tobacco: Addiction, prevention and treatment. *Nicotine Tob Res* 1999;1(1):21–44. doi: 10.1080/ 14622299050011131.

24. Centers for Disease Control and Prevention. National biomonitoring program: Tobacco. U.S. Department of Health and Human Services, Centers for Disease Control and Prevention. (https://www.cdc.gov/biomonitoring/ tobacco.html).

25. Pappas RS. Toxic elements in tobacco and in cigarette smoke: Inflammation and sensitization. *Metallomics* 2011. doi: 10.1039/c1mt00066g.

26. Pappas RS, Stanfill SB, Watson CH, Ashley DL. Analysis of toxic metals in commercial moist snuff and Alaskan iqmik. *J Anal Toxicol* 2008; 32(4):281–91.

27. Richter P, Hodge K, Stanfill S, Zhang L, Watson C. Surveillance of moist snuff: Total nicotine, moisture, pH, un-ionized nicotine, and tobacco-specific nitrosamines. *Nicotine Tob Res* 2008;10(11):1645–52. doi: 10.1080/14622200802412937.

28. Stanfill SB, Connolly GN, Zhang L, *et al*. Global surveillance of oral tobacco products: Total nicotine, unionised nicotine and tobacco-specific N-nitrosamines. *Tobacco Control* 2011;20(3):e2. doi: 10.1136/ tc.2010.037465.

29. Richter P, Spierto FW. Surveillance of smokeless tobacco nicotine, pH, moisture, and unprotonated nicotine content. *Nicotine Tobacco Res* 2003;5(6):885–9. doi: 10.1080/14622200310001614647.

30. Tyx RE, Stanfill SB, Keong LM, Rivera AJ, Satten GA, Watson CH. Characterization of bacterial communities in selected smokeless tobacco products using 16S rDNA analysis. *PLoS ONE* 2016;11(1):e0146939. doi: 10.1371/journal.pone.0146939.

31. Rivera AJ, Tyx RE, Keong LM, Stanfill SB. Microbial communities and gene contributions in smokeless tobacco products. *Appl Microbiol Biotechnol* 2020;104:10613–29 https://doi.org/10.1007/s00253-020-10999-w.

32. Bernard KA, Funke G. Corynebacterium. In *Bergey's Manual of Systematics of Archaea and Bacteria*, W.B. Whitman, F. Rainey, P. Kämpfer, *et al.*, eds. 1–70. 2015.

33. Idris AM, Nair J, Friesen M, *et al.* Carcinogenic tobacco-specific nitrosamines are present at unusually high levels in the saliva of oral snuff users in Sudan. *Carcinogenesis* 1992;13(6):1001–5. doi: 10.1093/carcin/13.6.1001.

34. Thun MJ, Henley SJ, Gansler T. Inflammation and cancer: An epidemiological perspective. *Novartis Found Symp* 2004;256:6–21; discussion 22–8, 49–52, 266–9. PMID: 15027481.

35. Stellman SD. Ernst Wynder: A remembrance. *Prev Med* 2006;43(4):239–45. doi: 10.1016/j.ypmed.2006.08.007.

36. Wynder EL, Graham EA. Tobacco smoking as a possible etiologic factor in bronchiogenic carcinoma; A study of 684 proved cases. *J Am Med Assoc* 1950;143(4):329–36. doi: 10.1001/jama.1950.02910390001001.

37. Wynder EL, Hoffmann D. Experimental tobacco carcinogenesis. *Science* 1968;162(3856):862–71. doi: 10.1126/science.162.3856.862.

38. International Agency for Research on Cancer. Some N-nitroso compounds. In: *IARC Monographs on the Evaluation of the Carcinogenic Risk of Chemicals to Humans, vol. 17* (Lyon, FR: IARC, 1978).

39. Hoffmann D, Hecht SS, Ornaf RM, Wynder EL. N′-nitrosonornicotine in tobacco. *Science* 1974;186(4160):265–7. doi: 10.1126/science.186.4160.265.

40. Hecht SS, Chen CB, Hirota N, Ornaf RM, Tso TC, Hoffmann D. Tobacco-specific nitrosamines: Formation from nicotine in vitro and during tobacco curing and carcinogenicity in strain A mice. *J Natl Cancer Inst* 1978;60(4):819–24. doi: 10.1093/jnci/60.4.819.

41. Amin S, Desai D, Hecht SS, Hoffmann D. Synthesis of tobacco-specific N-nitrosamines and their metabolites and results of related bioassays. *Crit Rev Toxicol* 1996;26(2):139–47. doi: 10.3109/10408449609017927.

42. Hecht SS. Tobacco carcinogens, their biomarkers and tobacco-induced cancer. *Nat Rev Cancer* 2003;3(10):733–44. doi: 10.1038/nrc1190.

43. Peterson LA, Balbo S, Fujioka N, *et al.* Applying tobacco, environmental and dietary-related biomarkers to understand cancer etiology and evaluate prevention strategies. *Cancer Epidemiol Biomarkers Prev* 2020;29(10):1904–1919. doi: 10.1158/1055-9965.Epi-19-1356.

44. Carmella SG, Akerkar S, Hecht SS. Metabolites of the tobacco-specific nitrosamine 4-(methylnitrosamino)-1-(3-pyridyl)-1-butanone in smokers' urine. *Cancer Res* 1993;53(4):721–4.

45. Hecht SS, Carmella SG, Murphy SE, *et al.* Similar exposure to a tobacco-specific carcinogen in smokeless tobacco users and cigarette smokers. *Cancer Epidemiol Biomarkers Prev* 2007;16(8):1567–72. doi: 10.1158/1055-9965.epi-07-0227.

46. Stepanov I, Hecht SS. Tobacco-specific nitrosamines and their pyridine-*N*-glucuronides in the urine of smokers and smokeless tobacco users. *Cancer Epidemiol Biomarkers Prev* 2005;14(4):885–91. doi: 10.1158/1055-9965.epi-04-0753.

47. Hatsukami DK, Ebbert JO, Feuer RM, Stepanov I, Hecht SS. Changing smokeless tobacco products: New tobacco-delivery systems. *Am J Prev Med* 2007;33(6, Supplement 1):S368–78. doi: 10.1016/j.amepre.2007.09.005.

48. Stepanov I, Jensen J, Hatsukami D, Hecht SS. New and traditional smokeless tobacco: Comparison of toxicant and carcinogen levels. *Nicotine Tobacco Res* 2008;10(12):1773–82. doi: 10.1080/14622200802443544.

49. Hatsukami DK, Stepanov I, Severson H, *et al.* Evidence supporting product standards for carcinogens in smokeless tobacco products. *Cancer Prev Res (Phila)* 2015;8(1):20–6. doi: 10.1158/1940-6207.Capr-14-0250.

50. U.S. Food and Drug Administration. Tobacco product standard for *N'*-nitrosonornicotine level in finished smokeless tobacco products (proposed rule). *Fed Regist* 2017;82:8004–8053.

51. Pirkle JL, Brody DJ, Gunter EW, *et al.* The decline in blood lead levels in the United States. The National Health and Nutrition Examination Surveys (NHANES). *JAMA* 1994;272(4):284–91.

52. Rostron BL, Chang CM, van Bemmel DM, Xia Y, Blount BC. Nicotine and toxicant exposure among U.S. smokeless tobacco users: Results from 1999 to 2012 National Health and Nutrition Examination Survey Data. *Cancer Epidemiol Biomarkers Prev* 2015;24(12):1829–1837. doi: 10.1158/1055-9965.epi-15-0376.

53. Cheng YC, Reyes-Guzman CM, Christensen CH, *et al.* Biomarkers of exposure among adult smokeless tobacco users in the population assessment of tobacco and health study (wave 1, 2013-2014). *Cancer Epidemiol Biomarkers Prev* 2020;29(3):659–67. doi: 10.1158/1055-9965.Epi-19-0766.

54. Stepanov I, Hatsukami D. Call to establish constituent standards for smokeless tobacco products. *Tobacco Reg Sci* 2016;2(1):9–30. doi: 10.18001/TRS.2.1.2.

55. Centers for Disease Control and Prevention. *Best Practices for Comprehensive Tobacco Control Programs — 2014.* (Atlanta, GA: Centers for Disease Control and Prevention, National Center for Chronic Disease Prevention and Health Promotion, Office on Smoking and Health, 2014).

56. Levy DT, Mays D, Boyle RG, Tam J, Chaloupka FJ. The effect of tobacco control policies on US smokeless tobacco use: A structured review. *Nicotine Tobacco Res* 2017;20(1):3–11. doi: 10.1093/ntr/ntw291.

57. Weinberg RA. How cancer arises. *Sci Am* 1996;275(3):62–70. doi: 10.1038/scientificamerican0996-62.

58. Boyland E. Tumour initiators, promoters, and complete carcinogens. *Br J Ind Med* 1985;42(10):716–8. doi: 10.1136/oem.42.10.716.

59. Smith MT, Guyton KZ, Gibbons CF, *et al.* Key characteristics of carcinogens as a basis for organizing data on mechanisms of carcinogenesis. *Environ Health Perspect* 2016;124(6):713–21. doi:10.1289/ehp.1509912.

60. Root HD, Aust JB, Sullivan A, Jr. Snuff and cancer of the ear. Report of a case. *N Engl J Med* 1960;262:819–20. doi: 10.1056/nejm196004212621608.

61. Ernster VL, Grady DG, Greene JC, *et al.* Smokeless tobacco use and health effects among baseball players. *JAMA* 1990;264(2):218–24.

62. Mason TJ, McKay FW, Hoover R, Blot WJ, Fraumeni JF. *Atlas of Cancer Mortality for U.S. Counties, 1950–1969.* DHEW Pub. No. (NIH) 75–780. (Bethesda, MD: U.S. Department of Health, Education, and Welfare, Public Health Service, National Institutes of Health, 1975).

63. Blot WJ, Harrington JM, Toledo A, Hoover R, Heath CW, Jr., Fraumeni JF, Jr. Lung cancer after employment in shipyards during World War II. *N Engl J Med* 1978;299(12):620–4. doi: 10.1056/nejm197809212991202.

64. Blot WJ, Fraumeni JF, Jr. Geographic patterns of oral cancer in the United States: Etiologic implications. *J Chronic Dis* 1977;30(11):745–57. doi: 10.1016/0021-9681(77)90003-0.

65. Ellington TD, Henley SJ, Senkomago V, *et al.* Trends in incidence of cancers of the oral cavity and pharynx — United States 2007–2016. *MMWR Morb Mortal Wkly Rep* 2020;69(15):433–438. doi: 10.15585/mmwr.mm6915a1.

66. Vogler WR, Lloyd JW, Milmore BK. A retrospective study of etiological factors in cancer of the mouth, pharynx, and larynx. *Cancer* 1962;15: 246–58. doi: 10.1002/1097-0142(196203/04)15:2<246::aid-cncr2820150206> 3.0.co;2-5.

67. Schottenfeld D. Snuff dipper's cancer. *N Engl J Med* 1981;304(13):778–9. doi: 10.1056/nejm198103263041309.

68. Winn DM, Blot WJ, Shy CM, Pickle LW, Toledo A, Fraumeni JF, Jr. Snuff dipping and oral cancer among women in the southern United States. *N Engl J Med* 1981;304(13):745–9. doi: 10.1056/nejm198103263041301.

69. National Institutes of Health. Health implications of smokeless tobacco use. *NIH Consens Statement* 1986;6(1):1–17.

70. International Agency for Research on Cancer. Tobacco habits other than smoking: betel-quid and areca-nut chewing and some related nitrosamines. In: *IARC Monographs on the Evaluation of the Carcinogenic Risk of Chemicals to Humans, vol. 37* (Lyon, FR: IARC, 1985).

71. International Agency for Research on Cancer. Betel-quid and areca-nut chewing and some areca-nut-derived nitrosamines. In: *IARC Monographs on the Evaluation of Carcinogenic Risks to Humans, vol. 85* (Lyon, FR: IARC, 2004).

72. International Agency for Research on Cancer. Personal Habits and Indoor Combustions. In: *IARC Monographs on the Evaluation of Carcinogenic Risks to Humans, vol. 100E* (Lyon, FR: IARC, 2012).

73. Andreotti G, Freedman ND, Silverman DT, *et al.* Tobacco use and cancer risk in the agricultural health study. *Cancer Epidemiol Biomarkers Prev* 2017;26(5):769–78. doi: 10.1158/1055-9965.Epi-16-0748.

74. Gupta S, Gupta R, Sinha D, Mehrotra R. Relationship between type of smokeless tobacco & risk of cancer: A systematic review. *Indian J Med Res* 2018;148(1):56–76. doi: 10.4103/ijmr.IJMR_2023_17.

75. Henley S, Thun M. Chapter 4: Health consequences of smokeless tobacco use. In *Smokeless Tobacco and Public Health: A Global Perspective*, Hatsukami DK ZM, Gupta P, Parascandola M, Asma S, eds. (Bethesda, MD: U.S. Department of Health and Human Services, Centers for Disease Control and Prevention and National Institutes of Health, National Cancer Institute, 2014).

76. Wilson KM, Markt SC, Fang F, *et al.* Snus use, smoking and survival among prostate cancer patients. *Int J Cancer* 2016;139(12):2753–9. doi: 10.1002/ ijc.30411.

77. Gupta R, Gupta S, Sharma S, Sinha DN, Mehrotra R. A systematic review on association between smokeless tobacco & cardiovascular diseases. *Indian J Med Res* 2018;148(1):77–89. doi: 10.4103/ijmr.IJMR_2020_17.

78. Siddiqi K, Shah S, Abbas SM, *et al.* Global burden of disease due to smoke-less tobacco consumption in adults: Analysis of data from 113 countries. *BMC Med* 2015;13:194. doi: 10.1186/s12916-015-0424-2.

79. World Health Organization. *WHO Report on the Global Tobacco Epidemic 2008 — The MPOWER Package.* (Geneva: World Health Organization, 2008). https://apps.who.int/iris/handle/10665/43818.

https://doi.org/10.1142/9789811239533_0006

Chapter 6

Alternative Nicotine Delivery Systems

Maciej L. Goniewicz*

1. Introduction

Chapters 4 and 5 described the most popular forms of tobacco use in the world as sources of nicotine and carcinogens: cigarette smoking and smokeless tobacco. Although the best way to avoid the cancer risks associated with smoking and smokeless tobacco use is to quit these habits altogether, the application of a harm reduction strategy could result in substantial reductions in mortality and morbidity related to cancer. One such approach would be to promote the substitution of alternative, less toxic and carcinogenic means of delivering nicotine, assuming that these did not cause any additional health risks.

The concept behind alternative nicotine delivery products originates from the principle that the biological mechanisms driving combustible tobacco cigarette smoking as a cause of a diverse spectrum of cancers are due in large part to the wide array of carcinogens present in cigarette smoke, many of which are generated by the combustion of the tobacco. In a conventional tobacco cigarette, the temperature of the burning cone can reach 900 °C with a median temperature across the rod of 600 °C.[1] This leads to a myriad of thermal reactions, including combustion, pyrolysis, and pyrosynthesis that result in the >7,000 compounds identified as components of tobacco smoke, including more than 70 cancer-causing agents.[2,3]

---

*Roswell Park Comprehensive Cancer Center, USA. maciej.goniewicz@roswellpark.org

Although burning tobacco is a very efficient method for "volatilizing" nicotine, it is ultimately unnecessary. So, alternative means for liberating nicotine from tobacco in an inhalable form without combustion have been explored; such means might have the potential to modify the cancer risk relative to conventional tobacco cigarettes. Alternative nicotine delivery systems like e-cigarettes and heated tobacco products (HTPs) represent a new stage in which nicotine is delivered in a method that simulates smoking but without involving a tobacco combustion process. These methods might also serve as safer alternatives to smokeless tobacco use (see Table 1).

2. E-cigarettes

Electronic cigarettes (e-cigarettes) are engineered to heat a liquid solution of nicotine so that the aerosol generated (colloquially called "vapor") can

Table 1: Comparison of product performance characteristics and primary ingredients of combustible cigarettes, HTPs and e-cigarettes.

	Combustible cigarettes	HTPs	E-cigarettes
Nicotine	YES	YES	YES
Tobacco	YES	YES	NO (nicotine in a form of liquid solution)
Combustion	YES	NO (a potential risk of incomplete combustion)	NO (a potential risk of thermal degradation of nicotine solution ingredients)
Temperature	YES (very high during puffs)	YES (generally lower than in combustible cigarettes)	YES (generally lower than in combustible cigarettes)
Electronic system	NO	YES	YES
Example of the Product			

be inhaled by the user. The act of inhaling aerosols generated from e-cigarettes is commonly referred to as "vaping". E-cigarettes were introduced to the global market in the mid-2000s. A Chinese pharmacist, Hon Lik, is credited with the invention of contemporary e-cigarettes, but tobacco companies had worked on designs for a nicotine aerosolizing device as early as the 1960s.[4] For example, British American Tobacco worked on project Ariel that aimed to develop a device containing nicotine in a solution form or coating the cylinder walls. When heated, nicotine would vaporize, or a nicotine-containing solution would create an inhalable aerosol.[5] Philip Morris also developed a similar product, the "Premier" Capillary Aerosol Generator, which heated liquid to an aerosol in a small capillary tube.[6] Since their commercialization and widespread introduction in the US market in 2007, contemporary e-cigarette products were mostly manufactured and sold by companies that were independent of global manufacturers of tobacco cigarettes. Over the last 10 years since their introduction, e-cigarettes have gained considerable popularity, especially among youth and former smokers.

Common features of e-cigarettes include a heating element that heats a propylene glycol and/or vegetable glycerin based solution ("e-liquid"/"e-juice") that contains stabilizers, flavorings (tobacco, menthol, fruit, candy or beverage themed, and more) and nicotine. When the user inhales through a plastic or metal mouthpiece, a sensor is activated, either manually or automatically (Figure 1). Activation of the sensor then leads to heating of a filament (a coil) in the atomizer. Coils may differ by the metal type, shape, orientation, and dimensions. The coil then heats the liquid, turning it into an aerosol which is inhaled through the mouthpiece.

While it is common to hear the term e-cigarettes, this is a broad term referring to a heterogeneous class of devices that differ in shape, size, and functional characteristics (Figure 2). The *first generation* of e-cigarettes emerged on the market in 2007. They were commonly called "cig-a-likes", due to their close resemblance to conventional cigarettes. Many of these products even had an LED light at the end, simulating the glow of a lit cigarette. First generation e-cigarettes used fixed, low-voltage batteries. *Second generation* e-cigarettes are generally larger than first generation products; most resemble a pen or a laser pointer. E-cigarettes in this

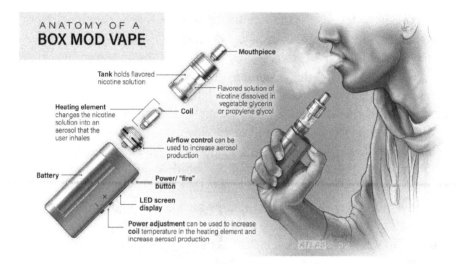

ANATOMY OF A
BOX MOD VAPE

Mouthpiece

Tank holds flavored nicotine solution

Flavored solution of nicotine dissolved in vegetable glycerin or propylene glycol

Heating element changes the nicotine solution into an aerosol that the user inhales

Coil

Airflow control can be used to increase aerosol production

Battery

Power/ "fire" button

LED screen display

Power adjustment can be used to increase coil temperature in the heating element and increase aerosol production

Figure 1:   Common features of e-cigarettes (example of 3rd generation device).

1st Gen	2nd Gen	3rd Gen	4th Gen
Small "cig-a-likes" that mimic cigarettes	Thin pen-style tank systems	Large mods and box mods	Small pod-based devices

Figure 2:   Various types of e-cigarettes and vaping devices.

category are re-chargeable rather than disposable, and many features are customizable. Batteries in this group have significantly larger capacity than batteries in cig-a-like models. Additionally, some second-generation e-cigarettes may allow the user to adjust the device power, providing more aerosol for inhalation. *Third generation* e-cigarettes bear no resemblance to traditional cigarettes; they are much larger and more variable in shape than first- and second-generation products. Known as "mods" or "box mods", third-generation e-cigarettes are highly customizable. The battery's output voltage can be adjustable by the user and the heating coil can be replaced with low-resistance material. Those modifications lead to an increase in the device's power that generally results in an increased production of aerosols. *Fourth generation* e-cigarettes, also known as "pods", are sleek with a high-tech design. They tend to be significantly smaller than prior generations, easily fitting in the palm of one's hand. In place of the refillable tank found in prior generations, the nicotine solution in fourth generation models is sold in disposable pods, which contain highly concentrated nicotine.

3. Heated Tobacco Products

With the introduction of HTPs (also called *Heat-not-Burn* products), the landscape of tobacco product exposure has changed yet again. HTPs have been developed by large tobacco companies and are for sale worldwide. The concept of heating rather than burning tobacco initially emerged in the 1980s from US-based tobacco companies Philip Morris and RJ Reynolds with Accord and Premier, respectively, the earlier generation HTPs. Those early models of HTPs did not reach a significant number of consumers and were withdrawn from the market. However, these products and ones conceptually similar have continued to evolve and now have reached the point where they may be poised to capture a significant market share. The introduction and growing popularity of e-cigarettes may have facilitated conditions to allow such products to succeed, in part by changing social norms and perceptions around use of alternative nicotine delivery systems. Contemporary HTPs include brands like IQOS from Philip Morris International (PMI), Ploom TECH from Japan Tobacco International, and Glo from British American Tobacco.[7] HTPs have gained worldwide popularity over the past few years and are now available in approximately 50 markets.[8] This popularity is attributed to several factors including, but not limited to, aggressive marketing by manufacturers, users' perception that HTPs represent a safer alternative to combustible cigarette smoking, their capacity to deliver nicotine to users, variety of flavors including tobacco and menthol flavors, advances in technology and the variability of products and product features currently available in the market.

The HTP system has three common components: (1) an insert (such as a stick, capsule, or pod) that contains the processed tobacco, (2) a way to heat the tobacco (i.e., a heating blade or carbon tip), and (3) a charger for electrically heated devices. HTPs heat tobacco and vaporize the tobacco constituents into an inhalable nicotine-containing aerosol (Figure 3). HTPs purport to deliver nicotine while reducing exposure to toxicants compared with combustible nicotine products such as tobacco cigarettes by avoiding burning of tobacco and instead heating it. In conventional cigarettes, once tobacco is heated above 600 °C, combustion occurs, and smoke containing harmful chemicals is released. HTPs have an electrical heating component, like e-cigarettes, that heats the processed tobacco to 350 °C releasing nicotine and other volatile components in tobacco. However, HTPs rely on a different operating system relative to e-cigarettes: these products contain tobacco material, as compared to liquid in the case of e-cigarettes.

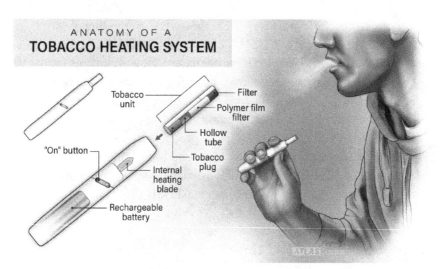

Figure 3:   Common features of a Heated Tobacco Product (HTP).

4. Key Findings

The cancer risk associated with the use of alternative nicotine delivery products hypothetically would be expected to be less than combustible tobacco cigarettes based on the rationale that e-cigarettes and HTPs emit less carcinogens and would therefore result in a reduced burden of carcinogens delivered to the user. Moreover, compared with combustible tobacco smoke, potentially carcinogenic components of e-cigarette and HTP aerosols may be orders of magnitude less carcinogenic compared with those present in tobacco smoke.[9,10] Due to the relatively short existence of alternative nicotine delivery products, data on the long-term health effects, including cancer risk, of e-cigarettes and HTP use are not currently available. In the interim, evidence from *in vitro* and *in vivo* laboratory studies, animal studies, observational human studies, and short-term clinical trials may provide important information on the potential harms of alternative nicotine delivery systems.[11]

5. Evidence from *In Vitro* Studies

Many laboratory studies conducted on alternative nicotine delivery systems have focused on the measurement of potentially harmful chemicals that may be produced by these products. Nicotine solutions used in e-cigarettes vary with respect to concentrations of toxicants. Chemicals identified in aerosols emitted from e-cigarettes and HTPs include nicotine, tobacco-specific nitrosamines (TSNAs), metals, polycyclic aromatic hydrocarbons (PAHs), volatile organic compounds (VOCs), and aldehydes. Within these classes, there are several respiratory irritants and toxicants as well as carcinogenic substances linked to the development of respiratory cancers. The presence of several potentially toxic and carcinogenic compounds like formaldehyde, acetaldehyde, and acrolein has been reported in e-cigarette and HTP emissions.[12,13] Overall, concentrations of toxicants and cancer-causing agents identified in e-cigarette aerosols are orders of magnitude lower than those found in cigarette smoke.[12] The presence of reactive aldehydes, particularly formaldehyde, in e-cigarette aerosols is of concern for potential risk of nasopharyngeal and lung cancer. The levels of formaldehyde in e-cigarette aerosols can vary by many orders of magnitude, depending in large part on the device parameters (e.g., power), type of solvent (e.g., propylene glycol and glycerol), and user characteristics (e.g., puff topography).[14] Concerns have also been raised about the presence of metal particles in e-cigarette aerosols (particularly nickel and chromium, two main elements in heating coils).[15]

In the operation of the HTPs an aerosol stream is formed. Hypothetically, reducing the aerosol generation temperature can result in lower emissions of tobacco combustion byproducts and reduced toxicity as compared to conventional tobacco cigarettes. In general, yields of volatile carbonyls and aromatic compounds (except for nicotine) in HTPs have been shown to be between one and two orders of magnitude lower than yields of combustible cigarettes, but relatively similar to those of e-cigarettes. Studies conducted by PMI, a manufacturer of IQOS — a leading brand of HTPs, showed that the aerosol generated from this brand of HTP is very different in chemical composition from the smoke formed by the combustion of tobacco in cigarettes. According to claims made by PMI, very limited low temperature pyrolysis phenomena may occur since temperatures during operation are lower than 350 °C.[16] PMI studies showed that the aerosol generated from the IQOS is composed mainly of compounds derived from the evaporation of substances present in the original tobacco substrate.[16] However, recently published independent evaluation of chemicals emitted from IQOS showed that aerosol released from that brand of HTP contains thermal degradation products the same as harmful constituents of tobacco smoke, including VOCs, PAHs, and carbon monoxide.[13] A study by the National Institute of Public Health in Japan found that with respect to the total gaseous and particulate compounds, no considerable difference was noted between HTPs and combustible cigarettes.[17] Although many combustion byproducts may be eliminated in HTPs, carcinogenic nitrosamines are generated in the process of tobacco curing rather than during combustion, and may be transferred from the HTP into the aerosol that it generates. An industry-independent study revealed that although HTPs emit lower levels of tobacco-specific nitrosamines as compared to combustible cigarettes, the levels are significantly higher than detected in e-cigarettes.[18]

The size of the particulate matter generated from alternative nicotine delivery products affects pulmonary nicotine absorption and determines settlement of particulate matter into various parts of the upper or lower airways. There is likely substantial variation across generations of e-cigarette and HTP devices, and across brands. While inhalation of high levels of particulate matter has been linked to greater mortality risk from cardiopulmonary illnesses, the available data indicate that e-cigarette particulate emissions expose users at a level far lower than those of conventional cigarettes.

6. Evidence from *In Vivo* Studies

Some of the chemical constituents found in e-cigarette and HTP aerosols that are discussed above, especially the reactive aldehydes formaldehyde and acrolein, can react with DNA and in some instances are capable of inducing mutations *in vitro* and following exposure *in vivo*.[19] Several laboratory studies on cytotoxic effects of e-cigarette chemical constituents have also identified negative effects on DNA. In one *in vitro* experiment, e-cigarette liquids aerosolized at biologically relevant doses induced increased DNA strand breaks and cell apoptosis in both "normal epithelial" and head and neck squamous cell carcinoma cell lines, independently of nicotine concentration.[20] Moreover, *in vitro* experiments have shown that e-cigarette aerosols have demonstrated cytotoxic effects on epithelial cell lines and acted as DNA-strand breaking agents.[21] Importantly, *in vitro* studies described above also showed that cell viability and metabolic activity were more adversely affected by conventional cigarettes than e-cigarettes. Exposure of cells to aerosols from HTPs generally resulted in decreased cell viability as compared to air controls, suggesting intrinsic toxic effects of HTP emissions.[16] However, HTP products also showed overall reduced cytotoxicity as compared to tobacco cigarettes but increased toxicity compared to e-cigarettes.[22,23]

Animal studies have provided some conflicting results regarding potential *in vitro* mutagenicity of e-cigarettes. As summarized in the NASEM report on the health consequences of e-cigarette use, of three studies examining mutagenicity of e-cigarettes in animal models, the two that looked directly at the liquid extracts did not find any evidence of mutagenicity, although the study that exposed rats *in vivo* to e-cigarette aerosols did find an increase in the mutagenicity of urine.[11]

Also relevant to a consideration of the potential association between alternative nicotine delivery systems and cancer are studies of exposure to emitted aerosols in relation to inflammation and oxidative stress. Chronic inflammation is thought to drive the development and progression of lung cancer.[24] The inflammation-promoting effects of tobacco smoke inhalation are undisputed, and emerging evidence indicates that e-cigarette aerosols also promote inflammation in the respiratory system, albeit at lower levels.[25] For instance, mice exposed to tobacco flavored e-cigarette aerosols containing nicotine had an increase in pro-inflammatory cytokine and chemokine secretion,[26] as well as increased infiltration of neutrophils and macrophages.[27] Exposure of cells *in vitro* or mice *in vivo* to aerosols from HTPs generally resulted in increased release of interleukins and cytokines as compared to air controls, suggesting intrinsic pro-inflammatory effects of HTP emissions.[22,28] The pro-inflammatory effects of aerosols emitted from alternative nicotine delivery systems may be mediated, at least partially, by generation of reactive oxygen species (ROS).[25] ROS are chemically reactive species that contain a radical oxygen or a non-radical oxygen such as hydrogen peroxide. Excessive ROS levels in cells lead to oxidative stress, which is defined as an imbalance between the production of ROS and their elimination by antioxidant enzymes. In cigarette smoke, ROS are produced during the combustion process. Although the combustion process should have been eliminated in alternative nicotine delivery products (as discussed above), aerosols from e-cigarettes and HTPs contain reactive aldehydes that cause release of pro-inflammatory cytokines and ROS in pulmonary and endothelial cells. Several laboratory studies reported the presence of ROS in emissions from e-cigarettes dependent on the e-cigarette brand, flavor, and puffing regime and *in vivo* experiments confirmed that e-cigarette aerosols also induce ROS production by the cells themselves.[29,30]

7. Evidence from Human Studies

Given multiple potential etiologic mechanisms related to incident case development coupled with the long latency period in developing illness, there is currently no definitive evidence on the role of alternative nicotine products in increasing cancer risk. As an intermediate assessment, cross-sectional biomarker data can be suggestive of possible carcinogen exposures related to cancer development, however these studies do not provide causal links and are subject to number of limitations. For instance, Shahab *et al.*[31] examined a large panel of biomarker data among e-cigarette users, cigarette users, and users of both products ("dual users"). The e-cigarette-only users had significantly lower metabolite levels of tobacco-specific nitrosamines, particularly NNAL, a metabolite of the potent lung carcinogen NNK.[31,32] An observational longitudinal study also showed a substantial reduction in exposure to NNK and several VOCs including respiratory toxicants or carcinogens like acrolein, acrylamide, acrylonitrile, 1,3-butadiene, and ethylene oxide among smokers who switched to e-cigarettes.[33] Although evidence from biomarker studies is insufficient to evaluate causative mechanisms, these studies do show that users of e-cigarettes have lower levels of biomarkers of lung carcinogens such as the tobacco-specific nitrosamine NNK, when compared to smokers.

Manufacturers of HTPs have conducted several short-term (5 days) and long-term (90 days) clinical trials to evaluate effects of their HTPs on biomarkers of exposure and subjective effects in smokers who switched to HTPs.[34–37] In summary, all studies have shown reduced exposure to harmful and potentially harmful smoke constituents after use of HTPs compared to smoking tobacco cigarettes. The trials also showed improvements in clinically relevant risk markers linked to mechanistic pathways involved in smoking-related diseases. On July 7, 2020, the US FDA accepted a modified-risk tobacco product (MRTP) application submitted by Phillip Morris for their HTP brand IQOS. The FDA decision was based on scientific studies that switching completely from conventional cigarettes to the IQOS system significantly reduces the body's exposure to harmful or potentially harmful chemicals.[38]

In summary, current evidence suggests that smokers who switched completely from tobacco cigarettes to alternative nicotine delivery products experience substantially lower exposure to toxicants. Long-term e-cigarette use, but not dual use of e-cigarettes with combustible cigarettes, is associated with substantially reduced exposure to carcinogens relative to smoking combustible cigarettes. Complete switching away from cigarettes will depend in part on the levels of nicotine achieved and the speed at which nicotine is delivered by these alternative nicotine delivery systems.

8. Gaps

Inhalation of complex mixtures like aerosols emitted from e-cigarettes and HTPs can cause a wide range of adverse health effects, ranging from simple irritation to systemic diseases. Knowledge about individual ingredients and emissions from alternative nicotine delivery products is currently limited. The health effects of many aerosolized constituents from nicotine solutions, tobacco inserts, and the other constituents in the alternative products, including solvents for nicotine and flavorings, are largely unknown. Testing and research are required to determine their ultimate effects on the health of users and bystanders. *In vitro* and *in vivo* studies are imperative to develop models in order to define the pathology of potential health conditions associated with use of alternative nicotine delivery products and the mechanistic pathways involved. The identification, validation and dissemination of robust *in vitro* and *in vivo* methods for the evaluation of emerging nicotine delivery products and their constituents could also advance regulatory decision-making to protect human health. Utilizing complex models such as rodent inhalation exposures could yield results relatively quickly. The animal models have several important advantages in furthering our understanding of health effects of alternative nicotine delivery products by permitting controlled exposures to individual ingredients of products that would not be feasible in humans.

Alternative nicotine delivery systems also present numerous regulatory challenges. The amount of nicotine and non-nicotine toxicants depends on the product features, such as nicotine concentration in e-cigarette solution, tobacco insert composition, the temperature of the heating element, and device design and characteristics. Understanding how these features influence several important product characteristics, including the temperature of the device, and nicotine and non-nicotine toxicant emissions, is key to the design of effective regulations that limit the toxicity profile of these products. There is currently a wide variability of devices on the market, and users have control over many of the devices' features that affect emissions, including numerous harmful chemicals, such as aldehydes, metals, VOCs, and ROS. Since emerging products may potentially emit chemicals that are not present in conventional combustible cigarettes, it is important to expand chemical assessment of emissions from alternative products beyond those found in cigarette smoke. Additionally, the technology of alternative nicotine delivery systems is rapidly evolving. New and more advanced devices are constantly entering the market; therefore, keeping track of the variability of the products that are on the market is key to assess how new features may impact aerosol toxicant emissions and therefore users' health.

It is currently not clear what the long-term health consequences of using alternative nicotine delivery products are, and whether these differ by disease type. Claims of lowered disease risk for HTPs compared to combustible tobacco cigarettes are based almost exclusively on industry-funded research, and except for a limited number of product testing studies, independent research is very limited to support these claims as of 2021. Research independent from industry is therefore urgently needed to provide a balanced view on their potential detrimental health impact.

It is important to understand whether alternative nicotine delivery products could potentially play a role in reducing the risks to smokers due to reduced exposure to certain toxic chemicals relative to conventional tobacco smoke. The current evidence suggests that alternative nicotine delivery systems, although not safe, likely pose less direct hazard to the individual smoker than tobacco cigarettes. The use of alternative nicotine products as a harm reduction strategy among cigarette smokers who are unwilling to quit warrants further studies. On the one hand, there is the possibility of potentially reducing risk to smokers, on the other, the prospect of inflicting serious risks to health. Therefore, further research is needed to evaluate long-term effects of switching, including potential health effects of continued use of e-cigarettes or HTPs. The strongest evidence to characterize the potential association between use of alternative nicotine delivery products and the risk of human cancer will be methodologically rigorous epidemiological studies with human cancer as the outcome. However, many users of alternative nicotine delivery products will be current or former cigarette smokers and the effects of current and former smoking will be a challenging confounder to account for in observational studies.[11]

An important concern about alternative nicotine delivery products is that they could increase use of multiple different tobacco products. Although independent clinical trials on e-cigarettes and industry data on HTPs suggest that those products may serve as a long-term substitution in highly controlled settings, there is concern that "real-world" concurrent use of combustible cigarettes and alternative products ("dual use") might prolong smoking behaviors. Some smokers may initiate alternative products for situational use, rather than to switch from smoking completely. Current smokers may also not understand what "switching completely" means and that they must completely quit smoking cigarettes to achieve the claimed potential health benefits of alternative products. Understanding factors, including device characteristics and messaging, that will promote complete switching is another area of important study. Additionally, there is a lack of evidence regarding the ways in which alternative nicotine delivery devices may affect smokers' intentions to quit smoking.

A final question is the effects of using alternative nicotine delivery systems among youth and young adults who are naïve to any nicotine or tobacco use. In the US, there has been a significant increase in youth uptake of e-cigarettes and the health effects of persistent use of these products among this population are unknown. The same factors that might promote complete switching may also contribute to uptake of these products among a tobacco naïve population. The public health benefits and risks among both users and non-users of tobacco products need careful consideration.

9. Conclusions

Although combustible tobacco cigarettes remain the most popular and deadly nicotine-containing product, non-cigarette products are evolving rapidly. Alternative nicotine delivery systems, like e-cigarettes and HTPs represent a new stage in which nicotine is delivered in a method that simulates smoking but without involving a tobacco combustion process. They are an emerging class of products in many countries, and they vary significantly in design, nicotine content and delivery, toxicity, and potential health effects.

To date, findings from *in vitro, in vivo* and human studies have demonstrated that e-cigarettes are likely less harmful compared to conventional tobacco cigarettes, and any harmful side effects are noticeably milder compared with regular cigarettes. Claims of lowered risk or health benefits of HTPs compared to conventional cigarettes are based almost exclusively on industry-funded research, and evidence from independent studies is limited. Since alternative nicotine delivery systems have only been on the market for a decade, it is presently not possible to assess all potential long-term harmful effects of their use.

The cancer risk associated with the use of alternative nicotine delivery systems hypothetically would be expected to be less than that of combustible tobacco cigarettes based on the rationale that the number and amount of cancer-causing chemicals emitted from those products are lower than in tobacco smoke. Particularly, the nicotine solutions used in e-cigarettes do not contain appreciable amounts of tobacco-specific nitrosamines. However, there is uncertainty about the potential mutagenicity and carcinogenicity of other chemicals emitted from e-cigarettes and HTPs, such as flavorings and humectants, and their potential byproducts of thermal degradation that result from the heating and aerosolization of the liquid and tobacco inserts in these products.

There are several biologically plausible pathways by which components of e-cigarettes and HTP aerosols could conceptually influence cancer development. Laboratory tests of constituents and aerosols generated from e-cigarettes and HTPs have revealed that those products contain and emit several known or suspected human carcinogens, including formaldehyde, acetaldehyde, and arsenic. The presence of potentially mutagenic and cytotoxic constituents provides biologically relevant mechanisms by which long-term use of alternative nicotine delivery products could affect cancer risk. Numerous compounds identified in e-cigarette and HTP aerosols can form ROS and can be converted to reactive intermediates capable of binding to DNA. Some *in vitro* studies have identified cytotoxicity of e-cigarette and HTP aerosols, potentially contributing to tissue repair and mitogenic response, which is another important pathway in the development of chemically induced cancers. Human observational studies and clinical trials that measured biomarkers of exposure to potentially toxic chemicals, including cancer causing agents, consistently showed that users of alternative nicotine delivery products displayed elevated levels of selected biomarkers as compared to non-users, however those levels were significantly lower when compared to smokers.

In summary, the current evidence suggests that alternative nicotine delivery systems, although not safe, likely pose less direct hazard to the individual user than tobacco cigarettes. But it is also clear that aerosols emitted and inhaled from alternative nicotine delivery systems are not harmless and potential health effects from using those products may emerge after long-term use.

References

1. Stedman RL. Chemical composition of tobacco and tobacco smoke. *Chem Rev* 1968;68(2):153–207.
2. International Agency for Research on Cancer. Tobacco Smoking. In: *Personal Habits and Indoor Combustions: IARC Monographs on the Evaluation of Carcinogenic Risks to Humans, v. 100E* (Lyon, FR: IARC, 2012). https://publications.iarc.fr/122
3. U.S. Department of Health and Human Services. *How Tobacco Smoke Causes Disease: The Biology and Behavioral Basis for Smoking-Attributable Disease: A Report of the Surgeon General.* (Atlanta, GA: Centers for Disease Control and Prevention, National Center for Chronic Disease Prevention and Health Promotion, Office on Smoking and Health, 2010).
4. Kaisar MA, Prasad S, Liles T, Cucullo L. A decade of e-cigarettes: Limited research & unresolved safety concerns. *Toxicology* 2016;365:67–75.
5. Risi S. On the origins of the electronic cigarette: British American Tobacco's project Ariel (1962–1967). *Am J Public Health* 2017;107(7):1060–7.
6. Dutra LM, Grana R, Glantz SA. Philip Morris research on precursors to the modern e-cigarette since 1990. *Tobacco Control* 2017;26(e2):e97–105.
7. Sutanto E, Miller C, Smith DM, *et al.* Prevalence, use behaviors, and preferences among users of heated tobacco products: Findings from the 2018 ITC Japan Survey. *Int J Environ Res Public Health* 2019;16(23):4630.
8. Glantz SA. Heated tobacco products: the example of IQOS. *Tobacco Control* 2018;27(Suppl 1):s1–6.

9. Chen J, Bullen C, Dirks K. A comparative health risk assessment of elec-
    tronic cigarettes and conventional cigarettes. *Int J Environ Res Public Health*
    2017;14(4):382.

10. Stephens WE. Comparing the cancer potencies of emissions from vapourised
    nicotine products including e-cigarettes with those of tobacco smoke.
    Tobacco Control 2018;27(1):10.

11. National Academies of Sciences, Engineering and Medicine. *Public Health
    Consequences of E-cigarettes.* (Washington, DC: The National Academies
    Press; 2018). Available from: https://www.nap.edu/catalog/24952/public-
    health-consequences-of-e-cigarettes.

12. Goniewicz ML, Knysak J, Gawron M, *et al.* Levels of selected carcinogens
    and toxicants in vapour from electronic cigarettes. *Tobacco Control.*
    2014;23:133–9.

13. Auer R, Concha-Lozano N, Jacot-Sadowski I, Cornuz J, Berthet A. Heat-
    Not-Burn tobacco cigarettes: Smoke by any other name. *JAMA Intern Med*
    2017;177:1050–2.

14. Kosmider L, Sobczak A, Fik M, *et al.* Carbonyl compounds in electronic
    cigarette vapors: effects of nicotine solvent and battery output voltage.
    Nicotine Tobacco Res 2014;16(10):1319–26.

15. Lerner CA, Sundar IK, Watson RM, *et al.* Environmental health hazards of
    e-cigarettes and their components: oxidants and copper in e-cigarette aero-
    sols. *Environ Pollut.* 2015;198:100–7.

16. Schaller JP, Keller D, Poget L, *et al.* Evaluation of the tobacco heating sys-
    tem 2.2. Part 2: Chemical composition, genotoxicity, cytotoxicity, and physi-
    cal properties of the aerosol. *Regul Toxicol Pharmacol* 2016;81 Suppl
    2:S27–47.

17. Uchiyama S, Noguchi M, Takagi N, *et al.* Simple determination of gaseous
    and particulate compounds generated from heated tobacco products. *Chem
    Res Toxicol* 2018;31(7):585–93.

18. Leigh NJ, Palumbo MN, Marino AM, O'Connor RJ, Goniewicz ML.
    Tobacco-specific nitrosamines (TSNA) in heated tobacco product IQOS.
    Tobacco Control 2018;27(Suppl 1):s37–8.

19. Canistro D, Vivarelli F, Cirillo S, *et al.* E-cigarettes induce toxicological
    effects that can raise the cancer risk. *Sci Rep* 2017;7(1):2028.

20. Welz C, Canis M, Schwenk-Zieger S, *et al.* Cytotoxic and genotoxic effects
    of electronic cigarette liquids on human mucosal tissue cultures of the oro-
    pharynx. *J Environ Pathol Toxicol Oncol* 2016;35:343–54.

21. Yu V, Rahimy M, Korrapati A, *et al*. Electronic cigarettes induce DNA strand breaks and cell death independently of nicotine in cell lines. *Oral Oncol* 2016;52:58–65.

22. Leigh NJ, Tran PL, O'Connor RJ, Goniewicz ML. Cytotoxic effects of heated tobacco products (HTP) on human bronchial epithelial cells. *Tobacco Control* 2018;27(Suppl 1):s26–9.

23. Davis B, To V, Talbot P. Comparison of cytotoxicity of IQOS aerosols to smoke from Marlboro Red and 3R4F reference cigarettes. *Toxicol In Vitro* 2019;61:104652.

24. King PT. Inflammation in chronic obstructive pulmonary disease and its role in cardiovascular disease and lung cancer. *Clin Transl Med* 2015;4:68.

25. Traboulsi H, Cherian M, Abou Rjeili M, *et al*. Inhalation toxicology of vaping products and implications for pulmonary health. *Int J Mol Sci* 2020;21(10):3495.

26. Lerner CA, Sundar IK, Yao H, *et al*. Vapors produced by electronic cigarettes and e-juices with flavorings induce toxicity, oxidative stress, and inflammatory response in lung epithelial cells and in mouse lung. *PLoS ONE* 2015;10:e0116732.

27. Glynos C, Bibli SI, Katsaounou P, *et al*. Comparison of the effects of e-cigarette vapor with cigarette smoke on lung function and inflammation in mice. *Am J Physiol Lung Cell Mol Physiol* 2018;315:L662–72.

28. Bhat TA, Kalathil SG, Leigh N, *et al*. Acute effects of heated tobacco product (IQOS) aerosol-inhalation on lung tissue damage and inflammatory changes in the lungs. *Nicotine Tob Res* 2021;23(7):1160–1167.

29. Muthumalage T, Lamb T, Friedman MR, Rahman I. E-cigarette flavored pods induce inflammation, epithelial barrier dysfunction, and DNA damage in lung epithelial cells and monocytes. *Sci Rep* 2019;9:19035.

30. Muthumalage T, Lamb T, Friedman MR, Rahman I. Inflammatory and oxidative responses induced by exposure to commonly used e-cigarette flavoring chemicals and flavored e-liquids without nicotine. *Front Physiol* 2017;8:1130.

31. Shahab L, Goniewicz ML, Blount BC, *et al*. Nicotine, carcinogen, and toxin exposure in long-term e-cigarette and nicotine replacement therapy users: a cross-sectional study. *Ann Intern Med* 2017;166:390–400.

32. Goniewicz ML, Smith DM, Edwards KC, *et al*. Comparison of nicotine and toxicant exposure in users of electronic cigarettes and combustible cigarettes. *JAMA Netw Open* 2018;1(8):e185937.

33. Goniewicz ML, Gawron M, Smith DM, Peng M, Jacob P, 3rd, Benowitz NL. Exposure to nicotine and selected toxicants in cigarette smokers who

switched to electronic cigarettes: a longitudinal within-subjects observational study. *Nicotine Tob Res* 2017;19:160–7.

34. Lüdicke F, Picavet P, Baker G, *et al.* Effects of switching to the menthol Tobacco Heating System 2.2, smoking abstinence, or continued cigarette smoking on clinically relevant risk markers: A randomized, controlled, open-label, multicenter study in sequential confinement and ambulatory settings (Part 2). *Nicotine Tob Res* 2018;20:173–82.

35. Haziza C, de La Bourdonnaye G, Skiada D, *et al.* Evaluation of the Tobacco Heating System 2.2. Part 8: 5-Day randomized reduced exposure clinical study in Poland. *Regul Toxicol Pharmacol* 2016;81(Suppl 2):S139–50.

36. Tricker AR, Kanada S, Takada K, *et al.* Reduced exposure evaluation of an Electrically Heated Cigarette Smoking System. Part 6: 6-Day randomized clinical trial of a menthol cigarette in Japan. *Regul Toxicol Pharmacol* 2012;64(Suppl 2):S64–73.

37. Tricker AR, *et al.* Reduced exposure evaluation of an Electrically Heated Cigarette Smoking System. Part 4: Eight-day randomized clinical trial in Korea. *Regul Toxicol Pharmacol* 2012;64(Suppl 2):S45–53.

38. FDA Authorizes Marketing of IQOS Tobacco Heating System with 'Reduced Exposure' Information. (Press release); 2020. Available: https://www.fda.gov/news-events/press-announcements/fda-authorizesmarketing-iQOS-tobacco-heating-system-reduced-exposure-information.

https://doi.org/10.1142/9789811239533_0007

Chapter 7

Mechanisms and Biomarkers of Tobacco Carcinogenesis

Stephen S. Hecht*

1. Introduction

The preceding chapters have described the amazing variety of carcinogens and toxicants found in all tobacco products, ranging from simple organics such as formaldehyde and inorganic metal salts to alkaloid-derived nitrosamines to relatively complex organic combustion products such as polycyclic aromatic hydrocarbons (PAHs). One wonders why otherwise sane humans would willingly and regularly expose themselves to such potentially hazardous products. The answer of course is simple: the products are highly efficient nicotine delivery systems, but unfortunately not very clean ones. We now know that cigarette smoking causes at least 16 different types of cancer, while smokeless tobacco use causes cancers of the oral cavity, esophagus, and pancreas, but there is no convincing evidence for the carcinogenicity of nicotine itself. There is no reason to doubt that the cancer-causing effects of combusted tobacco products and smokeless tobacco are dependent on the presence in these products of multiple carcinogens and a variety of substances that enhance carcinogenicity.

* Masonic Cancer Center, University of Minnesota, USA. hecht002@umn.edu

Mechanisms of carcinogenesis comprise the series of steps that convert a normal cell to a cancer cell. Mechanisms are ever evolving concepts dependent on rigorous hypothesis testing; they withstand the test of time. Some mechanistic concepts need to be discarded when new information proves them incorrect. Thus, as science and technology evolve, mechanisms become established as bedrock, while incorrect hypotheses fall by the wayside. This is how science works — an ever evolving search for truth. The mechanisms described here are built on the shoulders of giants — eminent scientists who explored and defined basic concepts of chemical carcinogenesis. These concepts, often studied and confirmed with respect to specific types of carcinogens, can be assembled to provide an evidence based description of the ways tobacco products transform cells and cause cancer.

A biomarker is defined by Oxford Languages as a measurable substance in an organism whose presence is indicative of some phenomenon such as disease, infection, or environmental exposure. Mechanisms and biomarkers are interrelated and interdependent concepts. If the mechanism is true, the related biomarker will be useful. When considering tobacco products, the United States Food and Drug Administration has classified biomarkers into "biomarkers of exposure" and "biomarkers of potential harm". Biomarkers of exposure are relatively straightforward, as they are related to specific constituents of tobacco products. An example is cotinine, a major metabolite of nicotine. Cotinine, measured in saliva, blood, or urine, is a biomarker of exposure to nicotine. Biomarkers of potential harm are sometimes more difficult to define as they relate to the complex steps involved in mechanisms, which may or may not be proven.

This chapter will present an overview of our current understanding of mechanisms by which tobacco products cause cancer and application of some related biomarkers of exposure and potential harm.

These studies require teamwork encompassing a broad range of expertise. I became aware of the team concept in cancer prevention research while working at the American Health Foundation, a cancer prevention organization founded by the eminent epidemiologist Ernst Wynder who, along with Sir Richard Doll, carried out the first large epidemiological studies linking cigarette smoking with lung cancer. Wynder recognized the necessity for strong interdisciplinary collaborations among scientists with different expertise and designed the Foundation with this in mind. He worked together with Dietrich Hoffmann, a talented and innovative chemist, to perform some of the groundbreaking studies on carcinogens in tobacco smoke, such as isolation of crystalline benzo[*a*]pyrene (BaP) from pounds of "tobacco tar" and discovery of tumor enhancing properties of tobacco tar subfractions. Scientists at the Foundation came from multiple disciplines and focused their research not only on tobacco and cancer, but also on various other aspects of cancer prevention including the possible roles of diet, alcohol, exercise, and other lifestyle factors. I followed this concept when I moved to Minnesota, where I met Professor Dorothy Hatsukami, a behavioral scientist and co-editor of this volume. At a luncheon meeting in 1997 with Dorothy and biochemist Sharon Murphy, we initiated a collaboration to study the chemistry, biochemistry, and behavioral aspects of tobacco addiction and cancer. The team expanded over the years including many wonderful and talented individuals. I note in particular Steven Carmella and Joni Jensen, who have been on the front lines of most of our studies. There is no doubt that Wynder's teamwork concept has been crucial in our research.

2. A Mechanistic Framework for Tobacco Carcinogenesis

The mechanistic framework originally proposed in 1999 for lung carcinogenesis by tobacco smoke,[1] and illustrated in Figure 1, has withstood the test of time and has been recapitulated in different ways in reports of the US Surgeon General and the International Agency for Research on Cancer (IARC).[2,3] Figure 1 illustrates this mechanistic pathway.

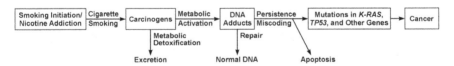

Figure 1: Overall mechanistic pathway of tobacco carcinogenesis, illustrated for lung cancer, essentially as originally proposed.[1] The overall mechanism is likely similar for other cancers caused by smoking and for relating smokeless tobacco use to head and neck cancer, as discussed in the text. Reproduced from Ref. 1 by permission of National Cancer Institute.

Following the description of the structure of DNA by Watson and Crick, cancer researchers in the US and England focused on DNA as the critical target in carcinogenesis, and it is central in this accepted mechanistic pathway. Each box and arrow represents a huge area of research which will be described here from a view at 30,000 feet, as the details of each can fill volumes.

2.1. Initiation of tobacco use

As discussed in Chapter 12, nicotine is addictive! This simple fact is likely not appreciated by the millions of teenagers who begin experimenting with cigarettes and, lately, with e-cigarettes, which are both efficient delivery systems for nicotine. According to the American Cancer Society and the US Surgeon General, most smokers start as teenagers, and those who have friends or parents who smoke are more likely to start than those who don't. The tobacco industry knows this and is endlessly creative in finding new and legal ways to deliver their message to teenagers. The American Cancer Society quotes the 2012 Surgeon General's report which nicely describes the ultimate effects of teenage experimentation with smoking as follows: "Of every 3 young smokers, only 1 will quit, and 1 of those remaining smokers will die from tobacco-related causes. Most of these young people never considered the long-term health consequences associated with tobacco use when they started smoking; and nicotine, a highly addictive drug, causes many to continue smoking well into adulthood, often with deadly consequences."[4,5]

2.2. Exposure to nicotine and carcinogens

Carcinogens — agents that cause cancer — form the link between cigarette smoking, DNA damage, and cancer. As described in Chapter 4, there are at least 70 chemical carcinogens in cigarette smoke that are classified by IARC as carcinogenic to either humans or laboratory animals. Smokeless tobacco is also a source of more than 20 IARC carcinogens (Chapter 5). These undeniable facts, established by years of pioneering and validated research by academic and government institutions worldwide, and confirmed by published studies from the tobacco industry, clearly demonstrate that tobacco — whether smoked, sucked, or chewed — is a dangerous delivery system for nicotine because it is always accompanied by a mixture of established carcinogens. While amounts of individual carcinogens vary widely among products, there is no conventional smoking product or smokeless tobacco product that is carcinogen free or safe.

The carcinogens in cigarette smoke have different sources and cancer-causing activities. Some such as PAHs and aromatic amines are combustion products mainly formed during smoking, while others such as tobacco-specific nitrosamines and metals are transferred from tobacco into smoke.[3] The carcinogens also have wide ranging activities and affect different target tissues based on studies in laboratory animals. PAHs often affect the tissues of contact such as the lung in smokers, while tobacco-specific nitrosamines are frequently organ specific in their effects.[1,6] The tobacco-specific nitrosamine 4-(methylnitrosamino)-1-(3-pyridyl)-1-butanone "**n**icotine-derived **n**itrosamino **k**etone", NNK is a potent lung carcinogen in multiple animal species.[6] Aromatic amines are often associated with bladder cancer, while aldehydes and metals have a variety of targets.[3,7] Benzene and 1,3-butadiene cause blood cancers.[8] The most prevalent strong carcinogens in smokeless tobacco are the tobacco-specific nitrosamines.[9] N'-nitrosonornicotine (NNN) in particular demonstrates potent carcinogenicity in the oral mucosa and esophagus, known target tissues for cancer in smokeless tobacco users.[10]

Smoking a cigarette is a quick way to obtain a dose of nicotine, the pharmacologically active component of tobacco; some important properties of nicotine and details of its metabolism are discussed further in Chapters 8 and 12. The absorption of nicotine through the membranes of the oral mucosa and in cells of the lung is dependent on pH which varies with tobacco types.[11] In general, higher pH facilitates absorption because the nicotine is chemically free (unprotonated) and passes easily through membranes. Upon inhalation of tobacco smoke, nicotine reaches the small airways and alveoli of the lung and enters the bloodstream, reaching the brain within 10–20 seconds of a cigarette puff. The rapid absorption of nicotine allows the smoker to titrate its levels in the brain and control its pharmacological effects. Similarly, smokeless tobacco users obtain their nicotine dose through the membranes of the oral mucosa at a slower absorption rate than cigarette smoking, yet the nicotine delivery is fast and high enough to result in addiction.

When nicotine is obtained in a relatively pure form, as in nicotine replacement treatment products such as nicotine patch or nicotine gum, it has the desired pharmacological effects without being accompanied by undesirable compounds in cigarette smoke and smokeless tobacco. But smoking a cigarette is a faster way of reaching peak nicotine concentrations in the blood than nicotine replacement treatments. Unfortunately, this entails exposure to more than 7,000 other compounds in cigarette smoke, of which at least 70 are carcinogens, which are absorbed through the membranes of the oral cavity and cells of the lung, along with nicotine.[12,13]

2.3. *Absorption, distribution, metabolism, and excretion*

Nicotine, carcinogens, and the other constituents of cigarette smoke and smokeless tobacco are foreign compounds that are processed by the body in essentially the same way as common pharmaceuticals. This overall process is known as ADME, an abbreviation for absorption, distribution, metabolism, and excretion. ADME is an overview of the fate in the body of a foreign compound. Absorption encompasses the passage of the compound through cellular membranes into the bloodstream. A number of factors can affect absorption. With respect to nicotine and related tobacco alkaloids, pH is important because at lower pH, such as in the stomach, absorption will be slower.[13] After absorption, the foreign compound undergoes distribution to various tissues and organs of the body. Distribution can be affected by the chemical structure of each compound and by multiple pharmacological properties such as binding to plasma proteins or tissues, but most compounds will predominantly reach the liver. The next step is metabolism, and this is critical in the carcinogenic process, as discussed further below. The purpose of most foreign compound metabolism is to render the compound more readily excreted, for example in the urine, and this is generally accomplished by enzymes that will increase each compound's water solubility by increasing its polarity. Then the final stage of the process is excretion whereby the foreign compounds which enter the body from tobacco use are finally removed, most commonly in urine or feces, but also for more volatile compounds through exhaled air. Metabolism of foreign compounds and drugs is described in three phases. In Phases I and II, the main objective is to modify the compound by adding an oxygen atom (Phase I) or a polar group such as glucuronic acid (Phase II), thus increasing their water solubility and facilitating excretion. Phase III incorporates further changes and the activities of certain transporters that increase removal of the foreign compounds.

2.4. *Metabolic activation and detoxification*

With respect to carcinogenesis, Phases I and II are critical. While the objective of Phase I metabolism is increased polarity for removal of the foreign substance, the intermediates formed in this process may be quite reactive with cellular constituents. Specifically, the intermediates with chemical structures that are "electrophilic" (electron seeking) can react with "nucleophilic" (nucleus seeking) components of the cell, resulting in the formation of new compounds which are addition products called "adducts". This process is known as metabolic activation and is critical in the carcinogenic process as illustrated in Figure 1. Two examples of metabolic activation are illustrated in Figure 2. In one, BaP, a highly carcinogenic and fat soluble combustion product found in tobacco smoke, is converted by Phase I metabolism in several steps to benzo[a]pyrene diol epoxide (BPDE), which is more polar than BaP and consequently has more potential to be excreted, but it is also highly electrophilic and reacts with nucleophilic sites in DNA, RNA, and proteins to form adducts.[14] DNA adducts are particularly important in carcinogenesis for the reasons discussed below. Another example is the tobacco-specific nitrosamine NNK. When this compound is metabolized, one of the products is the α-hydroxyNNK intermediate shown in Figure 2. This compound is more polar than NNK but is also highly reactive and spontaneously decomposes releasing a highly electrophilic intermediate, methane diazohydroxide, which reacts with DNA to form adducts.[15] NNK is also metabolized to NNAL, which is a useful biomarker of NNK uptake, as discussed in the next section of this chapter.

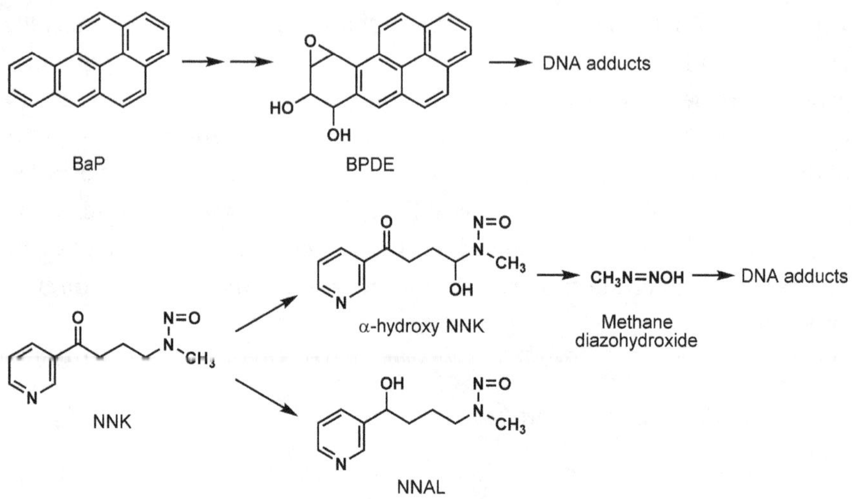

Figure 2: Overview of metabolism of BaP and NNK leading to DNA adducts. BaP, which is relatively unreactive, is metabolized by cytochrome P450 enzymes and epoxide hydrolase to produce BPDE, which easily reacts with DNA to produce adducts. NNK is also unreactive. In the body, it is converted by P450 enzymes to α-hydroxyNNK, an unstable intermediate that spontaneously yields methane diazohydroxide, which easily reacts with DNA to produce adducts among which is the miscoding adduct O^6-methylguanine (O^6-methyl-G). NNK is also converted by metabolism in the body to NNAL, which is excreted in the urine and serves as a biomarker of NNK exposure.

In most cases, the "metabolic detoxification" pathways predominate and the multiple foreign compounds in tobacco products are converted to more polar products which are excreted in the urine and often serve as biomarkers of tobacco product exposure, as discussed later in this chapter. Conversion of tobacco smoke compounds to more polar hydroxyl substituted derivatives, glucuronides, and glutathione conjugates are typical modes of metabolic detoxification leading to excretion in the urine or feces.

2.5. *DNA adducts, mutations, and repair*

The next critical step in the process is reaction of electrophiles formed in the metabolic activation process with cellular targets, most notably DNA. With respect to carcinogenesis, DNA is considered the major target molecule in the cell based on years of research demonstrating that DNA adducts cause mutations.[16,17] Thus, a DNA adduct is not recognized as a normal DNA base during replication. An example of this phenomenon is the DNA adduct O^6-methylguanine (O^6-methyl-G), which can be formed during the metabolism of NNK (see Figure 2). The normal DNA bases on the phosphate and sugar DNA backbone are guanine (G), adenine (A), cytosine (C), and thymine (T), and normal base pairing in the DNA double helix is between G and C, and between A and T. The structures of G and O^6-methylG are shown in Figure 3. The presence of the methyl group on the oxygen atom of G in O^6-methylG changes its base pairing properties, such that instead of pairing with C, it pairs with T. Then in the next round of replication, A is incorporated opposite to T. The overall result is a G–C to A–T mutation, which is permanent.[18] So the genetic information transmitted by the original G–C pair has now been altered permanently. This mutation was due to the DNA adduct O^6-methylG. This has been established by elegant experiments in which a single O^6-methylG is inserted at a known position in a DNA molecule using the tools of molecular biology, and that DNA is then replicated in cells, and the resulting mutations identified. These types of experiments, carried out with multiple different types of DNA adducts, demonstrate that DNA adducts cause permanent mutations in DNA.[17]

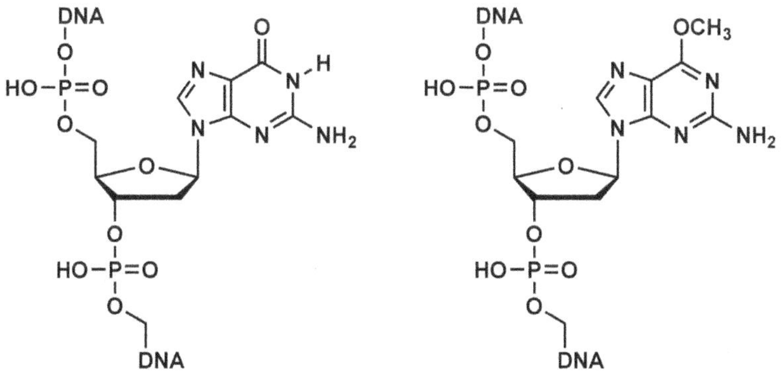

Figure 3: Structures of deoxyguanosine in DNA (left), comprising the guanine base (G), deoxyribose, and phosphates, and O^6-methyldeoxyguanosine (right), comprising the O^6-methyl-G base, deoxyribose and phosphates. During DNA replication, G normally pairs with C (not shown), but O^6-methyl-G instead pairs with T. Then, in the next round of replication, A is placed opposite that T, so the original G–C pair has been replaced by an A–T pair resulting in a permanent mutation.

Mammalian systems have repair proteins and enzymes that can remove DNA adducts and restore the original DNA structure. An example is O^6-methylguanine-DNA methyl transferase which removes the methyl group from the O^6-position of G converting O^6-methylG back to G.[19] In this way it can protect against the mutagenic properties of O^6-methylG in DNA. But a limitation of this protein is that it can act only a single time because it is then degraded.[19] Thus, in mice treated with NNK, when the dose produces levels of O^6-methylG that exceed DNA repair capacity, there is a sharp increase in lung tumor formation.[20] DNA repair systems are critical in maintaining the fidelity of DNA.[21] Faulty DNA repair can have immensely negative consequences. One example is the disease *xeroderma pigmentosum*, caused by a defect in repair of UV dimers due to sunlight exposure; individuals with this disease must strictly avoid exposure to sunlight to prevent the development of multiple skin tumors and an untimely death.

Cells with unrepaired and damaged DNA can be removed by the process of apoptosis, or programmed cell death. This is a normal and highly regulated process which can dispose of unwanted or damaged cells, as opposed to necrosis which is a process of traumatic cell death resulting for example from injury. Thus, apoptosis is considered a protective mechanism in the cell.

2.6. *Mutations in critical genes*

Multiple large scale sequencing studies have examined mutations in critical growth control genes such as *TP53* and *K-RAS*. *TP53* is the prototype of a tumor suppressor gene, which can slow or stop the development of tumors. It is commonly mutated in many types of human cancer. The *K-RAS* gene is an oncogene. When mutated, it provides instructions for the cell to proliferate and is critical in cancer development. The Cancer Genome Atlas Research Network performed a study of mutations in squamous cell carcinoma of the lung, and reported highly complex genomic alterations, including hundreds of mutations in exons as well as genomic rearrangements and copy number alterations in each tumor; *TP53* mutations were found in almost all specimens, and many other critical genes were mutated as well.[22] Other studies show commonly mutated *K-RAS* and multiple other genes in lung adenocarcinoma[23] and mutational signatures specifically associated with tobacco smoking in multiple cancer types, as well as a mutation frequency 10 times higher in smokers than non-smokers.[24,25] Collectively, these studies elegantly confirm the mechanistic framework illustrated in Figure 1, leading from exposure to cigarette smoke carcinogens to mutations in DNA to alterations in critical growth control genes to cancer development.

While exposure to the multiple DNA damaging agents in cigarette smoke is clearly the critical mechanistic step in cancer development, there are other processes occurring simultaneously that can exacerbate these effects. Cigarette smoke contains tumor promoters, co-carcinogens, and inflammatory agents which can enhance the effects of DNA damage and enhance carcinogenicity, although they are not considered carcinogenic in themselves. Oxidative DNA damage which can be secondary to these processes is another commonly observed phenomenon.

3. Biomarkers of Tobacco Carcinogenesis

3.1. *Biomarkers of exposure*

The most straightforward biomarkers are the biomarkers of exposure to specific important constituents of tobacco products. Nicotine is the unique addictive compound in all tobacco products that keeps smokers and smokeless tobacco users addicted. Nicotine is metabolized in humans to cotinine, and cotinine is further metabolized to 3'-hydroxycotinine. The structures of these compounds are shown in Figure 4.

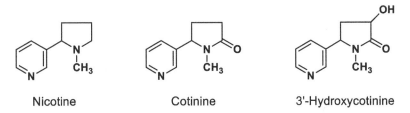

Figure 4: Chemical structures of the major tobacco alkaloid nicotine, and its metabolites cotinine and 3'-hydroxycotinine which are excreted in human urine and serve as biomarkers of nicotine exposure.

Cotinine has a longer lifetime in the body (16 h) than nicotine (2 h) and is therefore favored as a biomarker to quantify nicotine uptake, by measurements in saliva, blood, or urine.[26] The sum of nicotine, cotinine, and 3'-hydroxycotinine plus their glucuronide conjugates is called total nicotine equivalents and is frequently measured as a biomarker of nicotine uptake. "Cytochrome P450 2A6" is the main human enzyme that catalyzes the conversion of nicotine to cotinine, and of cotinine to 3'-hydroxycotinine. The ratio of urinary 3'-hydroxycotinine to cotinine is an excellent measurement of the activity of this enzyme which can vary widely due to ethnic differences and other factors. Relatively low average activity of cytochrome P450 2A6 has been observed in Japanese American smokers from Hawaii and has been proposed as an explanation for their relatively low risk of lung cancer (compared to other ethnic groups in Hawaii) because they have more unmetabolized nicotine in their bodies and therefore need to smoke less intensely. This is discussed further in Chapters 8 and 9.

Nicotine and its metabolites can be used as biomarkers of all tobacco products including cigarettes and related products featuring tobacco combustion as well as smokeless tobacco products. Nicotine biomarkers will also be found in the urine of people who use e-cigarettes or nicotine replacement therapy products.

The NNK metabolite NNAL (Figure 2) is another very useful urinary biomarker, particularly for studies related to tobacco use and cancer. NNAL (nicotine-derived nitrosamino alcohol) was born in the 1980s when Andre Castonguay, Ruth Sciame, and I studied the metabolism of NNK in rat liver. We were staring at Ruth's data showing a huge unknown metabolite when all of a sudden it occurred to me: it's the alcohol! Then Andre chimed in: "NNAL!", and the name stuck! Both NNK and NNAL are powerful pulmonary carcinogens in laboratory animals, and NNK and the related tobacco-specific nitrosamine NNN are considered "carcinogenic to humans" by IARC.[9] The persistence of NNAL in the body is longer than that of nicotine metabolites, and it can be detected in urine weeks after a person stops smoking. Both NNK and NNAL are completely tobacco-specific, so detection of NNAL in urine definitely identifies use of tobacco products such as cigarettes or smokeless tobacco, but not e-cigarettes or nicotine replacement therapy because they do not contain tobacco. The detection of NNAL in the urine of non-smokers exposed to secondhand tobacco smoke was very useful in establishing the dangers of secondhand smoke exposure, particularly with respect to lung cancer.[27] Thus, NNAL is almost the ideal biomarker of lung carcinogen exposure because of its long lifetime, complete tobacco-specificity, and known lung carcinogenicity. Urinary cotinine and NNAL were related to lung cancer development in the prospective Shanghai Cohort Study and the Singapore Chinese Health Study, in which samples were collected from cigarette smokers decades before lung cancer appeared in some of the participants.[28] Therefore, cotinine and NNAL are not only biomarkers of exposure to tobacco products but also biomarkers of potential harm.

Exhaled carbon monoxide is a convenient exposure biomarker for very recent cigarette smoking. It can be measured directly in exhaled breath using a number of commercial devices. Recent smoking will cause a CO level in exhaled air of greater than 5–6 ppm, but this can vary depending on a number of factors including exposure to environmental CO and the brand of measurement device used.[26]

Biomarkers of PAH exposure are useful because PAHs such as BaP are considered likely causes of cancer in cigarette smokers and other users of combusted tobacco products, based on decades of research by multiple groups worldwide. Urinary 1-hydroxypyrene (1-HOP, Figure 5), a metabolite of the non-carcinogenic PAH pyrene, has been extensively used. PAHs are combustion products which always occur in mixtures, so levels of pyrene correlate with those of carcinogenic PAHs such as BaP. In the US government sponsored National Health and Nutrition Examination Survey (NHANES) study, levels of urinary 1-HOP were about 3 times higher in smokers than non-smokers.[29] Phenanthrene tetraol (PheT, Figure 5) is another useful urinary biomarker of PAH exposure plus

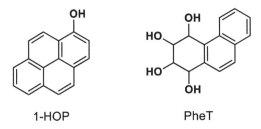

1-HOP   PheT

Figure 5:   Structures of 1-HOP and PheT, urinary biomarkers of PAH exposure.

metabolism and, like 1-HOP, is 2–3 times higher in cigarette smokers than non-smokers. An advantage of PheT is that the pathway of metabolism by which it forms mimics that of the carcinogenic pathway of BaP metabolism, but PheT concentration in urine is 500 times greater than that of the corresponding metabolite of BaP, and thus easier to measure.[30] PheT was significantly related to lung cancer incidence in cigarette smokers in the prospectively designed Shanghai Cohort Study.

Tobacco smoke contains a number of volatile carcinogens and toxicants such as benzene, 1,3-butadiene, acrolein, crotonaldehyde, and acrylonitrile. These compounds are all metabolized to mercapturic acids that are excreted in the urine.[31–36] The mercapturic acids form as the end products of the glutathione-*S*-transferase metabolism pathway that is important in the detoxification of these volatiles. Benzene and 1,3-butadiene are considered carcinogenic to humans by IARC, while acrolein, crotonaldehyde, and acrylonitrile are well-established toxicants with relatively modest or no carcinogenic activity. The measurement of these metabolites in the urine of smokers is practical and can provide important leads to cancer etiology. The metabolite of acrylonitrile is also useful in specifically identifying users of combusted tobacco products, thus providing a convenient method to distinguish cigarette smokers from users of other nicotine containing products such as smokeless tobacco, nicotine replacement products, or e-cigarettes.

3.2. *Biomarkers of potential harm*

These biomarkers are clearly less well established than biomarkers of exposure because the studies required to validate a biomarker of potential harm are more difficult and complex. There is no single biomarker that can predict whether or not a cigarette smoker or smokeless tobacco user will get cancer, but there are some clear directions. As noted above, several well-established biomarkers of exposure including NNAL, cotinine, total nicotine equivalents, and phenanthrene tetraol have been related to lung cancer in prospective epidemiology studies, indicating that they may also biomarkers of potential harm, but this requires further exploration. Combining these measures in a receiver operating characteristic analysis did not result in sufficient predictive ability for lung cancer, and further studies incorporating other biomarkers are necessary to construct a truly predictive model that could be used to identify those cigarette smokers at highest risk for cancer. Such a biomarker or model could truly be called a biomarker of potential harm.

The metabolism of nicotine is catalyzed by cytochrome P450 2A6 which exists in multiple variants or polymorphisms. The differing activities of these forms can affect the amount of nicotine remaining in the body, and therefore smoking intensity and cancer risk. Thus, variants in this enzyme may be biomarkers of potential harm. This topic is discussed in Chapter 8.

The next step in Figure 1 is DNA adduct formation, a central part of the cancer induction process in cigarette smokers and smokeless tobacco users. Accurate measurement of DNA adducts is challenging because they are formed in very small amounts (typically less than 1 adduct per million normal DNA bases), but currently available methods using mass spectrometry are quite capable of these measurements. Oral cells are a convenient source of DNA, and some studies have shown as much as 20-fold higher levels of DNA adducts of acrolein and products of lipid peroxidation in smokers than non-smokers. DNA in white blood cells is another feasible source of DNA adduct measurement; one study showed significant differences between smokers and non-smokers in levels of formaldehyde-DNA adducts. None of these measurements has yet been tested in a molecular epidemiology study to determine whether they may be biomarkers of potential harm. Other methods of DNA adduct quantitation in human tissue samples have also been applied to tissues and cells from cigarette smokers. The most widely used approaches were immunoassay in which antibodies raised against DNA adducts form the basis of the analysis, and ^{32}P-postlabelling in which DNA adducts are labeled with radioactive phosphorous as the basis for a very sensitive detection method. Multiple studies have used these basically semi-quantitative methods for DNA adduct detection in human tissues, but the results did not evolve into useful biomarkers of potential harm.[37]

Oxidative damage and inflammation are interrelated phenomena that are involved in tumor promotion, co-carcinogenesis, and related physiological pathways that enhance the effects of DNA damaging carcinogens. Considerable evidence supports their role in cancer induction by tobacco products. The isoprostanes are a group of compounds formed *in vivo* from the non-enzymatic free radical initiated oxidation of arachidonic acid, a polyunsaturated fatty acid present in the phospholipids of cellular membranes. Analysis of certain isoprostanes by mass spectrometry provides an excellent measure of oxidative damage in humans. A nested case-control study of 610 lung cancer cases and 610 matched controls within the prospective Shanghai Cohort Study demonstrated that concentrations of urinary isoprostane 8-*epi*PGF2α, a biomarker of oxidative stress, were significantly higher in current smokers than former smokers or never smokers, and that 8 *epi*PGF2α levels were significantly higher in lung cancer cases than their smoking-matched controls, but not different in never smokers. These results support the use of 8-*epi*PGF2α as a biomarker of potential harm, related to lung carcinogenesis in cigarette smokers.

Variations in the α5 nicotinic cholinergic receptor subunit gene (*CHRNA5*) on chromosome 15q25.1 have been associated with nicotine dependence, smoking intensity, and age at lung cancer diagnosis. In one study, a causal candidate variant in *CHRNA5*, rs16969968, was investigated with respect to the acute response to nicotine in smokers. The heavy smoking risk allele was associated with lower ratings of aversive effects. Thus, differential aversive response to nicotine was identified as one likely mechanism for the association of *CHRNA5-CHRNA3-CHRNB4* with heavy smoking, and rs16969968 may be a biomarker of potential harm.[38,39]

4. Summary

Addiction to nicotine traps otherwise rational humans into using tobacco products such as cigarettes and smokeless tobacco that are horrible nicotine delivery systems because they contain multiple carcinogens. When taken into the human body, these carcinogens, which are foreign compounds, are metabolized in the body's attempt to excrete them. This process may only be partially successful and some of the resulting metabolites and intermediates may react with DNA, the major target for cancer initiation. The resulting DNA adducts can cause mutations in critical genes such as *K-RAS* and *TP53* resulting in altered growth control mechanisms and cancer. In the past 20 years, aspects of this process have been captured as biomarkers of carcinogen exposure and potential harm. Some of these biomarkers have the potential to predict which tobacco users are at highest risk for cancer, so intensive preventive strategies can be initiated before it is too late.

References

1. Hecht SS. Tobacco smoke carcinogens and lung cancer. *J Natl Cancer Inst* 1999;91:1194–210.

2. U.S. Department of Health and Human Services. *How Tobacco Smoke Causes Disease: The Biology and Behavioral Basis for Smoking-attributable Disease: A Report of the Surgeon General.* (Washington, D.C.: U.S. Department of Health and Human Services, 2010).

3. International Agency for Research on Cancer. Tobacco smoke and involuntary smoking. In *IARC Monographs on the Evaluation of Carcinogenic Risks to Humans*, vol 83. (Lyon, FR: IARC, 2004).

4. U.S. Department of Health and Human Services. *Preventing Tobacco Use Among Youth and Young Adults: A Report of the Surgeon General.* (Washington, D.C.: U.S. Department of Health and Human Services, 2012).

5. Why People Start Smoking and Why It's Hard to Stop. American Cancer Society, 2015 (https://www.cancer.org/cancer/cancer-causes/tobacco-and-cancer/why-people-start-using-tobacco.html, accessed 9/18/2020).

6. Hecht SS. Biochemistry, biology, and carcinogenicity of tobacco-specific *N*-nitrosamines. *Chem Res Toxicol* 1998;11:559–603.

7. Vineis P, Pirastu R. Aromatic amines and cancer. *Cancer Causes Control* 1997;8:346–55.

8. International Agency for Research on Cancer. A review of human carcinogens: chemical agents and related occupations. In: *IARC Monographs on the Evaluation of Carcinogenic Risks to Humans, vol. 100F.* (Lyon, FR: IARC; 2012).

9. International Agency for Research on Cancer. Smokeless tobacco and tobacco-specific nitrosamines. In: *IARC Monographs on the Evaluation of Carcinogenic Risks to Humans, vol. 89.* (Lyon, FR: IARC; 2007:41–583).

10. Balbo S, James-Yi S, Johnson CS *et al.* (*S*)-*N'*-Nitrosonornicotine, a constituent of smokeless tobacco, is a powerful oral cavity carcinogen in rats. *Carcinogenesis* 2013;34:2178–83.

11. Benowitz NL, Hukkanen J, Jacob P, 3rd. Nicotine chemistry, metabolism, kinetics and biomarkers. *Handb Exp Pharmacol* 2009(192):29–60.
12. Hecht SS. Research opportunities related to establishing standards for tobacco products under the Family Smoking Prevention and Tobacco Control Act. *Nicotine Tob Res* 2012;14:18–28.
13. Rodgman A, Perfetti T. *The Chemical Components of Tobacco and Tobacco Smoke* (Boca Raton, FL: CRC Press, 2009).
14. International Agency for Research on Cancer. Some non-heterocyclic polycyclic aromatic hydrocarbons and some related exposures. In: *IARC Monographs on the Evaluation of Carcinogenic Risks to Humans, vol. 92.* (Lyon, FR: IARC; 2010:35–818).
15. Ma B, Stepanov I, Hecht SS. Recent studies on DNA adducts resulting from human exposure to tobacco smoke. *Toxics* 2019;7.
16. Smith MT, Guyton KZ, Gibbons CF, *et al.* Key characteristics of carcinogens as a basis for organizing data on mechanisms of carcinogenesis. *Environ Health Perspect* 2016;124:713–21.
17. Delaney JC, Essigmann JM. Biological properties of single chemical-DNA adducts: a twenty year perspective. *Chem Res Toxicol* 2008;21:232–52.
18. Basu AK, Essigmann JM. Site-specifically modified oligodeoxynucleotides as probes for the structural and biological effects of DNA-damaging agents. *Chem Res Toxicol* 1988;1:1–18.
19. Pegg AE. Multifaceted roles of alkyltransferase and related proteins in DNA repair, DNA damage, resistance to chemotherapy, and research tools. *Chem Res Toxicol* 2011;24:618–39.
20. Peterson LA, Hecht SS. O^6-Methylguanine is a critical determinant of 4-(methylnitrosamino)-1-(3-pyridyl)-1-butanone tumorigenesis in A/J mouse lung. *Cancer Res* 1991;51:5557–64.
21. Kiwerska K, Szyfter K. DNA repair in cancer initiation, progression, and therapy-a double-edged sword. *J Appl Genet* 2019;60:329–34.
22. Cancer Genome Atlas Research Network. Comprehensive genomic characterization of squamous cell lung cancers. *Nature* 2012;489:519–25.
23. Campbell JD, Alexandrov A, Kim J, *et al.* Distinct patterns of somatic genome alterations in lung adenocarcinomas and squamous cell carcinomas. *Nat Genet* 2016;48:607–16.
24. Alexandrov LB, Ju YS, Haase K, *et al.* Mutational signatures associated with tobacco smoking in human cancer. *Science* 2016;354:618–22.
25. Govindan R, Ding L, Griffith M, *et al.* Genomic landscape of non-small cell lung cancer in smokers and never-smokers. *Cell* 2012;150:1121–34.

26. Benowitz NL, Bernert JT, Foulds J, *et al.* Biochemical verification of tobacco use and abstinence: *Nicotine Tob Res* 2020;22:1086–1097.

27. Hecht SS, Stepanov I, Carmella SG. Exposure and metabolic activation biomarkers of carcinogenic tobacco-specific nitrosamines. *Acc Chem Res* 2016;49:106–14.

28. Yuan JM, Butler LM, Stepanov I, Hecht SS. Urinary tobacco smoke-constituent biomarkers for assessing risk of lung cancer. *Cancer Res* 2014;74:401–11.

29. Suwan-ampai P, Navas-Acien A, Strickland PT, Agnew J. Involuntary tobacco smoke exposure and urinary levels of polycyclic aromatic hydrocarbons in the United States, 1999 to 2002. *Cancer Epidemiol Biomarkers Prev* 2009;18:884–93.

30. Hochalter JB, Zhong Y, Han S, Carmella SG, Hecht SS. Quantitation of a minor enantiomer of phenanthrene tetraol in human urine: correlations with levels of overall phenanthrene tetraol, benzo[*a*]pyrene tetraol, and 1-hydroxypyrene. *Chem Res Toxicol* 2011;24:262–8.

31. Boldry EJ, Yuan JM, Carmella SG, *et al.* Effects of 2-phenethyl Isothiocyanate on metabolism of 1,3-butadiene in smokers. *Cancer Prev Res (Phila)* 2020;13:91–100.

32. Haiman CA, Patel YM, Stram DO, *et al.* Benzene uptake and glutathione S-transferase T1 status as determinants of *S*-phenylmercapturic acid in cigarette smokers in the Multiethnic Cohort. *PLoS One* 2016;11:e0150641.

33. Chen M, Carmella SG, Li Y, Zhao Y, Hecht SS. Resolution and quantitation of mercapturic acids derived from crotonaldehyde, methacrolein, and methyl vinyl ketone in the urine of smokers and nonsmokers. *Chem Res Toxicol* 2020;33:669–77.

34. Chen M, Carmella SG, Sipe C, *et al.* Longitudinal stability in cigarette smokers of urinary biomarkers of exposure to the toxicants acrylonitrile and acrolein. *PLoS One* 2019;14:e0210104.

35. Carmella SG, Chen M, Zhang Y, Zhang S, Hatsukami DK, Hecht SS. Quantitation of acrolein-derived 3-hydroxypropylmercapturic acid in human urine by liquid chromatography-atmospheric pressure chemical ionization-tandem mass spectrometry: effects of cigarette smoking. *Chem Res Toxicol* 2007;20:986–90.

36. Luo X, Carmella SG, Chen M, *et al.* Urinary cyanoethyl mercapturic acid, a biomarker of the smoke toxicant acrylonitrile, clearly distinguishes smokers from non-smokers. *Nicotine Tobacco Res* 2020;22(10):1744–7.

37. Phillips DH, Venitt S. DNA and protein adducts in human tissues resulting from exposure to tobacco smoke. *Int J Cancer* 2012;131:2733–53.

38. Chen LS, Hung RJ, Baker T, *et al.* CHRNA5 risk variant predicts delayed smoking cessation and earlier lung cancer diagnosis — a meta-analysis. *J Natl Cancer Inst* 2015;107:doi: 10.1093/jnci/djv100.
39. Jensen KP, DeVito EE, Herman AI, Valentine GW, Gelernter J, Sofuoglu M. A CHRNA5 smoking risk variant decreases the aversive effects of nicotine in humans. *Neuropsychopharmacology* 2015;40:2813–21.

https://doi.org/10.1142/9789811239533_0008

Chapter 8

Nicotine Metabolism and Its Role in Cancer

Sharon E. Murphy*

1. Introduction

Nicotine is not a carcinogen, but it is arguably the compound in tobacco that is most responsible for the devastating cancer toll of tobacco use.[1] As recognized for more than 40 years and discussed in Chapter 12, nicotine is addictive and responsible for maintaining smoking. Cigarettes are uniquely efficient nicotine delivery systems. But, regretfully for smokers, cigarettes are equally efficient in the delivery of the myriad of carcinogens and toxicants present in tobacco smoke. These compounds and their role in tobacco-related cancers are discussed in Chapters 4–6, but without nicotine very little if any tobacco-related cancer would occur. As discussed in Chapter 14, the FDA was granted the authority more than 10 years ago to significantly reduce the nicotine content of cigarettes below an addictive level. But this has not yet happened. So, we continue to study the fate of nicotine in smokers and its influence on tobacco-related disease.

Nicotine, like any drug, is metabolized to facilitate its excretion.[2] The ability of an individual to metabolize a compound is unique, dependent on

---

*Masonic Cancer Center and Department of Biochemistry, Molecular Biology and Biophysics, University of Minnesota, USA. murph062@umn.edu

the efficiency and abundance of the enzymes that carry out the reactions involved. The metabolites of nicotine are not addictive, and the more efficiently a smoker metabolizes nicotine the more often or more intensely they tend to smoke.[1,3] Therefore, poor nicotine metabolizers are exposed to a lower dose of tobacco smoke carcinogens than are normal metabolizers, decreasing their risk of lung cancer.

This chapter will present an overview of our understanding of how variation in nicotine metabolism influences a smoker's lung cancer risk. Three topics of research will be summarized: (1) nicotine metabolism pathways and the enzyme components of those pathways, (2) the relationship of genetic variants of the key nicotine metabolizing enzyme and other factors to smoking dose, and (3) the contribution of genetic variation in that enzyme, cytochrome P450 2A6 (P450 2A6), to lung cancer risk in different ethnic/racial groups. The integration of data from these areas of research has provided strong evidence to support the mechanism, illustrated in Figure 1, by which genetic variants in the enzyme P450 2A6 are associated with lung cancer in smokers.

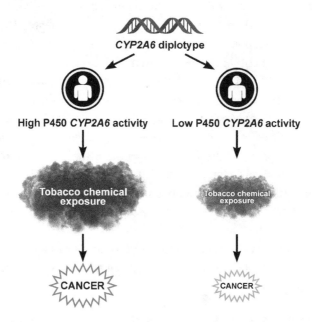

Figure 1:   Proposed relationship of *CYP2A6* to smoking intensity and cancer.

As discussed in Chapter 2, in 1950 Ernst Wynder published the first of several case control studies reporting a link between smoking and lung cancer. In 1982, I met Dr. Wynder when I interviewed for a postdoctoral position at the American Health Foundation (AHF), a small NCI designated Cancer Center, which he founded. Wynder reportedly said, in his characteristic blunt manor, "we need a biochemist", and that became me. I had no plan or even thought to study tobacco, and barely knew what epidemiology was, but metabolism is metabolism and that was my interest. The collaborative approach to research introduced to me by Steve Hecht, the editor of this book and then the director of research at the AHF, has allowed me to be a part of an amazing team that is focused on the prevention of cancer. Many players on that team, several of whom have authored chapters for this book, are in my "unbiased" opinion giants in the world of tobacco and cancer research. My role in collaborative studies with these players, Steve Hecht, Dorothy Hatsukami, and Loic Le Marchand among others, was defined by Dr. Wynder almost 40 years ago. I am "the biochemist".

2. Nicotine Metabolism

In my research at the AHF, one compound I focused on was *N'*-nitrosonornicotine (NNN), identified by Dietrich Hoffmann and Steve Hecht as a tobacco-specific carcinogen (Chapters 4, 5, 7). Not surprisingly since it is derived in part from nicotine, NNN "looks" like nicotine (Figure 2). The only difference is the presence of the "–CH$_3$", a methyl group, in nicotine and the "–N=O", a nitroso group, of NNN. These groups are chemically very different, but they may only modestly affect the fit of each molecule into the "pocket" of the enzyme, where it needs to sit for catalysis of the metabolic reaction to occur. The major site of

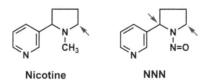

Nicotine   **NNN**

Figure 2:   Structures of nicotine and NNN (arrows indicate major sites of metabolism).

nicotine metabolism occurs at a position on the molecule (indicated by the arrow) that is also a major site of NNN metabolism. I was studying P450 2A enzymes as catalysts of nitrosamine metabolism and considered nicotine as a possible inhibitor. I was amazed to discover that, despite the use of tobacco products for hundreds of years, in 1990 the key enzyme responsible for nicotine metabolism was not yet known. By that time the main pathways, the chemical identity of the major products, and key intermediates in those pathways were well known, but not the enzyme. A few years later, P450 2A6, an enzyme I knew well due to my work on NNN and NNK, another nicotine derived carcinogen (discussed in Chapter 7), was identified as the key enzyme responsible for nicotine metabolism.[2,4-7]

2.1. *Pathways of nicotine metabolism*

In smokers, nicotine is primarily metabolized by three pathways: 5′-*C*-oxidation, *N*-glucuronidation, and *N*′-oxidation (Figure 3). The product of nicotine 5′-oxidation is further metabolized to cotinine. The formation of cotinine is quantitatively the most important nicotine metabolism pathway.[2,7] Cotinine, like nicotine, is metabolized by three major pathways: 3′-oxidation to *trans*-3′-hydroxycotinine, cotinine *N*-glucuronidation and cotinine *N*-oxidation (Figure 3). *Trans*-3′-hydroxycotinine is further metabolized to an *O*-glucuronide conjugate. In most smokers, cotinine and its metabolites account for greater than 75% of a smoker's nicotine dose.

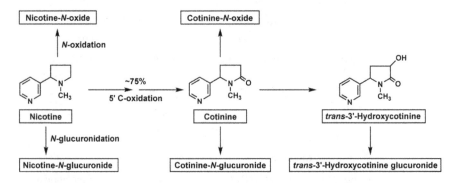

Figure 3:   Nicotine metabolism pathway.

The sum of the molar urinary concentrations of nicotine, cotinine, *trans*-3′-hydroxycotinine and their glucuronide conjugates plus nicotine *N*-oxide, referred to as total nicotine equivalents (TNEs), is an excellent biomarker of tobacco exposure.[8] Biomarkers are defined as quantifiable substances whose presence is indicative of, in the case of a smoker, a lifestyle exposure. The use of biomarkers of tobacco exposure to elucidate mechanisms of tobacco carcinogenesis is discussed in Chapter 7.

There are ethnic/racial differences in the abundance and activity of the enzymes that catalyze the pathways of nicotine metabolism,[9–11] therefore the relative distribution of the metabolites excreted will vary across different populations. This is illustrated for three groups — African Americans, Whites and Japanese Americans — in Figure 4. The C-oxidation pathway, i.e., the formation of cotinine, contributes significantly less to nicotine metabolism in Japanese American smokers than in the other two groups. This results in more unchanged nicotine being excreted by smokers in this group.

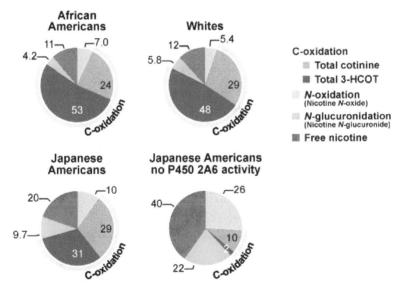

Figure 4: The percentage of TNEs excreted in urine by African American, White, and Japanese American smokers from the Multiethnic Cohort Study by the three major pathways of nicotine metabolism.[10] Some Japanese Americans have no P450 2A6 activity, and their nicotine metabolite distribution is also shown. Reproduced from Ref. 10 by permission of Oxford University Press.

2.2. *Nicotine metabolizing enzymes*

P450 enzymes (gene name *CYP*) are a large family of enzymes that catalyze oxidation reactions in many species. In humans, 10 hepatic P450 enzymes account for the biotransformation of 70–80% of all drugs.[12] One of the less abundant of these, P450 2A6, which metabolizes only 3% of these drugs, is the key enzyme catalyst of nicotine 5′-oxidation.[2,7] The only other hepatic P450 that metabolizes nicotine is P450 2B6, but it is not very efficient, nor is it very abundant.[13] Therefore, smokers with no P450 2A6 activity excrete little or no cotinine.[14] This is illustrated in Figure 4 for a subset of Japanese American smokers with no P450 2A6 activity. The prevalence of individuals with little or no P450 2A6 activity is much greater in Japanese than in Whites.

P450 2A6 is also the major, if not exclusive, catalyst of the conversion of cotinine to 3′-hydroxycotinine.[2] Therefore, due to the relatively long half-life of cotinine (compared to nicotine) the ratio of 3′-hydroxycotinine to cotinine (in either blood or urine) has been characterized as an excellent measure of P450 2A6 activity.[2] This measure has been used in numerous studies investigating the influence of P450 2A6 activity on smoking behaviors.

The enzymes responsible for catalyzing the other two pathways of nicotine metabolism, *N*-glucuronidation (the addition of a sugar molecule, to increase polarity) and *N*-oxidation are, like P450 2A6, members of enzyme families involved in the metabolism of drugs and other foreign compounds that we encounter. Nicotine *N*-glucuronidation is catalyzed by a UDP-glucuronsyl transferase, UGT2B10, and nicotine *N*-oxidation by a flavin monooxygenase, FMO3.[7] While nicotine metabolism through these pathways increases when a smoker has decreased or no P450 2A6 activity (Figure 4), it is not sufficient to make up for the significant decrease in nicotine C-oxidation. This results in a longer nicotine half-life. Therefore, to maintain their addiction, smokers with low P450 2A6 activity likely require fewer cigarettes and longer intervals between smoking each cigarette than "normal" *CYP2A6* activity smokers. That is, they effectively get more nicotine per puff of a cigarette than smokers with "normal" nicotine metabolism.

3. P450 2A6 Variants and Smoking Dose

Nicotine is addictive; the desire to consume nicotine is why people smoke. This characteristic of nicotine has been well recognized for decades and in 1988 the Surgeon General's Report on nicotine addiction was published.[15,16] Despite this, in 1994, before Congress and under oath, the CEOs of the seven biggest US tobacco companies denied that nicotine is addictive.

As discussed in Chapter 12, smokers titrate their nicotine dose to optimize their pleasure, to reduce stress and anxiety, and to avoid withdrawal symptoms. A smoker's rate of nicotine clearance contributes significantly to their nicotine intake and in turn their smoking behavior; that is, the number of cigarettes they smoke and how often and intensely they smoke them.[1] The relationship of nicotine clearance to nicotine intake was first quantitatively documented in a pharmacokinetic study of Chinese American smokers,[17] and a few years later the direct relationship of nicotine clearance to *CYP2A6* genotype was confirmed.[18]

There are numerous *CYP2A6* variants, many of which significantly impact nicotine metabolism.[3,9,11] The Human Cytochrome 450 Nomenclature database lists more than 75 different *CYP2A6* alleles (https://www.pharmvar.org/htdocs/archive/cyp2a6.htm). Several of these, including a deletion allele, *CYP2A6*4*, and an allele with a single amino acid change, *CYP2A6*2*, produce no functional enzyme. The variant allele frequency of these and three others that are relatively prevalent in one or more of five major populations are listed in Table 1. Importantly, the

Table 1:   Some genetic variants of the *CYP2A6* gene that code for P450 2A6 with reduced or no activity.

Allele	Variant type	Functional consequence	Allele frequency in various populations (%)				
			EUR	AFR	EAS	SAS	AMR
*1	No variant	"Normal" activity	64.6	65.1	**30.8**	65.6	71.9
*2	Missense (L160H)	No activity	**2.3**	0.5	0	1.1	1.2
*4	Whole gene deletion	No activity	1	1.5	**17**	7	4

(Continued)

Table 1:   *(Continued)*

Allele	Variant type	Functional consequence	Allele frequency in various populations (%)				
			EUR	AFR	EAS	SAS	AMR
*7	Missense (I471T)	Much reduced or no activity	<0.1	<0.1	**12.9**	0.3	0.3
*9	Disrupts TATA box	Reduced activity	11.1	8.3	**23**	14.4	13.8
*17	Missense (V365M)	Reduced activity	0	**11.2**	0	0	0.6

Notes: Frequency data are from Zhou *et al.*,[9] values are in bold for the group in which the allele is most prevalent. The groups are Europeans (EUR), Africans (AFR), East Asians (EAS), South Asians (SAS), and admixed Americans or Latino (AMR). Frequencies for *CYP2A6*1* are based on the frequencies of the variants listed here and another 18 variant alleles. Reproduced from Ref. 9 by permission of Wiley Periodicals, Inc.

prevalence of the individual alleles varies by ethnic/racial group. *CYP2A6*4* is prevalent in Japanese, with an allele frequency of up to 20%. Other variants are found exclusively in one population, for example *CYP2A*17* (allele frequency 11%), is found only in individuals of African ancestry and *CYP2A6*7* (allele frequency 13%) only in East Asians.[9,19] The prevalence of the *CYP2A6*4* and *7* alleles in Japanese Americans results in much of the decreased nicotine C-oxidation observed in these smokers relative to those of other ethnic/racial groups (Figure 4).

Several studies have observed a relationship between cigarettes per day (CPD) and *CYP2A6* genotype.[20–23] Many of these are in East Asian populations, which have a greater than 60% prevalence of functionally deficient *CYP2A6* alleles.[9] *CYP2A6* genotype has also been shown to influence smoking intensity (mean and total puff volume).[24] TNE levels are related to *CYP2A6* genotype in smokers of Asian and African American ancestry.[19,25] This relationship has not been demonstrated in White smokers, likely due to the relatively low prevalence of *CYP2A6* variants in this population. Both TNE and CPD are related to a smoker's nicotine metabolism, specifically the ratio of *trans*-3'-hydroxycotinine to cotinine, which is referred to as the nicotine metabolism ratio (NMR).[19,26] Several investigators are working to develop genetic risk models to predict the NMR.[27,28] Ideally these models could contribute to predicting tobacco exposure in the many ex-smokers who go on to develop lung cancer and allow targeted intervention studies.

It should be noted here that another factor strongly influencing nicotine addiction is variants in the genes encoding the α5-α3-β4 nicotinic receptor subunits which can predict nicotine dependence. Multiple genetic studies based on large numbers of subjects of European descent have confirmed the association of the chromosomal location of the nicotinic receptor subunits, 15q25.1, with extents of cigarette smoking.[29]

4. *CYP2A6* and Lung Cancer

The relative risk of lung cancer for those who have smoked an average of 10 CPD is significantly less than those who smoked 20 CPD for the same number of years. Similarly, those who smoke each cigarette more intensely are at a higher risk of lung cancer. Therefore, smokers who are poor nicotine metabolizers are expected to be "protected" from lung cancer compared to those who are "normal metabolizers", simply because they smoke less intensely per cigarette and fewer cigarettes overall as illustrated in Figure 1. Poor metabolizers would primarily be individuals who carry any *CYP2A6* variant allele that significantly impacts their ability to metabolize nicotine to cotinine, for example the variants listed in Table 1. Since the frequency of variant alleles is much greater in Asian populations than others, the effect would be greatest in that population.

A number of epidemiology studies have confirmed the protective effect of the *CYP2A6*4 deletion allele on a smoker's lung cancer risk.[20,21,30–34] In these studies, smokers who carry two *CYP2A6*4 alleles, and therefore have no P450 2A6 activity, were on average 60% less likely to get lung cancer. It was reported in a large early study of Japanese smokers[21] that those who carried one or more variant *CYP2A6* alleles smoked significantly fewer CPD than those who carried no variant alleles. However, even after adjustment for cigarette consumption, the risk of developing lung cancer was significantly lower for smokers whose genotypes were *CYP2A6*1/*4, *1/*7, *1/*9, *4/*4, *4/*7, *4/*9, *7/*7 and *7/*9 than those who possessed the *1/*1 genotype ($p < 0.05$). These data led to the suggestion that something beyond smoking dose, such as reduced carcinogen detoxification, was mediating the effect of *CYP2A6* genotype on lung cancer risk. The more likely explanation is that CPD is a poor measure of smoking dose, and that a smoker's *CYP2A6* genotype is "correcting" for differences in nicotine and carcinogen consumption per cigarette. That is, a smoker who carries variant *CYP2A6* alleles smokes each cigarette less intensely than a *CYP2A6**1/*1 smoker. More recent studies that use nicotine and carcinogen biomarkers to measure smoking dose support this hypothesis.[25,35–37]

In epidemiologic studies of either Shanghai or Singapore Chinese, the direct relationship of *CYP2A6* genotype to nicotine metabolism, smoking dose, and lung cancer risk was demonstrated.[25,35] In these epidemiologic cohort studies, *CYP2A6* genotype predicted a smoker's nicotine metabolism (Figure 5), as well as TNE concentrations in urine collected long before lung cancer was diagnosed. The risk of lung cancer was about 30% lower for poor metabolizers compared to normal/intermediate/slow (as defined in Figure 5). In the Shanghai Cohort Study, *CYP2A6* genotype was no longer significantly associated with lung cancer when TNE was

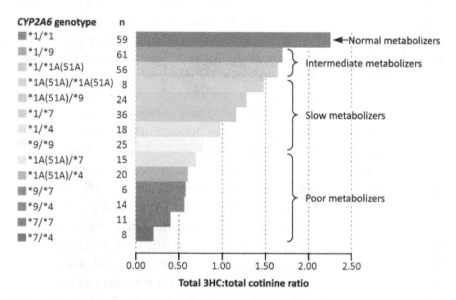

Figure 5:   Nicotine metabolism phenotype by *CYP2A6* diplotype in the Shanghai Cohort Study. The values are geometric means of the urinary total *trans*-3′-hydroxycotinine (3HC) to total cotinine ratio for smokers with different *CYP2A6* genotypes that are grouped by metabolizer phenotype.[25]

Source: Figure copyright © 2015, John Wiley and Sons, reused with permission.

included with CPD as the measure of smoking dose. These data are consistent with the conclusion that the association of *CYP2A6* with lung cancer risk is the result of its effect on smoking dose. In the Singapore cohort, when the relative risk of lung cancer was adjusted for CPD and TNE, the association of *CYP2A6* genotype was attenuated but still significant.

The variation in lung cancer risk by ethnic/racial group reported in the Multiethnic Cohort Study (MEC), a prospective epidemiologic study, is discussed by Loic Le Marchand in Chapter 9.[38–40] At relatively low reported CPD, (<10 or between 11 and 20), African Americans had about a 2-fold higher risk and Japanese Americans a 2-fold lower risk of lung cancer than Whites. However, as noted above, CPD is a crude and often poor measure of tobacco exposure.[41,42] For a subset of ~2,000 smokers in the MEC, TNE and biomarkers for several tobacco-related carcinogens (NNK, benzene and butadiene) were measured in urine collected years prior to lung cancer diagnosis.[10,38] The concentrations of these biomarkers were highest in African American smokers, intermediate in White smokers, and lowest in Japanese American smokers. Urinary TNE levels, unlike CPD, paralleled the lung cancer risk of these populations of smokers.

In a recent update to the MEC Study, the ethnic/racial differences in lung cancer were confirmed at 10 CPD.[40] In addition, a separate analysis was carried out that used predicted TNE in place of CPD to quantify smoking exposure. Predicted TNE was determined using data from the biomarker sub-study to estimate this measure of nicotine uptake in the entire MEC cohort. When predicted TNE was used in place of CPD as the measure of daily smoking, the relative risk for lung cancer of Japanese American and African American smokers was no different from that of White smokers at an intermediate TNE level of 35 nmol/mL. For smokers of Japanese ancestry, mean TNE levels are driven by the prevalence of *CYPA6* variants and smoking intensity.[19] In African Americans, *CYP2A6* low activity variants also result in lower TNE levels.[19] However, despite the contribution of *CYP2A6* variants to TNE levels in African American smokers, other factors must contribute to the higher average TNE levels observed for the entire population. These factors may be genetic or environmental, and may include variants of the nicotine receptor[23] or socioeconomic differences[43] that influence smoking behavior.[44]

Among the MEC smokers for whom biomarkers were analyzed, 92 lung cancer cases were prospectively identified.[37] After adjustment for age, sex, race/ethnicity, body mass index, and smoking duration, both P450 2A6 activity (the urinary NMR) and TNE were significantly associated with lung cancer risk. The association for P450 2A6 activity remained even after adjusting for CPD and TNE. These findings suggest that P450 2A6 activity, in all ethnic groups, provides information on lung cancer risk that is not captured by smoking history or TNE. It may be that P450 2A6 activity is a better predictor of lifetime smoking levels than is a single TNE measurement.

As noted previously, *CYP2A6* alleles that code for little or no active protein are relatively common in smokers of Japanese ancestry but are rare in Whites. And, only a handful of studies in non-Asian populations have found a significant relationship between *CYP2A6* genotype and lung cancer risk.[23,45,46] But more recently, a large collaborative study that used TNE and genetic data from the MEC and genetic data from the Transdisciplinary Research in Cancer of the Lung (TRICL) consortium has confirmed an association of *CYP2A6* genotype with lung cancer in over 13,000 cases of European descent.[36] These data provide strong support, in a non-Asian population with relatively few *CYP2A6* variants, for the hypothesis that lower *CYP2A6* activity leading to less intense smoking and decreased exposure to carcinogens results in a decreased risk of lung cancer.

Taken together, these lung cancer studies of *CYP2A6* genotype, P450 2A6 metabolism and TNE levels confirm the association of *CYP2A6* genotype with lung cancer risk in individual smokers independent of their ethnic/racial identity (Figure 1). At the population level, the relationship is most easily observed in those groups with a significant prevalence of variant alleles relative to other factors that affect smoking dose.

5. Conclusion

CYP2A6 genotype and P450 2A6-mediated nicotine metabolism are associated with lung cancer risk in smokers. In ethnic/racial groups with a relatively high prevalence of *CYP2A6* variants, this association contributes significantly to the population-level risk of disease. In other populations the contribution is much less. *CYP2A6* is highly polymorphic and the frequency of variant alleles differs significantly by ethnic/racial group (Table 1). To appropriately weigh the role of *CYP2A6* variants on an individual's lung cancer risk will require the development of genetic models of nicotine metabolism that predict smoking dose. The future development of these models is important to gain a better measure than reported CPD, in the many ex-smokers who will go on to develop lung cancer years after quitting. Ideally, this measure could be combined with other variables to more accurately identify ex-smokers at the highest risk of lung cancer, and to intervene accordingly.

References

1. Benowitz NL. Pharmacology of nicotine: Addiction, smoking-induced disease, therapeutics. *Ann Rev Pharmacol Toxicol* 2009;49:57–71.
2. Hukkanen J, Jacob PIII, Benowitz NL. Metabolism and disposition kinetics of nicotine. *Pharmacol Rev* 2005;57:79–115.
3. Tanner JA, Chenoweth MJ, Tyndale RF. Pharmacogenetics of nicotine and associated smoking behaviors. *Curr Top Behav Neurosci* 2005;23: 37–86.
4. Patten CJ, Smith TJ, Murphy SE, *et al*. Kinetic analysis of activation of 4-(methylnitrosamino)-1-(3-pyridyl)-1-butanone by heterologously expressed human P450 enzymes, the effect of P450 specific chemical inhibitors on this activation in human liver microsomes. *Arch Biochem Biophys* 1996;333:127–38.
5. Staretz ME, Murphy SE, Patten CJ, *et al*. Comparative metabolism of the tobacco smoke carcinogens benzo[a]pyrene, 4-(methylnitrosamino)-1-(3-pyridyl)-1-butanone, *N*′-nitrosonornicotine in human hepatic microsomes. *Drug Metab Disp* 1997;25:154–62.
6. Patten CJ, Smith TJ, Tynes R, *et al*. Evidence for cytochrome P450 2A6 and 3A4 as major catalysts for *N*′-nitrosonornicotine α-hydroxylation in human liver microsomes. *Carcinogenesis* 1997;18:1623–28.
7. Murphy SE. Biochemistry of nicotine metabolism and its relevance to lung cancer. *JBC Reviews* 2021;296;100722.

8. Benowitz NL, Bernert JT, Foulds J, *et al*. Biochemical verification of tobacco use and abstinence: 2019 update. *Nicotine Tobacco Res* 2020;22;1086–97.

9. Zhou Y, Ingelman-Sundberg M, Lauschke VM. Worldwide distribution of cytochrome P450 alleles: A meta-analysis of population-scale sequencing projects. *Clin Pharmacol Ther* 2017;102:688–700.

10. Murphy SE, Park SS, Thompson EF, *et al*. Nicotine *N*-glucuronidation relative to *N*-oxidation and *C*-oxidation and UGT2B10 genotype in five ethnic/racial groups. *Carcinogenesis* 2016;35:2526–33.

11. Tanner JA, Tyndale RF. Variation in CYP2A6 activity and personalized medicine. *J Pers Med* 2007;7:18. doi: 10.3390/jpm7040018.

12. Zanger UM, Schwab M. Cytochrome P450 enzymes in drug metabolism: Regulation of gene expression, enzyme activities, impact of genetic variation. *Pharmacol Ther* 2013;138:103–41.

13. Dicke K, Skrlin S, Murphy SE. Nicotine and 4-(methylnitrosamino)-1-(3-pyridyl)-butanone (NNK) metabolism by P450 2B6. *Drug Metab Dispos* 2005;33:1760–4.

14. Nakajima M, Yamagishi S, Yamamoto H, Yamamoto T, Kuroiwa Y, Yokoi T. Deficient cotinine formation from nicotine is attributed to the whole deletion of the CYP2A6 gene in humans. *Clin Pharmacol Ther* 2000;67:57–69.

15. Benowitz NL. Pharmacological aspects of cigarette smoking and nicotine addiction. *N Engl J Med* 1988;319:1318–30.

16. U.S. Department of Health and Human Services. *The Health Consequences of Smoking: Nicotine Addiction. A Report of the Surgeon General.* (Washington, DC: U.S. Department of Health and Human Services, Centers for Disease Control, Center for Health Promotion and Education, Office on Smoking and Health, 1988).

17. Benowitz NL, Perez-Stable EJ, Herrera B, Jacob PIII. Slower metabolism and reduced intake of nicotine from cigarette smoking in Chinese-Americans. *J Natl Cancer Inst* 2002;94:108–15.

18. Benowitz NL, Swan GE, Jacob PIII, Lessov-Schlaggar CN, Tyndale RF. CYP2A6 genotype and the metabolism and disposition kinetics of nicotine. *Clin Pharmacol Ther* 2006;80:457–67.

19. Park SL, Tiirikainen MI, Patel YM, *et al*. Genetic determinants of *CYP2A6* activity across racial/ethnic groups with different risks of lung cancer and effect on their smoking intensity. *Carcinogenesis* 2016;37:269–79.

20. Ariyoshi N, Miyamoto M, Umetsu Y, *et al.* Genetic polymorphism of CYP2A6 gene and tobacco-induced lung cancer risk in male smokers. *Cancer Epidemiol Biomarkers Prev* 2002;11:890–4.

21. Fujieda M, Yamazaki H, Saito T, *et al.* Evaluation of *CYP2A6* genetic polymorphisms as determinants of smoking behavior and tobacco-related lung cancer risk in male Japanese smokers. *Carcinogenesis* 2004;25:2451–8.

22. Pan L, Yang X, Li S, Jia C. Association of CYP2A6 gene polymorphisms with cigarette consumption: A meta-analysis. *Drug Alcohol Depend* 2015;14:268–71.

23. Wassenaar CA, Dong Q, Wei Q, Amos CI, Spitz MR, Tyndale RF. Relationship between CYP2A6 and CHRNA5-CHRNA3-CHRNB4 variation and smoking behaviors and lung cancer risk. *J Natl Cancer Inst* 2011;103:1342–6.

24. Strasser AA, Malaiyandi V, Hoffmann E, Tyndale RF, Lerman C. An association of CYP2A6 genotype and smoking topography. *Nicotine Tob Res* 2007;9:511–8.

25. Yuan JM, Nelson HH, Butler LM, *et al.* Genetic determinants of cytochrome P450 2A6 activity and biomarkers of tobacco smoke exposure in relation to risk of lung cancer development in the Shanghai cohort study. *Int J Cancer* 2016;138:2161–71.

26. Chenoweth MJ, Tyndale RF. Pharmacogenetic optimization of smoking cessation treatment. *Trends Pharmacol Sci* 2017;38:55–66.

27. Buchwald J, Chenoweth MJ, Palviainen T, *et al.* Genome-wide association meta-analysis of nicotine metabolism and cigarette consumption measures in smokers of European descent. *Mol Psychiatry* 2021;26:2212–23.

28. Loukola A, Buchwald J, Gupta R, *et al.* A Genome-wide association study of a biomarker of nicotine metabolism. *PLoS Genet* 2015;11:e1005498.

29. Chen LS, Horton A, Bierut L. Pathways to precision medicine in smoking cessation treatments. *Neurosci Let* 2018;669:83–92.

30. Miyamoto M, Umetsu Y, Dosaka-Akita H, *et al.* CYP2A6 gene deletion reduces susceptibility to lung cancer. *Biochem. Biophys Res Commun* 1999; 261:658–60.

31. Hosono H, Kumondai M, Arai T, *et al.* CYP2A6 genetic polymorphism is associated with decreased susceptibility to squamous cell lung cancer in Japanese smokers. *Drug Metab Pharmacokinet* 2015;30:263–8.

32. Liu YL, Xu Y, Li F, Chen H, Guo SL. CYP2A6 deletion polymorphism is associated with decreased susceptibility of lung cancer in Asian smokers: A meta-analysis. *Tumour Biol* 2013;34:2651–7.

33. Liu T, Xie CB, Ma WJ, Chen WQ. Association between CYP2A6 genetic polymorphisms and lung cancer: A meta-analysis of case-control studies. *Environ Mol Mutagen* 2013;54:133–40.

34. Johani FH, Majid MSA, Azme MH, Nawi AM. Cytochrome P450 2A6 whole-gene deletion (CYP2A6*4) polymorphism reduces risk of lung cancer: A meta-analysis. *Tob Induc Dis* 2020;18:50.

35. Yuan JM, Nelson HH, Carmella SG, *et al*. CYP2A6 genetic polymorphisms and biomarkers of tobacco smoke constituents in relation to risk of lung cancer in the Singapore Chinese Health Study. *Carcinogenesis* 2017;38:411–8.

36. Patel YM, Park SL, Han Y, *et al*. Novel association of genetic markers affecting *CYP2A6* activity and lung cancer risk. *Cancer Res* 2016;76:5768–76.

37. Park SL, Murphy SE, Wilkens LR, Stram DO, Hecht SS, Le Marchand L. Association of CYP2A6 activity with lung cancer incidence in smokers: The multiethnic cohort study. *PLoS One* 2017;12:e0178435.

38. Murphy SE, Park SL, Balbo S, *et al*. Tobacco biomarkers and genetic/epigenetic analysis to investigate ethnic/racial differences in lung cancer risk among smokers. *NPJ Precis Onco* 2018;2:17.

39. Haiman CA, Stram DO, Wilkens LR, *et al*. Ethnic and racial differences in the smoking-related risk of lung cancer. *N Engl J Med* 2006;354:333–42.

40. Stram DO, Park SL, Haiman CA, *et al*. Racial/ethnic differences in lung cancer incidence in the Multiethnic Cohort Study: An update. *J Natl Cancer Inst* 2019;111:811–19.

41. Joseph AM, Hecht SS, Murphy SE, *et al*. Relationships between cigarette consumption and biomarkers of tobacco toxin exposure. *Cancer Epidemiol Biomarkers Prev* 2005;14:2963–68.

42. Blank MD, Breland AB, Enlow PT, Duncan C, Metzger A, Cobb CO. Measurement of smoking behavior: Comparison of self-reports, returned cigarette butts, and toxicant levels. *Exp Clin Psychopharmacol* 2016;24:348–55.

43. Hovanec J, Siemiatycki J, Conway DI, *et al*. Lung cancer and socioeconomic status in a pooled analysis of case-control studies. *PLoS One* 2018;13:e0192 999.

44. Cropsey KL, Leventhal AM, Stevens EN, *et al*. Expectancies for the effectiveness of different tobacco interventions account for racial and gender differences in motivation to quit and abstinence self-efficacy. *Nicotine Tob Res* 2014;16:1174–82.

45. Wassenaar CA, Ye Y, Cai Q, *et al. CYP2A6* reduced activity gene variants confer reduction in lung cancer risk in African American smokers — Findings from two independent populations. *Carcinogenesis* 2015;36: 99–103.

46. Rotunno M, Yu K, Lubin JH, *et al.* Phase I metabolic genes and risk of lung cancer: Multiple polymorphisms and mRNA expression. *PLoS One* 2009;4:e5652.

Chapter 9

Ethnic Differences in the Risk of Lung Cancer Related to Cigarette Smoking

Loïc Le Marchand*

1. Introduction

Cigarette smoking is universally established as a major risk factor for lung cancer as it has been strongly related to the risk of this malignancy across the world. Indeed, public policies and smoking cessation efforts in the past few decades have resulted in a substantial reduction in lung cancer incidence in a number of countries. Interestingly, some early studies suggested notable variation in the strength of the smoking–lung cancer association among certain populations. Reasons for this observation were initially not investigated since priority was rightly given to addressing smoking as a major preventable cause of mortality and a global public health challenge. However, given that the majority of new lung cancer cases in the US currently occur among ex-smokers, there is a critical need for additional means of lung cancer prevention, beyond smoking cessation, to address the substantial lung cancer risk of long-term smokers who have already quit. Further, the observation of differences in tumor molecular characteristics across ethnic/racial groups suggests variation in the underlying biological pathways for lung cancer across ethnic/racial populations.[1] Finally, correcting the lung cancer disparities that persist in the

*Epidemiology Program, University of Hawaii Cancer Center, Honolulu, HI 96813, USA.
loic@cc.hawaii.edu

US will require understanding why some populations carry a stronger risk of smoking-related lung cancer, so that these differences can be addressed as we move closer to optimally curtailing smoking in those populations. Thus, there has been a renewed research interest in the ethnic/racial disparities that exist in the association of cigarette smoking and lung cancer, with the goal of elucidating risk factors and biological mechanisms that may lead to additional means of prevention. This chapter summarizes what has been learned to date from epidemiological and biomarker studies, as well as the implications of this new knowledge for lung cancer prevention.

2. Epidemiological Studies

The existence of ethnic/racial differences in lung cancer risk in relation to smoking was first suggested by descriptive studies and case-control studies conducted in the US and Asia. It was recognized that the rise in lung cancer mortality that followed the introduction of manufactured cigarettes in the early 20th century in the US occurred a decade earlier and with a steeper slope in Native Hawaiians compared to Whites and Asian Americans in Hawaii.[2] A similarly high incidence of lung cancer was reported for Maoris in New Zealand,[3,4] suggesting that Polynesians, as a group, may be particularly susceptible to the lung carcinogenic effect of tobacco smoking. An ecological study among a random sample of 8,636 Hawaii residents also supported a greater lung cancer risk in Native Hawaiians due to smoking, since their lifetime use of cigarettes was found to be similar to that of Japanese American smokers, despite the two-fold greater incidence rate in the Native Hawaiian population.[5] As a result, a population-based case-control study was conducted in Hawaii to formally test these ethnic differences in lung cancer risk. After adjusting for lifetime smoking, education and occupation, Native Hawaiian, Filipino and White male smokers were at 121%, 53% and 46% greater risk of lung cancer, respectively, compared to their Japanese counterparts.[6] Chinese smokers had a risk similar to that of Japanese smokers. These risk patterns were consistent between sexes and across tumor histological types, and were apparently not explained by the type of cigarettes smoked, level of inhalation or diet. The lower lung cancer risk of Hawaii East Asian

American smokers, compared to Whites, was consistent with the results of case-control studies conducted in Japan, China and Korea that all reported 4–10-fold smaller odds ratios for the smoking and lung cancer association, compared to studies conducted in the West.[7–9]

Evidence for a greater lung cancer risk due to cigarette smoking among African Americans compared to Whites was first provided by several case-control studies conducted in the US. An analysis of a hospital-based case-control study conducted by the American Health Foundation (AHF) in the 1970s and 1980s showed an 80% increased risk of lung cancer among African Americans compared to Whites for a given level of smoking.[10] A subsequent analysis of more recent data from the AHF study suggested that this difference only existed at a high smoking intensity (21+ cigarettes per day or 37.5 pack-years).[11] A population-based case-control study in Detroit also showed that African Americans aged 40–54 years were 2–4 times more likely to develop lung carcinoma than Whites after adjustment for self-reported lifetime smoking exposure.[12] However, no significant risk difference was observed among older participants. With regard to other ethnic/racial populations in the US, only a case-control study in New Mexico reported on Hispanics. This study did not show any significant difference in lung cancer risk between Hispanics and Whites after accounting for differences in smoking.[13] A recognized limitation of case-control studies is that they are often subject to biases (e.g., recall and selection biases). Prospective studies that collect exposure information before diagnosis and take into account confounders and competing risks are considered scientifically stronger.

The first prospective study of ethnic/racial differences in lung cancer risk related to cigarette smoking was conducted in the Multiethnic Cohort (MEC) which has been following 215,000 Hawaii and Los Angeles residents since 1993–1996.[14] Lung cancer risk differences were investigated among African American, Japanese American, Latino, Native Hawaiian, and White male and female participants. The analysis included 1,979 incident lung cancer cases identified over an eight-year average follow-up. Large lung cancer risk differences were observed among the five ethnic/racial groups, especially among smokers with low and moderate numbers of cigarettes per day (CPD). African Americans and Native Hawaiians had a similarly increased risk, compared to all other groups. Among those who smoked no more than 10 and those who smoked 11 to 20 CPD, the relative risks, as compared with African Americans, ranged from 0.21 to 0.39 (*p*'s <0.001) among Japanese Americans and Latinos and from 0.45 to 0.57 (*p*'s <0.001) among Whites.[14] However, these differences were much reduced at levels exceeding 30 CPD and were no longer statistically significant. These ethnic/racial patterns in lung cancer risk associated with smoking were observed among men and women.[14]

A recent update of this analysis with an additional 16 years of follow-up and 4,993 lung cancer cases that took into account differential quitting rates among ethnic/racial groups during follow-up showed the same ethnic/racial risk patterns as in the earlier analysis, with marked differences at low levels of smoking (10 CPD) which were no longer significant at high levels (35 CPD) (Figure 1).[15] These risk patterns were similarly observed for the two most common cell types of lung cancer, adenocarcinoma and squamous cell carcinoma.[15] Interestingly, results for small cell carcinoma showed that Native Hawaiians had significantly higher risk for this cell type compared to all other ethnic groups.

A few studies have also considered whether socioeconomic factors might contribute to lung cancer disparities, perhaps in synergy with

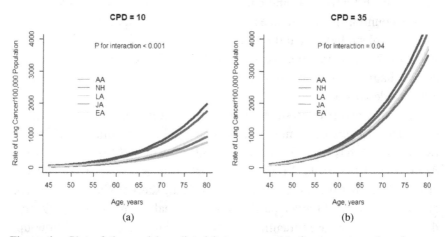

(a)   (b)

Figure 1:   Plot of the model-predicted lung cancer risk for current smokers by age according to ethnic/racial group and reported smoking intensity: (a) risk at 10 cigarettes per day; (b) risk at 35 cigarettes per day. Reproduced from Ref. 15 by permission of National Cancer Institute.

Notes: CPD = cigarettes per day; AA = African Americans; EA = European Americans; JA = Japanese Americans; LA = Latino Americans; NH = Native Hawaiians.

smoking. Krieger *et al.* postulated that area-level socioeconomic status (SES) may be a more comprehensive measure of socioeconomic status (SES) than individual-level SES because it captures social characteristics of communities that are not typically measured by questionnaire.[16] An analysis assigning a census block group SES index to the 60,756 participants in the VITamins And Lifestyle (VITAL) cohort examined the association between area-level SES and total and site-specific cancer incidence, adjusting for household income and individual education.[17] Compared with the highest-SES areas, living in the lowest-SES areas was associated with a statistically significant 43% higher lung cancer incidence.

The association between neighborhood deprivation and lung cancer risk was also investigated in the Southern Community Cohort Study with 1,334 lung cancer cases and 5,315 controls.[18] After adjustment for smoking status and individual-level measures of SES, there was no monotonic increase in risk with worsening neighborhood deprivation score overall or within sex and race groups. However, there was a trend of increasing risk with greater deprivation among current smokers and former smokers who quit less than 15 years ago ($p = 0.04$) but not among never and longer-term former smokers. These data suggest that social determinants of disease may act in synergy with recent smoking history in increasing lung cancer risk.

All the studies described above assessed cigarette smoking through self-report. Questionnaires addressing age at which the participant started smoking, CPD, duration of smoking, and the number of years since quitting smoking were used to estimate the lifetime exposure of a participant. As a result, ethnic/racial discrepancies in lung cancer risk could be due to group differences in self-reporting accuracy, or to subtle differences in smoking behavior (e.g. cigarette type, puff size and depth of inhalation) that are difficult to capture with questionnaires. However, inaccuracies in self-reported smoking history have been compared between African Americans and Whites and found to be similar.[19,20] Moreover, menthol cigarettes, which are generally preferred by African American smokers, have not been found to be associated with a greater risk of lung cancer.[21,22] For example, a recent study with 440 incident lung cancer cases and 2,213 matched controls nested within the Southern Community Cohort reported that smokers of menthol cigarettes had a significantly lower lung cancer risk and mortality than smokers of non-menthol cigarettes.[22]

3. Biomarker Studies

In recent years, biomarkers have been used to further characterize differences in smoking behavior among ethnic/racial groups beyond those described for CPD and duration. Cotinine, the main metabolite of nicotine, has most frequently been used to quantify smoking exposure. Data from a large US national survey — the Third National Health and Nutrition Examination Survey (NHANES) — showed that African Americans have higher levels of serum cotinine per cigarette smoked than Whites or Hispanics.[23] Most recently, total nicotine equivalents (TNE) — the sum of nicotine and six of its metabolites — has emerged as a more comprehensive marker of nicotine uptake. A study among 2,393 MEC smokers used overnight or first morning urine to assess TNE in five ethnic groups. After adjusting for age, sex, CPD and body mass index, African Americans had significantly higher TNE levels than Whites, and Whites had significantly higher TNE levels than Japanese Americans.[24] TNE levels were slightly lower in Native Hawaiians than in Whites and similar in Latinos and Whites. These results from the NHANES and MEC studies suggested that African American smokers take in more nicotine from each cigarette, and Japanese American smokers take in less nicotine, compared to White smokers. Because nicotine uptake serves as a marker of tobacco smoke carcinogen exposure,[25] these data are consistent with the higher lung cancer risk in African American smokers and the lower risk of Japanese American smokers.

Biomarkers have also, in some instances, provided clues to the biological mechanisms underlying ethnic/racial differences in smoking behavior and lung cancer risk. Additional studies in MEC have shown that the lower TNE per cigarette observed in Japanese Americans is primarily a result of their lower activity for CYP2A6, the main enzyme responsible for the metabolism of nicotine, resulting in a longer maintenance of nicotine in the circulation and a lesser need to smoke intensely.[26,27] Indeed, both a high CYP2A6 activity and genetic variants in the *CYP2A6* gene region associated with high CYP2A6 activity were found to be associated with risk of lung cancer.[28–30] It is also known that Japanese, as a group, have a greater frequency of *CYP2A6* variants and deletions that result in low or no CYP2A6 activity.[31]

To explore the possibility that the questionnaire measure of smoking intensity confounded ethnic/racial disparities originally observed in MEC smokers, data from the biomarker sub-study were used to estimate an objective measurement of nicotine uptake in the entire MEC cohort.[15] At set levels of predicted TNE, the apparent susceptibilities to lung cancer by ethnic/racial group were partially reordered (Figure 2). Both at low and high levels of predicted TNE (35 nmol/mL and 65 nmol/mL, respectively), the modeled risk of Japanese American smokers was predicted to be higher than that of White smokers and the modeled risk of African American smokers to be similar to that of White smokers.[15] At a high level of predicted TNE (65 nmol/ml), the Japanese were predicted to be similar to the high-risk Native Hawaiians, and African Americans and Latinos were predicted to remain at lower risk.[15] However, it is important to note that fewer Japanese American smokers have TNE as high as the other ethnic/racial groups and, thus, Japanese Americans remained a lower risk group. Nonetheless, these data suggested that the higher risk of African American smokers and lower risk of Japanese American smokers are due to their high and low nicotine uptake, respectively. In contrast, Native Hawaiians and Latinos remained the highest and lowest risk groups after

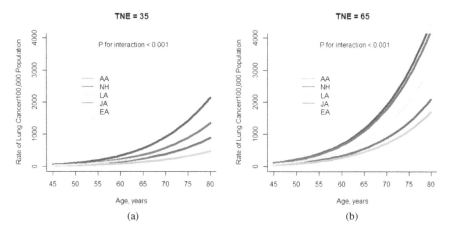

Figure 2: Plot of the model-predicted lung cancer risk for current smokers by age according to ethnic/racial group and predicted total nicotine equivalents: (a) risk at TNE = 35 nmol/mL; (b) risk at TNE = 65 nmol/mL. Reproduced from Ref. 15 by permission of National Cancer Institute.

Notes: TNE = total nicotine equivalents; AA= African Americans; CPD = cigarettes per day; EA = European Americans; JA = Japanese Americans; LA = Latinos Americans; NH = Native Hawaiians.

accounting for predicted TNE, indicating that subtle variation in smoking behavior did not explain their high and low susceptibility to lung cancer due to smoking.

Chronic inflammation, an established mechanism for cancer promotion and a consequence of smoking, has also been explored to explain the increased lung cancer risk of African Americans. The association with lung cancer of circulating levels of several key components of inflammation, including acute-phase proteins, pro- and anti-inflammatory cytokines, chemokines, growth factors, and angiogenesis factors, were initially investigated among African Americans and Whites in the National Cancer Institute-Maryland case-control study.[32] Statistically significant results were replicated in the prospective Prostate, Lung, Colorectal, and Ovarian Cancer Screening Trial and the Wayne State University Karmanos Cancer Institute case-control study.[32] Elevated IL6 and IL8 levels were found to be associated with lung cancer among both races in all three studies. Elevated IL1β, IL10, and TNFα levels were additionally associated with lung cancer among African Americans only. Serum cytokine levels are known to vary by race and might contribute to lung cancer differently between African Americans and European Americans.

4. Implications for Prevention

The National Lung Screening Trial (NLST) has shown that low-dose computed tomography (CT) screening can detect lung tumors at the millimeter range and reduce overall lung cancer mortality by 20%.[33] A number of screening facilities across the United States now utilize low-dose CT scans to screen individuals at high risk of lung cancer. The current US Preventive Services Task Force (USPSTF) guidelines, however, exclude a large number of individuals by limiting screening to smokers aged 55–80, who have a 30 pack-year smoking history and who quit no more than 15 years ago. Whether the proportion of lung cancer patients who would have been excluded based on these criteria differs between Whites and African Americans was investigated in the Southern Community Cohort Study.[34] It was found that, among participants diagnosed with lung cancer, a significantly smaller percentage of African American smokers with lung cancer would have been eligible for screening compared to White smokers with lung cancer (32% vs 56%). It was suggested that this racial disparity in screening eligibility could be eliminated by simple modifications to the current eligibility criteria. It was shown that by decreasing the pack-year smoking requirement to 20 years and beginning screening at age 50, sensitivity for lung cancer screening would improve for African Americans so that it would be almost identical to that among White smokers. Specificity for lung cancer screening would be similarly aligned with White smokers as well. These proposed changes have now been adopted by the USPSTF.[35]

For each lung cancer diagnosis, the NLST study identified approximately 50 individuals with false positive nodules, requiring follow-up procedures that entail significant morbidity (e.g., surgical biopsy), distress and cost. In the NLST, the 60% of participants at highest risk for lung cancer death accounted for 88% of screening-prevented lung cancer deaths, while the 20% of participants at lowest risk accounted for only 1% of prevented lung cancer deaths.[36] Thus, the ability to identify individuals at highest risk is crucial in making lung cancer screening efficient. As a search for lung cancer risk biomarkers is now on-going,[37] it will be important to investigate whether these biomarkers are as predictive in African Americans and Native Hawaiians, the two US populations with the highest risk for lung cancer, as in Whites. It is also possible that the risk biomarkers discovered by exploring ethnic differences in lung cancer risk may be useful to identify individuals at high risk among all ethnic/racial populations and, in the case of CYP2A6, especially among East Asians, a population in which CYP2A6 may be particularly predictive of risk.[31]

5. Conclusions and Future Directions

Although the data are still relatively limited, especially regarding the numbers of ethnic/racial groups studied, some consistent patterns of ethnic/racial differences in lung cancer risk have emerged for cigarette smokers. African Americans and Native Hawaiians have a higher risk, and East Asians and Latinos have a lower risk than Whites at a given level of smoking exposure. These data should not be interpreted as suggesting that cigarette smoking is less harmful in the latter two populations since, among them, smoking is also a major health hazard and results in a shorter life expectancy. Instead, investigating these differences offers the opportunity to expand our understanding of the relationships of smoking behavior and biological mechanisms with lung cancer risk and may lead to new approaches to address ethnic/racial disparities for a disease which remains the leading cause of cancer death in men and women.

Differences in smoking intensity as measured by TNE per cigarette have been proposed to at least partially explain the lung cancer risk differences among African American, East Asian and White smokers. The lower TNE per cigarette observed in East Asians is likely to reflect their slower nicotine metabolism resulting from a greater frequency of *CYP2A6* variants conferring low or no enzyme activity. The high TNE per cigarette of African Americans could be related to yet uncharacterized modifiers of smoking behavior resulting in a higher carcinogen load. In this regard, the investigation of the social determinants of disease risk are of particular interest. In contrast, the lower lung cancer risk in Latino smokers and the higher risk in Native Hawaiian smokers remain unexplained. Current investigations are exploring other biomarkers (e.g., metabolomics, DNA methylation profiles) that may reflect these uncharacterized biological differences underlying lung cancer risk.[38,39] With the advent of lung cancer screening via low-dose CT, such biomarkers may be useful in a precision prevention approach to identify smokers at the highest risk for lung cancer and help to address ethnic/racial disparities that exist for this very lethal malignancy.

References

1. Schabath MB, Cress WD, Munoz-Antonia T. Racial and ethnic differences in the epidemiology of lung cancer and the lung cancer genome. *Cancer Control* 2016;23:338–46.
2. Le Marchand L, Kolonel LN. in *Social Process in Hawaii, Vol 32: The Health of Native Hawaiians: A Selective Report on Health Status and Health Care in the 1980s,* E.L. Wegner (ed.). p 134–148 (The University of Hawaii Press, 1989).
3. Henderson BE, Kolonel LN, Foster F. Cancer in polynesians. *Natl Cancer Inst Monogr* 1982;62:73–8.

4. Dachs GU, Currie MJ, McKenzie F, *et al.* Cancer disparities in indigenous Polynesian populations: Māori, Native Hawaiians, and Pacific people. *Lancet Oncol* 2008;9:473–84.

5. Kolonel L. Smoking and drinking patterns among different ethnic groups in Hawaii. *Natl Cancer Inst Monogr* 1979:81–7.

6. Le Marchand L, Wilkens LR, Kolonel LN. Ethnic differences in the lung cancer risk associated with smoking. *Cancer Epidemiol Biomarkers Prev* 1992;1:103–107.

7. Jung KJ, Jeon C, Jee SH. The effect of smoking on lung cancer: Ethnic differences and the smoking paradox. *Epidemiol Health* 2016;38:e2016060. doi:10.4178/epih.e2016060.

8. Stellman SD, Takezaki T, Wang L, *et al.* Smoking and lung cancer risk in American and Japanese men: An international case-control study. *Cancer Epidemiol Biomarkers Prev* 2001;10:1193–9.

9. Sobue T, Yamamoto S, Hara M, *et al.* Cigarette smoking and subsequent risk of lung cancer by histologic type in middle-aged Japanese men and women: The JPHC study. *Int J Cancer* 2002;99:245–51.

10. Harris RE, Zang EA, Anderson JI, Wynder EL. Race and sex differences in lung cancer risk associated with cigarette smoking. *Int J Epidemiol* 1993;22:592–9.

11. Stellman SD, Chen Y, Muscat JE, *et al.* Lung cancer risk in white and black Americans. *Ann Epidemiol* 2003;13:294–302.

12. Schwartz AG, Swanson GM. Lung carcinoma in African Americans and whites. A population-based study in metropolitan Detroit, Michigan. *Cancer* 1997;79:45–52.

13. Humble CG, Samet JM, Pathak DR, Skipper BJ. Cigarette smoking and lung cancer in 'Hispanic' whites and other whites in New Mexico. *Am J Public Health* 1985;75:145–8.

14. Haiman CA, Stram DO, Wilkens LR, *et al.* Ethnic and racial differences in the smoking-related risk of lung cancer. *N Engl J Med* 2006;354:333–42.

15. Stram DO, Park SL, Haiman CE, *et al.* Racial/ethnic differences in lung cancer incidence in the Multiethnic Cohort Study: An update. *J Natl Cancer Inst* 2019;111:811–9.

16. Krieger N, Williams DR, Moss NE. Measuring social class in US public health research: Concepts, methodologies, and guidelines. *Annu Rev Public Health* 1997;18:341–78.

17. Hastert TA, Beresford SA, Sheppard L, White E. Disparities in cancer incidence and mortality by area-level socioeconomic status: A multilevel analysis. *J Epidemiol Community Health* 2015;69:168–76.

18. Sanderson M, Aldrich MC, Levine RS, *et al*. Neighbourhood deprivation and lung cancer risk: A nested case-control study in the USA. *BMJ Open* 10;8:e021059. doi: 10.1136/bmjopen-2017-021059.

19. Clark PI, Gautam SP, Hlaing WM, Gerson LW. Response error in self-reported current smoking frequency by black and white established smokers. *Ann Epidemiol* 1996;6:483–9.

20. Wills TA, Cleary SD. The validity of self-reports of smoking: Analyses by race/ethnicity in a school sample of urban adolescents. *Am J Public Health* 1997;87:56–61.

21. Carpenter CL, Jarvik ME, Morgenstern H, McCarthy WJ, London SJ. Mentholated cigarette smoking and lung-cancer risk. *Ann Epidemiol* 1999;9:114–20.

22. Blot WJ, Cohen SS, Aldrich M *et al*. Lung cancer risk among smokers of menthol cigarettes. *J Natl Cancer Inst* 2011;103: 810–6.

23. Caraballo RS, Giovino GA, Pechacek TF, *et al*. Racial and ethnic differences in serum cotinine levels of cigarette smokers: Third National Health and Nutrition Examination Survey, 1988–1991. *JAMA* 1998;280:135–9.

24. Murphy SE, Park SS, Thompson EF, *et al*. Nicotine N-glucuronidation relative to N-oxidation and C-oxidation and UGT2B10 genotype in five ethnic/racial groups. *Carcinogenesis* 2014;35:2526–33.

25. Patel YM, Park SL, Carmella SG, *et al*. Metabolites of the polycyclic aromatic hydrocarbon phenanthrene in the urine of cigarette smokers from five ethnic groups with differing risks for lung cancer. *PLoS One* 2016;11:e0156203.

26. Derby KS, Cuthrell K, Caberto C, *et al*. Nicotine metabolism in three ethnic/racial groups with different risks of lung cancer. *Cancer Epidemiol Biomarkers Prev* 2008;1712:3526–35.

27. Park SL, Tiirikainen MI, Patel YM, *et al*. Genetic determinants of CYP2A6 activity across racial/ethnic groups with different risks of lung cancer and effect on their smoking intensity. *Carcinogenesis* 2016;373:269–79.

28. Park SL, Murphy SE, Wilkens LR, *et al*. Association of CYP2A6 activity with lung cancer incidence in smokers: The Multiethnic Cohort Study. *PLoS One*. 2017;125:e0178435.

29. Yuan JM, Nelson HH, Butler LM, *et al*. Genetic determinants of cytochrome P450 2A6 activity and biomarkers of tobacco smoke exposure in relation to risk of lung cancer development in the Shanghai cohort study. *Int J Cancer* 2016;138:2161–71.

30. Patel YM, Park SL, Han Y *et al*. Novel association of genetic markers affecting CYP2A6 activity and lung cancer risk. *Cancer Res* 2016; 76:5768–76.

31. Murphy SE. Nicotine metabolism and smoking: Ethnic differences in the role of P450 2A6. *Chem Res Toxicol* 2017;30:410–9.

32. Meaney CL, Mitchell KA, Zingone A, *et al.* Circulating inflammation proteins associated with lung cancer in African Americans. *J Thorac Oncol* 2019;14(7):1192–203.

33. Aberle DR, Adams AM, Berg CD, *et al.* National lung screening trial research team. Reduced lung-cancer mortality with low-dose computed tomographic screening. *N Engl J Med* 2011;365:395–409.

34. Aldrich MC, Mercaldo SF, Sandler KL, *et al.* Evaluation of USPSTF lung cancer screening guidelines among African American adult smokers. *JAMA Oncol* 2019;5:1318–24.

35. US Preventive Services Task Force. Screening for lung cancer: US preventive services task force recommendation statement. *JAMA* 2021;325(10): 962–70.

36. Kovalchik SA, Tammemagi M, Berg CD, *et al.* Targeting of low-dose CT screening according to the risk of lung-cancer death. *New Engl J Med* 2013;369:245–54.

37. Ostrin EJ, Sidransky D, Spira A, Hanash SM. Biomarkers for lung cancer screening and detection. *Cancer Epidemiol Biomarkers Prev* 2020;29:2411–15. doi: 10.1158/1055-9965.EPI-20-0865.

38. Dator R, Villalta PW, Thomson N, *et al.* Metabolomics Profiles of Smokers from Two Ethnic Groups with Differing Lung Cancer Risk. *Chem Res Toxicol* 2020;33:2087–98. doi: 10.1021/acs.chemrestox.0c00064.

39. Park SL, Patel YM, Loo L, *et al.* Association of internal smoking dose with blood DNA methylation in three racial/ethnic populations. *Clinical Epigenetics* 2018;10:110. doi:10.1186/s13148-018-0543-7.

https://doi.org/10.1142/9789811239533_0010

Chapter 10

Chemoprevention of Tobacco-Associated Lung Cancer

Gary D. Stoner*

1. Introduction

1.1. *Tobacco carcinogenesis in humans*

Tobacco use accounts for about 30% of all cancer deaths in the United States. The association between tobacco use and human cancer is clearly strongest for tobacco smoking and lung cancer; there were an estimated 135,720 lung cancer deaths in the US in 2020.[1] However, tobacco use also causes multiple other human cancers including cancer of the oral cavity, pharynx, larynx, esophagus, nasal cavity, paranasal sinuses, nasopharynx, stomach, liver, pancreas, kidney, uterine cervix, renal pelvis, bladder and blood (myeloid leukemia).[2] It is well established that nicotine addiction is the major cause for continued use of tobacco; however, nicotine itself is not considered to be a carcinogen[3] (see Chapters 9 and 13).

Investigations in animal model systems and in humans have shown that there are at least 70 carcinogens in tobacco smoke including polycyclic aromatic hydrocarbons (PAHs), *N*-nitrosamines and multiple other organic and inorganic compounds.[3] Most of these carcinogens must be

*Department of Medicine, The Ohio State University College of Medicine, Columbus, OH, USA. gary.stoner@osu.mc

metabolized by body tissues to cause cancer, i.e., they serve as substrates for Phase I enzymes (cytochromes P450) that activate them into metabolites that cause DNA damage and produce mutations in key genes leading to cancer (see Chapter 7). Among the prominent genes found to be mutated in human cancers are the *RAS* oncogenes and the *TP53* tumor suppressor gene. Carcinogens also serve as substrates for Phase II enzymes (glutathione-*S*-transferases, UDP-glucuronosyl transferases, sulfotransferases, and others) that conjugate them with cellular glutathione, glucuronic acid and sulfates leading to their detoxification and excretion from the body. Tobacco smoke also contains other constituents such as tumor promoters, co-carcinogens, methylating agents, and reactive oxygen species (ROS) that produce oxidative damage, all of which contribute importantly to the carcinogenesis process.

One of the important issues in tobacco carcinogenesis is to identify tobacco users who are at highest risk for cancer development, especially cigarette smokers and lung cancer. Although approximately 80–90% of lung cancer patients are smokers, only 10–20% of the heavy smokers actually develop lung cancer, suggesting a potential for genetic predisposition to this disease.[2] Interestingly, metabolic studies performed in the 1970s and 1980s utilizing cultured human lung tissues revealed that humans vary markedly in their ability to metabolically activate and detoxify the tobacco carcinogens benzo[a]pyrene (BaP) and 4-(methylnitrosamino)-1-(3-pryidyl)-1-butanone (NNK), and in the levels of damage these carcinogens produce in their DNA.[4–6] This is likely to be the case for other tobacco carcinogens as well. Attempts have been made to take advantage of this information, as well as more recent data on the numerous polymorphisms in genes for enzymes involved in carcinogen metabolism, to identify smokers at high risk for lung cancer.[7] Similarly, investigations are ongoing to identify differences among smokers and never smokers in their ability to repair damaged DNA with the goal of identifying reliable biomarkers of lung cancer risk.[8,9] However, to date, there is no acceptable method to identify smokers at highest risk for lung cancer and this remains an important goal in tobacco carcinogenesis research.

1.2. *Chemoprevention*

Epidemiologic studies showing the relationship between tobacco smoking and lung cancer were published initially in 1950 by Doll[10] and Wynder[11] (see Chapter 2). Clearly, these were very important observations for which Doll was knighted in England. At that time, approximately 50% of US males smoked cigarettes, but the smoking prevalence among women was much lower because women did not begin smoking at progressively increasing rates until during and after World War II. Because of the increasing awareness of US citizens of the relationship between smoking and lung cancer, as well as other diseases, there has been a continuing decrease in age-adjusted lung cancer mortality in the past several decades.[3] This is due largely to reduced cigarette smoking and illustrates the power of primary cancer prevention. Nevertheless, the current overall smoking prevalence amongst US citizens remains at about 14%. Thus, there is a need for additional measures to prevent smoking-induced cancers in humans, and this chapter discusses the use of secondary prevention, or chemoprevention, as a potential approach to reduce risk for lung cancer development in tobacco users.

Chemoprevention, a term initially defined by Sporn in 1976,[12] is "the use of both dietary and synthetic chemicals to inhibit the development of invasive cancer either by blocking the DNA damage that initiates carcinogenesis and/or by arresting or reversing the progression of premalignant cells to cancer". Chemoprevention did not become a major area of research activity in cancer until the early 1980s when the National Cancer Institute (NCI) established chemoprevention as a component of its Division of Cancer Prevention and offered expertise and funding for chemoprevention research.[13] Prior to the 1980s, there were relatively few scientists investigating the potential cancer-inhibitory effects of dietary and synthetic chemicals because most investigators were focused on identifying *cancer-causing chemicals* and determining their mechanisms of action. Indeed, there was considerable skepticism regarding the use of chemicals to prevent a disease caused in large part by chemicals! Nevertheless, there were a few leading scientists such as Lee Wattenberg of the University of Minnesota, Michael Sporn of the NCI and currently at Dartmouth, and Paul Talalay of Johns Hopkins University who published data documenting the efficacy of chemoprevention agents, mainly in animal model systems, that propelled the chemoprevention field. Since the 1980s and principally through assistance from the NCI, investigators have evaluated more than 1,000 naturally occurring dietary compounds and synthetic agents for chemopreventive activity in animal models and some of these have been tested in Phase I, II and III human clinical trials.[13,14] It is important to recognize that chemoprevention studies in animal models have been critical for the identification and selection of agents to be evaluated for chemopreventive activity in humans. Because of the expense and time required to conduct Phase III human trials involving large numbers of test subjects, there have been relatively few Phase III chemoprevention trials, including trials for prevention of lung cancer. Figure 1 depicts the most desirable characteristics of chemoprevention agents which must be taken into consideration before proceeding to human clinical trials.

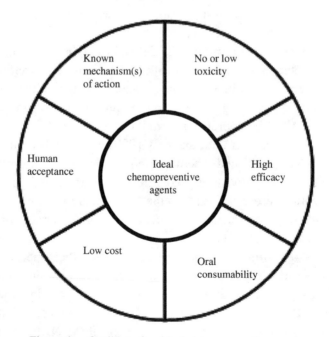

Figure 1:   Qualities of an ideal chemopreventive agent.

Table 1: Chemoprevention agents.

Types	Mechanisms of action
Anti-initiation	• Influence carcinogen activation and detoxification
	• Reduce oxidative damage
	• Stimulate DNA repair
Anti-promotion/ progression	• Inhibit cell proliferation, inflammation, angiogenesis, enzymes involved in tissue invasion and metastasis
	• Stimulate differentiation, apoptosis, cell to cell communication
	• Demethylate tumor suppressor genes

Historically, animal model studies have resulted in the classification of chemoprevention agents as either anti-initiation or anti-promotion/ progression agents (Table 1).[15–17] *Anti-initiation agents* reduce the damage that carcinogen metabolites produce in DNA by either inhibiting Phase I enzymes (P450s) involved in the metabolism of carcinogens to DNA damaging agents or by stimulating the expression of Phase II enzymes (glutathione S-transferases, UDP glucuronosyl transferases, *N*-acetyltransferases, etc.) associated with carcinogen detoxification. Some agents coordinately enhance the expressions of both Phase I and Phase II enzymes leading to more rapid detoxification and excretion of carcinogen metabolites. There have been relatively few chemoprevention studies to identify compounds that stimulate DNA repair pathways, a neglected area of chemoprevention research. *Anti-promotion/progression agents* function principally to inhibit the stepwise progression of premalignant cells to benign tumors and finally to invasive cancers. On a cellular level, these agents reduce cell proliferation, inflammation and angiogenesis (new blood vessel formation) and stimulate cell differentiation and apoptosis (programmed cell death). They can also promote restoration of normal cell to cell communication and inhibit the expression of enzymes associated with the invasion of cancer cells into normal tissues. On a molecular level, anti-promotion/progression agents influence the expression of genes in signaling pathways associated with all of these cellular activities. The most effective chemoprevention agents appear to be those that are capable of influencing both anti-initiation and anti-promotion/

progression events suggesting that reducing DNA damage and targeting multiple genes in key cell signaling pathways is important for optimal chemopreventive efficacy.

This chapter will discuss the use of animal model systems to identify and evaluate chemoprevention agents for tobacco carcinogen-induced lung cancer. As indicated below, most studies have been conducted in rodent models of lung cancer induced by the tobacco carcinogens NNK and BaP. It should be stated that animal models for other tobacco-associated human cancers such as oral cavity, esophagus and bladder do exist, but most chemoprevention studies with these models have used carcinogens that are not tobacco related, e.g., 4-nitroquinoline-1-oxide and 7,12-dimethylbenz[*a*])anthracene for oral cavity cancer, and *N*-butyl-*N*-(4-hydroxybutyl)nitrosamine for bladder cancer. Therefore, these studies will not be discussed as the focus in this chapter is on tobacco carcinogens and lung cancer prevention.

2. Animal Model Systems for Studies of Lung Carcinogenesis and Chemoprevention

2.1. *Mouse lung*

The lung adenoma model in strain A mice has been used the most extensively for the identification of chemoprevention agents for lung cancer. Strain A mice were originated in 1936 by L. C. Strong, a mouse geneticist at the Jackson Laboratories in Bar Harbor, Maine.[18] They are referred to as A/Jax or more commonly A/J mice due to the location in which they were developed. A/J mice are highly susceptible to the development of lung tumors in that they readily develop spontaneous lung tumors with roughly 80–100% incidence at 1 year, and tumors are often detected within the first 6 months of age.[19–21] Most tumors are derived from either type II cells of the alveolar epithelium[19,22] or Clara cells of the terminal bronchioles[23] and remain as benign adenomas during the lifetime of the mice. However, some progress to adenocarcinomas and possess the histologic features seen in human non-small cell lung adenocarcinomas (Figure 2). Shimkin[24] in 1940 first applied lung tumors in mice to quantitative bioassays of chemicals for carcinogenic activity. Since this initial

Adenoma   Adenocarcinoma

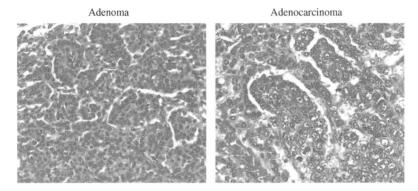

Figure 2: Mouse lung adenoma and adenocarcinoma.

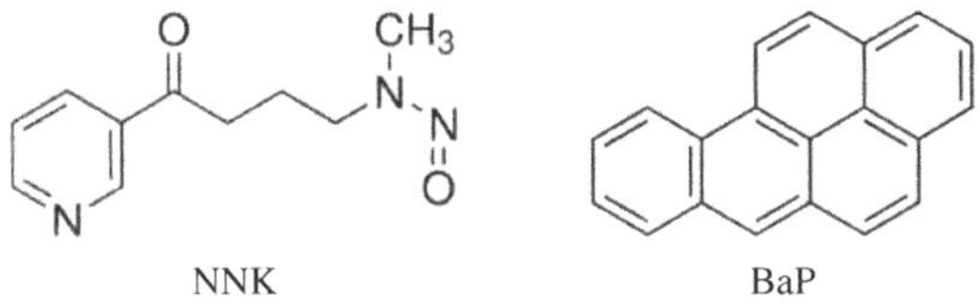

Figure 3: NNK and BaP.

publication, strain A mice (usually A/J) have been used extensively in bioassays to identify environmental carcinogens from numerous sources and chemical classes including polycyclic hydrocarbons, nitrosamines, carbamates, metals, chlorinated hydrocarbons, aziridines, aflatoxin, and many others.[19,20,25] Various tobacco-related carcinogens as well as cigarette smoke itself[21] induce lung tumors in A/J mice; tumor induction in strain A mice by BaP and NNK have been widely used models (Figure 3).

You *et al.*[27] initially reported that the predominant molecular altera-tion found in nearly all spontaneous and chemically induced lung tumors in A/J mice is mutational activation of the *K-ras* oncogene. Mutations in *K-ras* occur most commonly in two specific sites in the gene leading ulti-mately to the production of abnormal proteins that cause loss of growth control in mutated lung cells. The reader is referred to the publication by Vikis *et al.*[28] for an extensive description of the molecular events involved in the development of chemically induced lung tumors in A/J mice and other mouse strains. Additional mouse strains that have been used for chemoprevention studies of lung cancer include Swiss albino Mice,[29]

FVB/N mice[30] and various transgenic mouse strains.[31] In general, these strains have a lesser susceptibility to both spontaneous and chemically induced lung tumors than A/J mice, but the biological characteristics of lung tumors in most mouse strains are similar. Below, we discuss agents shown to inhibit the development of tobacco carcinogen-induced lung tumors in mice and, where determined, their known mechanism(s) of inhibition.

2.1.1. *Tobacco carcinogens*

2.1.1.1. Cigarette smoke

One of the major problems in tobacco research for many years was the inability to induce lung tumors in animals with cigarette smoke itself. Hecht[32] described multiple attempts to induce lung and other tumors in animals with cigarette smoke and suggested that failure to accomplish this was probably due to the very low doses of known tobacco carcinogens in the smoke. Thus, the observation by Witschi *et al.*[33–35] that it was possible to reproducibly induce lung tumors in A/J mice with cigarette smoke was an important advance in tobacco carcinogenesis. In their studies, A/J mice were exposed for 6 h/day, 5 days/week, to a mixture of 89% cigarette sidestream smoke and 11% mainstream smoke. After 5 months of treatment, the animals were *taken off* cigarette smoke and given air for another 4 months (4-month recovery period). At 9 months, the mice were killed and surface lung tumors counted. In multiple studies, this treatment resulted in a tumor multiplicity of about 2.5 tumors per lung in smoked mice versus about 1.0 lung tumor per mouse in air controls. Although the lung tumor response in mice exposed to smoke is low, it is significant relative to air controls. Interestingly, continuous exposure of A/J mice to cigarette smoke under the same conditions for the entire 9 months does not result in a significant increase in lung tumor development.[33,36] The reason (s) for this result is unknown but may be due to toxic effects of cigarette smoke on initiated cells preventing them from progressing to tumors.

In an initial chemoprevention study, Witschi *et al.*[37] reported that treatment of smoked mice for 9 months with 250 mg/kg each of the chemoprevention agents, phenethyl isothiocyanate (PEITC) and benzyl isothiocyanate (BITC) failed to result in a significant reduction in the lung tumor response relative to smoked mice not given these agents (controls). Similarly, the known chemoprevention agents, green tea, acetylsalicylic acid, *N*-acetyl cysteine, D-limonene, and 1,4-phenylenebis(methylene)-selenocyanate (p-XSC) were ineffective in this model.[38] In contrast, smoked mice given a diet supplemented with *myo*-inositol and dexamethasone (10 g and 0.5 mg/kg diet, respectively) had a significantly reduced tumor multiplicity relative to smoked controls.[39] From a mechanistic standpoint, it is difficult to draw conclusions regarding the relative effectiveness of chemoprevention agents in this model because of the complexity of cigarette smoke itself and the many cellular and molecular changes it produces. However, PEITC, BITC, D-limonene, *N*-acetyl cysteine and p-XSC have demonstrated anti-initiation effects in other models, suggesting that the potential effects of these agents on the metabolism of cigarette smoke carcinogens in the studies of Witschi *et al.* were not sufficient to inhibit lung tumorigenesis. In contrast, the inhibitory effects of dexamethasone and *myo*-inositol may have been due to the well-known anti-inflammatory effects of dexamethasone coupled with the recent observation of the ability of *myo*-inositol to reduce the expression of mutant K-*ras* in mouse lung tumors.[40] Due to the minimal lung tumor response to cigarette smoke in the Witschi A/J mouse lung adenoma model, and its inability to identify chemoprevention agents that are active in other animal model systems, it seems unlikely that this model will ever be used for routine chemoprevention studies to identify inhibitors of tobacco carcinogenesis. The model is also complicated by the observation that smoked mice do not gain weight as quickly as those treated with filtered air, and the requirement for the 4-month recovery period is poorly understood.

In a study by Hutt *et al.*,[41] whole body exposure of B6C3F1 mice to mainstream cigarette smoke (250 mg/m^3) for 6 h/day, 5 days/week, for 920 days, resulted in significantly increased incidences and numbers of benign pulmonary adenomas as well as increased adenocarcinomas and distant metastases. These results were remarkable in that actual invasive cancers were produced in a mouse strain that is relatively resistant to spontaneous lung tumor development. However, this model is not likely to be used for routine identification of chemoprevention agents for lung cancer because of the long period of treatment required to induce tumors and the associated expense. Clearly, there is a need to develop a suitable animal model to investigate the mechanisms by which cigarette smoke and its associated carcinogens induce lung cancer in animals, as well as to identify chemoprevention agents, either alone or in combination, that effectively prevent cigarette smoke-induced lung cancer.

2.1.1.2. NNK

Cigarette smoke contains a number of N-nitrosamine carcinogens. One of the most abundant is the tobacco-specific carcinogen, NNK, initially identified as a lung carcinogen in mice at the American Health Foundation in Valhalla, New York by S.S. Hecht and colleagues.[42] NNK is a potent lung carcinogen capable of inducing lung tumors in rats, mice, hamsters and ferrets.[43] Hecht *et al.*[44] have investigated the metabolism of NNK extensively and found that, to induce cancer, NNK must undergo metabolic activation by P450 enzymes that convert it to metabolites that produce adducts in DNA. O^6-Methylguanine (O^6-MeGua) is one of the most important DNA adducts for mutagenesis and carcinogenesis by NNK. The detoxification pathway for NNK involves its conversion to the carcinogen 4-(methylnitrosamino)-1-(3-pyridyl)-1-butanol (NNAL), followed by glucuronidation of NNAL to produce glucuronide metabolites that are excreted in urine.[45] The molecular events produced in tissues and cells as a result of NNK metabolism have been described in detail by Ge *et al.*[46]

As stated above, NNK-induced lung tumors in A/J mice have been used extensively to identify chemoprevention agents for lung carcinogenesis. In a standard bioassay, A/J mice are maintained on a semi-synthetic diet and, at 6–8 weeks of age, administered a single intraperitoneal dose of 2 mg (10 μmol) of NNK. Preferably, A/J mice should not be older than 8 weeks of age at the beginning of the bioassay because the older the mouse at the beginning, the higher the spontaneous tumor response in control mice and the lower the tumor response to carcinogens.[19–21] After 16 weeks, nearly all NNK-treated mice will have about 8–12 tumors per lung. In contrast, when the mice are maintained on a regular "chow" diet, the lung tumor response to NNK is significantly lower,[47] presumably because the "chow" diet contains compounds with chemopreventive activity. This was an important observation and indicates that animal bioassays must be strictly standardized to obtain reproducible results and to compare the relative efficacy of chemoprevention agents. To assess their potential *anti-initiation effects*, test agents are administered in the diet at two or three dose levels, either *before or during* NNK administration to permit them to influence Phase I cytochrome P450 activation enzymes and/or Phase II detoxification enzymes involved in NNK metabolism (Figure 4). Typically, this leads to a dose-dependent reduction in the formation of O^6-MeGua adducts in lung DNA and a corresponding reduction in the lung tumor response to NNK. To evaluate their potential *anti-promotion/ progression effects*, test agents are generally administered in the mouse diet at two or three dose levels beginning 1 or 2 weeks *after* NNK treatment and throughout the remaining period of the bioassay (Figure 4). Biomarkers of efficacy in this "post-initiation" bioassay include quantitation of the progression of early focal lesions in the lung to adenomas and the conversion of adenomas to carcinomas with the use of a microscope. Other biomarkers include the use of quantitative immunohistochemistry to measure the ability of the test agent to (a) slow the growth rate of premalignant lung cells by staining for the cell growth markers, proliferating cell nuclear antigen (PCNA) or Ki-67,[48] (b) inhibit the formation of new blood vessels (angiogenesis) by measuring microvessel density,[49] and (c) enhance the death rate of initiated cells (apoptosis) by using a technique called TUNEL.[50] Potential molecular biomarkers more recently discovered are described by Ge *et al.*[46]

A. Anti-initiation protocol

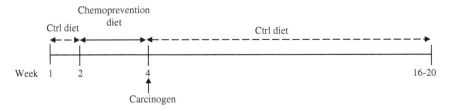

B. Anti-promotion/progression protocol

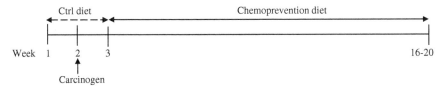

Figure 4:   Protocols to identify anti-initiation and anti-promotion/progression agents.

Numerous compounds and mixtures have been shown to exhibit chemopreventive activity in the NNK-induced A/J mouse lung adenoma model. Extensive lists and discussions of effective agents and their modes of action have been provided by Hecht,[26] Khan and Mukhtar,[51] Ge *et al.*[46] and Zheng and Takano.[52] It will not be possible to discuss all of these agents and their modes of action in the context of this chapter so focus will be on a few agents illustrating some relevant mechanisms of inhibition (Table 2).

Table 2:   Some chemopreventive agents for NNK-induced mouse lung tumors.

Agent	Anti-initiation/ mechanism	Anti-promotion/ progression/mechanism	References
PEITC	↓ NNK activation ↑ NNK detoxification ↓ DNA adducts	↓ cell proliferation ↑ apoptosis	55–57,62
p-XSC	↑ NNK detoxification ↓ DNA adducts	↓ promotion/progression, mechanism unknown	65,67
Tea (PE)	↓ 8-OH-dG	↓ cell proliferation ↓ c-Jun, ERK ↓ angiogenesis ↑ apoptosis	68–73
I3C	↓ DNA adducts	↓ cell proliferation ↓ c-Jun, ERK ↓ angiogenesis ↑ apoptosis	74–77
Dexamethasone/ *myo*-inositol	n.d.	anti-inflammation ↓ mutant RAS expression	78
Sulindac sulfone	n.d.	↓ cyclooxygenases	81,82
Metformin	n.d.	↓ mTOR ↑ AMPK	84
CS3D	n.d.	↓ STAT3 ↓ VEGFA, IL-6, COX-2, p-NF-κB	85

Notes: PEITC, phenethyl isothiocyanate; p-XSC, 1,4-phenylenebis(methylene)-selenocyanate; PE, polyphenon E; I3C, indole-3-carbinol; CS3D, circular oligonucleotide STAT3 decoy; n.d., not determined.

(a) Isothiocyanates

Among the most effective inhibitors of tumor initiation in A/J mouse lung are the isothiocyanates (ITCs). ITCs are present in cruciferous vegetables as glucosinolates and are converted to ITCs by the enzyme myrosinase.[53] They are released by the cutting and chewing of vegetables as well as the action of intestinal microflora.[54] Morse *et al.*[55] evaluated the ability of a group of ITCs of increasing chain length [PEITC, 3-phenylpropyl isothiocyanate (PPITC), 4-phenylbutyl isothiocyanate (PBITC), 5-phenylpentyl isothiocyanate (PPeITC) and 6-phenylhexyl isothiocyanate (PHITC)] for their relative ability to inhibit NNK tumorigenesis in A/J mouse lung. PEITC is a naturally occurring compound found abundantly in watercress and certain other cruciferae[54] and the other ITCs are synthetic. All ITCs were found to inhibit lung tumors in A/J mice when administered by gavage at a dose of 5 μmol/mouse for 4 days prior to i.p. treatment with 10 μmol NNK. The inhibitory effects of the ITCs on the number of NNK-induced lung tumors in the mice correlated with their chain length as the longer chain compounds (PBITC, PPeITC, PHTIC) were more effective in inhibiting the metabolism of NNK to DNA damaging metabolites than the shorter chain compounds (PEITC, PPITC). Detailed investigations of the effects of these ITCs on NNK metabolism in mouse lung and liver tissues[56,57] and lung microsomes[58] clearly showed that their inhibitory effect on NNK carcinogenesis is due to inhibition of the metabolic activation of NNK to metabolites capable of producing methylated adducts (especially O^6-MeGua) and pyridyloxobutylated adducts in DNA. Interestingly, a shorter chain ITC, BITC, was found to be ineffective in inhibiting NNK-induced lung tumors in A/J mice, but was effective against BaP-induced lung tumors.[59,60] This led Hecht *et al.*[61] to evaluate whether a combination of dietary BITC and PEITC might be effective in reducing lung tumorigenesis in A/J mice treated with both BaP and NNK. They observed that PEITC and BITC in combination were effective against these two important tobacco carcinogens suggesting that the use of combination chemoprevention with ITCs could be a plausible approach to the prevention of lung carcinogenesis in tobacco smokers.

PEITC is also a chemopreventive against lung tumor development in A/J mice when administered post-initiation. Conaway *et al.*[62] investigated the effects of PEITC and sulforaphane (an ITC found abundantly in broccoli[63]) and the conjugates these two ITCs produce with *N*-acetyl cysteine during progression of lung adenomas to adenocarcinomas in A/J mice. They observed a decrease in the incidence of adenocarcinomas in the PEITC alone, PEITC-NAC and sulforaphane-NAC treated groups compared to NNK controls. The decreases in adenocarcinoma incidence correlated with decreased cell proliferation and increased apoptosis in the lungs of mice treated with the chemoprevention agents relative to NNK controls.

(b) Selenium

Epidemiological studies have suggested that an increased risk of certain cancers in humans is related to insufficient intake of selenium.[64] This led to the evaluation of selenium, mainly in the form of inorganic sodium selenite, as a chemoprevention agent in laboratory animals, but it proved to be too toxic for routine chemoprevention. These results led El Bayoumy *et al.*[65] and Prokopczyk *et al.*[66] to examine the ability of a synthetic form of selenium, 1,4-phenylenebis(methylene)-selenocyanate (p-XSC), for chemopreventive potential in the A/J mouse lung adenoma model using NNK as the carcinogen. Importantly, p-XSC was found to be better tolerated in mice than sodium selenite or the organic forms of selenium, selenocysteine and selenomethionine, and it was highly effective in inhibiting NNK-induced lung tumorigenesis. Metabolism studies showed that p-XSC reduced both 7-methyl guanine (7-MeGua) and O^6-MeGua adducts produced by NNK metabolites in liver and lung DNA, and induced multiple Phase II detoxification enzymes including glutathione peroxidase suggesting that it may protect against oxidative damage. A subsequent study by Prokopczyk *et al.*[67] showed that p-XSC has both anti-initiation and anti-promotion/progression potential in the A/J mouse lung tumor model.

(c) Tea and its polyphenols

Tea, derived from the plant *Camellia sinensis,* is the most commonly consumed beverage globally. More than 20 studies of the effect of tea on lung tumorigenesis have been published, and most investigations have used A/J mice and either NNK or BaP as the carcinogens.[68] Green tea has been evaluated the most extensively for chemoprevention potential and much of its effects appear to be related to its major polyphenolic compound, (–)epigallocatechin gallate (EGCG).[68] Polyphenon E, an extract of green tea high in EGCG and other polyphenols, administered in drinking water along with caffeine significantly inhibited the progression of lung adenomas and adenocarcinomas induced by NNK in A/J mice.[69] This was associated with inhibition of cell proliferation and the induction of apoptosis, and a decrease in the levels of the cancer growth genes, c-Jun and p-extracellular signal-related kinase (ERK)1/2 in tumor tissues. In another study, polyphenon E (0.25% or 0.5% in drinking water) in combination with atorvastatin (Lipitor, a blood cholesterol lowering agent) significantly inhibited NNK-induced lung tumorigenesis in A/J mice. This inhibition was associated with enhanced apoptosis and suppression of the gene, myeloid leukemia 1 (Mcl-1), in adenomas.[70] Liao et al.[71] investigated the effects of 0.1%, 0.2%, 0.4% and 0.6% green tea in drinking water on NNK-induced lung tumors in female A/J mice and found that only the 0.6% dose reduced lung tumor multiplicity. This result was associated with inhibition of angiogenesis as measured by microvessel density and induction of apoptosis as determined by TUNEL in lung adenomas. Another study showed that the levels of 8-hydroxydeoxyguanosine (8-OHdG), a biomarker of oxidative DNA damage, were significantly suppressed in NNK-treated mice treated with green tea or ECGC.[72] Although less well studied, black tea and its constituent theaflavins have also been shown to inhibit NNK-induced lung carcinogenesis in A/J mice and the inhibitory effects of black tea are nearly comparable to those of green tea.[73] This is important because, overall, the consumption of black tea worldwide exceeds that of green tea.

(d) Indole-3-carbinol

Indole-3-carbinol (I3C) occurs in commonly eaten cruciferous vegetables such as cabbage, cauliflower, kale, broccoli and Brussels sprouts as a glucosinolate called glucobrassicin. Upon hydrolysis by the enzyme myrosinase, glucobrassicin yields predominately I3C. In an anti-initiation bioassay, Morse et al.[74] reported that I3C administered by gavage to A/J mice at doses of 25 or 125 µmol/mouse/day for 4 days before i.p. treatment with NNK caused a significant reduction in NNK-induced lung tumors. This correlated with lowered O^6-MeGua levels in lung DNA.

Qian *et al*.[75] found that when administered to A/J mice post-initiation, I3C reduced the number of NNK-induced lung adenomas and adenocarcinomas and these results were due, at least in part, to inhibitory effects on the phosphatidylinositol-3-kinase (P13K)/Akt cell signaling pathway. In another study from the same laboratory, treatment of A/J mice with dietary I3C and silibinin, a compound derived from milk thistle seeds, caused reduction in the number of NNK-induced lung adenomas and a decrease in adenocarcinomas. These results were associated with decreased expressions of genes in multiple cell signaling pathways.[76] Similar results were obtained when I3C was evaluated for its ability to inhibit the lung tumor response in A/J mice treated with both NNK and BaP.[77] In this study, I3C reduced tumor multiplicity through inhibition of cell proliferation and induction of apoptosis.

(e) Anti-inflammatory agents

Dexamethasone is a glucocorticoid that binds to and activates the glucocorticoid receptor on the cell surface. Wattenberg and Estensen[78] reported that dexamethasone inhibited the promotion/progression stages of NNK- and BaP-carcinogenesis in A/J mouse lung and was particularly effective in combination with *myo*-inositol. As stated above, this combination was highly effective likely due to the anti-inflammatory effects of dexamethasone coupled with the ability of *myo*-inositol to inhibit the expression of mutant *Ras* in mouse lung tumors.[40] Non-steroidal anti-inflammatory drugs (NSAIDs) have also been used to reduce inflammation. These drugs target enzymes called cyclooxygenases (COXs) that are involved in the conversion of arachidonic acid in cells to prostaglandins. COX-1 is normally expressed in cells while COX-2 must be induced to be expressed. Increased expression of COX-2 is found in many tumor types including mouse lung tumors[79] and their type 2 epithelial cell precursors.[80] Multiple NSAIDs including sulindac, its metabolite sulindac sulfone, aspirin, and other NSAIDS, are effective in inhibiting lung tumors in NNK-treated mice.[81,82] However, celecoxib, a drug that specifically inhibits COX-2, had no effect on lung tumor multiplicity in A/J mice in spite of its ability to reduce inflammation.[83]

(f)   Inhibitors of other signaling pathways

Activation of a cell signaling pathway called mTOR is an important and early event in tobacco-induced lung cancer, thus agents that target this pathway could be useful for the prevention and treatment of lung cancer. Metformin, a drug that is widely prescribed for the treatment of type II diabetes, was hypothesized to be a viable candidate for lung cancer chemoprevention because it activates an enzyme called AMP-activated protein kinase (AMPK) which inhibits the mTOR pathway. To test this hypothesis, A/J mice were treated with oral metformin after exposure to NNK. Interestingly, metformin reduced the lung tumor burden (number and size) by up to 53% at plasma concentrations that are achievable in humans. In the lung, metformin did not activate AMPK but it inhibited the activation of multiple cell signaling pathways including ERK, IGF-IR/IR, Akt and mTOR. When administered i.p., metformin decreased the lung tumor burden (number and size) by 72%, which correlated with decreased cell proliferation and a marked inhibition of mTOR in the tumors. The authors concluded that these data support the testing of metformin in cancer chemoprevention clinical trials for lung and potentially other cancers.[84] Indeed, as discussed below, metformin is currently being evaluated for chemopreventive efficacy against lung cancer in humans.

Signal transducer and activator of transcription (STAT) proteins represent novel therapeutic targets for cancer prevention and therapy. In particular, STAT3 serves critical roles by influencing multiple cellular processes, including the cell cycle, apoptosis, and tumorigenesis. The STAT-3 cell signaling pathway is overactive in human non-small cell lung cancers (NSCLCs) for which lung tumors in A/J mice serve as a model. Njatcha *et al.*[85] treated mice previously exposed to NNK with a circular oligonucleotide STAT-3 decoy (CS3D) to examine its effect on lung tumorigenesis. CS3D contains a double-stranded STAT3 DNA response element that interrupts STAT3 signaling by binding to STAT3 dimers, rendering them unable to initiate transcription at native STAT3 DNA binding sites. Intermittent CS3D treatment decreased airway precancerous lesions by 42% at 1 week after treatment, progression of the precancerous lesions to adenomas by 54% at 8 weeks, and reduced the number and size of lung tumors by 49% and 29.5%, respectively, at 20 weeks. Importantly, no toxic effects were observed following CS3D treatment. These effects of CS3D were independent of the KRAS mutational status of the tumors. From a molecular standpoint, the authors found that downregulation of STAT3 activity using CS3D led to reductions in the expression of multiple other cell signaling pathways leading to lung cancer.

2.1.1.3. BaP

Tobacco smoke contains a number of polycyclic hydrocarbon carcinogens of which the most extensively investigated is BaP. In addition to its presence in tobacco smoke, BaP is present in the atmosphere through the burning of fossil fuels and wood, and in food from the smoking of meat and fish. The metabolism of BaP has been studied extensively and the major DNA adduct produced by the ultimate cancer-inducing metabolite of BaP was first identified in the late 1970s.[86,87] BaP produces a spectrum of tumors in animal models and of relevance to this chapter is its ability to induce lung tumors in A/J mice and other mouse strains.

In the BaP model, female A/J mice at 5–8 weeks of age are given either a single i.p. dose of 100 mg BaP/kg body weight or three intragastric gavages of 2 mg BaP in 0.2 mL of a suitable solvent such as vegetable oil with 3–4 days between doses. The mice are held for about 16 weeks to allow the development of pulmonary tumors. Typically, 8–10 adenomas develop per animal with 100% incidence. In this model, chemopreventive agents have been administered in the diet, by gavage or by aerosol. As is the case with the NNK model described above, a large number of naturally occurring and synthetic agents have been evaluated for their ability to inhibit BaP-induced lung tumors in A/J mice and it will not be possible to discuss all of them in this chapter. The reader is referred to the publications of Hecht,[26,47] Steele and Lubet,[14] Khan and Mukhtar[51] and, more recently, Kasala *et al.*[88] for more extensive lists and discussions of chemoprevention agents for BaP-induced lung tumors in A/J mice and other mouse strains. This chapter will discuss a few agents that exhibit different modes of chemopreventive activity in the BaP model (Table 3).

Table 3:   Some chemopreventive agents for BaP-induced mouse lung tumors.

Agent	Anti-initiation/ mechanism	Anti-promotion/progression/ mechanism	References
BITC	↓ BaP metabolism ↓ DNA adducts	n.d.	59,60,90
Tea (PE)	n.d.	↑ apoptosis ↓ cell proliferation ↓ inflammation ↓ cyclin D1, bcl-2, p21, p53, p27	90,91,94
ATB	n.d.	↓ cell signaling pathways, NOTCH, FGF, PDGFα, Ras-MAPK, caspase 3, BAD	95
Kava	n.d.	↓ cell proliferation no effect on apoptosis	96
Budesonide	n.d.	modulated expression of genes for cell cycle, signal transduction, apoptosis	101–104

Notes: BITC, benzyl isothiocyanate; PE, polyphenon E; ATB, antitumor B.

(a) Isothiocyanates

ITCs have also been evaluated for their ability to inhibit BaP-induced lung tumors in A/J mice, and other mouse strains. Protocols to identify agents for anti-initiation and anti-promotion/progression activities in BaP-treated mouse lung have been similar to those described above for NNK. Perhaps the most interesting observation in these studies is the lack of ability of PEITC to inhibit BaP-induced lung tumorigenesis in A/J mice whereas BITC was effective.[59,61,89] These findings are consistent with metabolism studies which indicated that BITC is a more effective inhibitor of BaP metabolism and DNA adduct formation in A/J mouse liver and lung, respectively, than PEITC.[90] As indicated above, given this information, Hecht *et al.*[61] showed that a combination of dietary PEITC and BITC was effective in inhibiting lung tumorigenesis in A/J mice treated with both NNK and BaP. This combination may well be useful for the prevention of lung cancer in active tobacco smokers.

(b) Tea and its constituents

Dietary Polyphenon E was evaluated in the BaP-A/J mouse lung tumor model for its effects on tumor development when administered in the drinking water post-initiation.[91] It reduced tumor multiplicity by 46% and tumor load (number × volume) by 94%. Two other agents, the herb ginseng and the drug rapamycin, were also tested in this same study and both were found to be effective in inhibiting the tumor load (number and size of tumors). Although the mechanisms of inhibition by these agents were not investigated, Polyphenon E and ginseng have a variety of cellular and molecular effects leading to reduced cell proliferation and enhanced apoptosis.[72,92] As stated above, rapamycin is an inhibitor of mTOR, a protein kinase that plays a central role in regulating cell proliferation. In another study, Anderson *et al.*[93] evaluated dietary Polyphenon E and aerosolized difluoromethylornithine (DFMO, an inhibitor of polyamine synthesis leading to reduced cell growth) for their ability to inhibit lung tumor progression in A/J mice treated with BaP. Polyphenon E was found to be effective in reducing the tumor load but not tumor number. DFMO was ineffective in this model when administered by aerosol. Manna *et al.*[94] examined the effect of tea polyphenols on BaP-induced lung tumors in A/J mice using histopathological and molecular parameters. Progression of lung lesions was restricted at the early lesion stage and this was associated with reduction in cell proliferation and increased apoptosis. Further, the tea polyphenols inhibited the inflammatory response and decreased the expression of genes associated with cell proliferation and apoptosis.

(c) Antitumor B and other mixtures

Antitumor B (ATB) is a mixture of Chinese herbs composed of six plants. Clinical studies have shown a significant chemopreventive efficacy of ATB against human esophageal and lung cancers. Zhang *et al.*[95] examined the effect of ATB given post-initiation on BaP-induced lung tumors in A/J mice harboring a defective p53 tumor suppressor gene and deleted (absent) Ink4a/Arf tumor suppressor genes. Treatment with ATB resulted in an approximate 40% decrease in tumor number and a 70% decrease in tumor load in both wild type mice and in mice with loss of the Ink4a/Arf genes. The effects of ATB treatment on lung tumor development in mice with a defective p53 gene and deleted Ink4a/Arf genes were somewhat greater (50% decrease in tumor multiplicity and 90% decrease in tumor load). Molecular analysis indicated that most of the genes modulated by ATB belong to several cell signaling pathways associated with cell proliferation and apoptosis.

Kava, a crop from the Pacific Islands, is used as an herbal medicine. It elicits sedative, anesthetic and euphoric effects. Johnson *et al.*[96] examined the effect of a commercially available form of kava extract on the development of BaP- induced lung tumors in A/J mice. Kava was found to decrease tumor multiplicity in a dose-dependent manner. It reduced cell proliferation but had no effect on cell death, indicating that kava primarily suppressed lung tumorigenesis in A/J mice via inhibition of cell growth. At all doses tested, Kava did not induce detectable toxic effects, particularly with respect to the liver. Carlton *et al.*[97] evaluated the effect of a synthetic diet containing 10% lyophilized strawberry powder on the development of both NNK- and BaP- induced lung tumors in A/J mice and found the strawberries to be ineffective against both carcinogens. These results are in contrast to the demonstrated ability of 10% lyophilized strawberries in the diet to inhibit the development of esophageal tumors in rats induced by the nitrosamine carcinogen, *N*-nitrosomethylbenzylamine (NMBA).[98,99] Although the reason(s) for the inability of the strawberries to inhibit lung tumors in mice is unknown, it is possible that the biologically active constituents in strawberries do not reach the lung in sufficient amounts to be effective since strawberries contain high levels of ellagitannins and anthocyanins which are not well absorbed into blood.[100] In contrast, these compounds are absorbed locally into esophageal tissues which is likely responsible for their ability to inhibit esophageal tumors in rats.

(d) Budesonide alone and in combination with other agents
Budesonide is another glucocorticoid that binds to and activates the glucocorticoid receptor. Wattenberg *et al.*[101] were the first to demonstrate the ability of budesonide to inhibit the development of lung tumors in mice. Budesonide was effective in inhibiting BaP-induced lung adenoma formation in A/J mice when given in the diet, but more effective when

administered by aerosol. Remarkably, budesonide given by aerosol for 1 min 6 times a week at doses of 23, 72, and 126 μg/kg body weight resulted in more than 80% inhibition of BaP-induced lung tumors; all three dose levels were highly effective. In a subsequent study, Wattenberg *et al.*[102] found that the combination of aerosolized budesonide and 0.3% *myo*-inositol in the diet was more effective in inhibiting lung tumorigenesis than budesonide alone. Yao *et al.*[103] used a technique called DNA array analysis, which measures changes in messenger RNA (mRNA) expression levels of multiple cellular genes, to compare changes in gene expression in mouse lung tumors induced by BaP alone versus those induced in mice treated with BaP and budesonide. They found that 363 genes were changed in levels of expression between lung tumors induced by BaP alone versus similar tumors from mice treated with BaP and budesonide. Among these genes, 243 were elevated in expression (overexpressed) and 120 were reduced in expression (underexpressed) after budesonide treatment. Fifty of the overexpressed genes and 58 of the underexpressed genes were modulated back to normal levels of expression by budesonide, and these genes are known to be associated with different pathways including cell cycle control, signal transduction, and apoptosis. They concluded that budesonide exerts its effects on chemoprevention of lung tumorigenesis through inhibition of cell proliferation. In a more recent study,[104] budesonide given by aerosol coupled with nicotinamide (a form of vitamin B3) in the diet were tested for their effects on BaP-induced lung tumors in A/J mice. Nicotinamide fed at a dietary concentration of 0.75% significantly inhibited the number of BaP-induced lung tumors. The efficacy of nicotinamide was enhanced by aerosolized budesonide. The authors concluded that combination chemoprevention with these agents is well tolerated and an effective strategy that could be clinically advanced to human studies.

2.2. *Rat lung*

The rat lung has not been used extensively for studies in cancer chemoprevention. The reasons for this include the long time period (about 2 years) for tumor development, the requirement for extensive histopathology to identify and quantify the tumors, and the associated costs of the studies. Two tobacco carcinogens, NNK and BaP, have been shown to produce lung tumors in rats. Nearly 25 years ago, F.L. Chung *et al.*,[105] then at the American Health Foundation, investigated the ability of the ITCs, PHITC and PEITC, and of *N*-acetyl cysteine (NAC), a precursor of cellular glutathione, to inhibit NNK-induced lung tumors in F-344 rats. Male rats were treated with NNK by subcutaneous injection at a dose of 1.5 mg/kg body weight 3 times weekly for 20 weeks. This dose regimen induced a 67% tumor incidence in the lung. PHITC and PEITC administered in the diet for 22 weeks, a period covering from 1 week before to 1 week after NNK treatment, produced a significant inhibition of NNK-induced lung tumors. The tumor incidences in NNK-treated rats given two dose levels of PHITC were 24% and 19%, and PEITC were 9% and 17%, compared to 67% in NNK controls. In contrast, NAC given at two dose levels in the diet had no effect on NNK-induced lung tumorigenesis. The mechanism(s) by which PHITC and PEITC inhibited lung tumor development in the rats were not investigated, but potentially were due to both the anti-initiation and anti-promotion/progression effects of these agents, as determined in NNK- and BaP-treated mouse lung.

In a subsequent investigation, Chung *et al.*[106] examined the effect of black tea and caffeine on lung tumor development in F-344 rats treated with NNK. NNK was administered by subcutaneous injection for 20 weeks as described above. Rats were given either black tea as drinking water at concentrations of 2%, 1% or 0.5%, or caffeine in drinking water at concentrations identical to those in 2% and 0.5% tea for 22 weeks. The NNK-treated group given 2% black tea showed a significant reduction in total lung tumor (adenomas, adenocarcinomas, and adenosquamous carcinomas) incidence from 47% to 19%, whereas the groups given 1% and 0.5% tea had no change relative to NNK controls. Interestingly, the group treated with 680 ppm caffeine alone had a 47% to 10% reduction in tumors. This is the concentration of caffeine found in 2% black tea. The authors concluded that the protective effect of black tea on NNK-tumorigenesis in rat lung could be due to its content of caffeine.

In another study in which BaP was used as the carcinogen for rat lung, an ethanolic extract of *Marsdenia condurango* (commonly called Condurango) was evaluated for its effects on already developed lung tumors.[107] Male and female Sprague-Dawley rats were treated with BaP orally twice a week for 1 month and then with Condurango orally twice daily after lung tumors had developed. Each tumor bearing rat was fed one drop (0.06 ml) of Condurango twice a day with a fine pipette for 1, 2 or 3 months after tumors had developed. Histological analysis revealed gradual regression of lung tumors in BaP-treated rats given Condurango. This was attributed to the ability of Condurango to generate ROS and to influence the expression of genes associated with apoptosis. Although these results are interesting, the study did not specify the concentration of BaP used to induce the lung tumors or provide information regarding the bioactive constituents in Condurango.

3. Extrapolation to Human Lung Cancer — Clinical Trials

Chemoprevention of human lung cancer has met with limited success. Perhaps this is not surprising because most, if not all, clinical trials to date have involved the administration of single chemopreventive agents which are not likely to significantly affect the multitude of cellular events elicited by the many carcinogenic agents in tobacco smoke. Early trials with agents such as β-carotene and the retinoids either increased the occurrence of lung cancer in active smokers or were proven to be too toxic for routine chemoprevention. The reader is encouraged to read the reviews of Soria *et al.*[108] and Gray *et al.*[109] for a summary of the early trials. However, with recent advances in the understanding of lung carcinogenesis and the identification of intermediate biomarkers, the prospects for effective chemoprevention of lung cancer have improved. Needless to say, results from the above-described and other studies in animal models of lung cancer chemoprevention have been invaluable for the selection of agents for human trials and the choice of biomarkers to employ in these trials. The remaining portion of this chapter will summarize some of the above mentioned chemoprevention agents that have been evaluated in human clinical trials.

A Phase II clinical trial of PEITC was undertaken to determine if it has the same inhibitory properties on the metabolic activation of NNK in smokers as it does in F-344 rats and A/J mice.[110] Cigarette smokers were asked to smoke cigarettes containing deuterium labeled [pyridine-D_4]NNK for a period of 1 week. Then subjects were randomized to one of two arms: PEITC followed by placebo and placebo followed by PEITC.

After 1 week of PEITC treatment, the NNK metabolic activation ratio [pyridine-D_4]hydroxy acid/total [pyridine-D_4]NNAL was measured in urine. Overall, the ratio was reduced by 7.7% with PEITC treatment ($p = 0.023$). Another objective of the trial was to determine if smokers who are carriers of homozygous deletions in the glutathione S-transferase (*GST*) genes, *GSTM1* and *GSTT1*, might derive more or less benefit from PEITC treatment. The reason for testing this objective is that it had been hypothesized from epidemiologic studies that individuals with *GSTM1* and *GSTT1* null-null genotypes could be protected from cancer more effectively by ITCs than those with competent GST enzymes because the ITCs would be less effectively metabolized and excreted from the body. The results indicated that PEITC had a stronger inhibitory effect on metabolism of NNK in subjects with the null genotype of *GSTT1* but not *GSTM1*. In addition, the inhibitory effect of PEITC on NNK metabolism was comparable in subjects who lacked both or possessed both genes. The authors concluded that although the effect of PEITC on NNK metabolism in smokers was modest, irrespective of *GST* genotype, the results provide a basis for further investigation of PEITC as an inhibitor of lung carcinogenesis.

Lam *et al.*[111] conducted a Phase I dose-escalation clinical trial to assess the safety and determine the maximum tolerated dose (MTD) of *myo*-inositol in smokers with bronchial precancerous lesions (dysplasia). The compound was found to be safe and the MTD was determined as 18 g/day in the diet. In a subsequent Phase IIb trial, Lam *et al.*[112] administered *myo*-inositol to smokers at a concentration of 9 grams (2×/day, 18 g total) for 6 months. *Myo*-inositol treatment resulted in a moderate reduction in the dysplasia rate relative to placebo controls and caused a significant decrease in epithelial gene expression for P13Kinase activity. It also significantly reduced interleukin 6 (IL-6) levels in bronchoalveolar lavage fluid over 6 months. The authors concluded that these results were modest in effect and that chemoprevention of lung cancer would be improved by using a targeted therapy approach based on molecular alternations rather than a single agent approach.

Pharmacokinetic studies of green tea polyphenols and their biological effects in human chemoprevention trials of oral, prostate and colon cancer have been summarized by Lambert.[113] However, there are no reports of chemoprevention studies involving green or black tea against lung cancer in humans.

Limburg *et al.*[114] conducted a randomized, Phase II chemoprevention trial of the COX enzyme inhibitor sulindac in current and former cigarette smokers to examine its potential effects on the number and histologic grade of dysplastic lesions and its effects on cell proliferation by measuring the Ki-67 labeling index. Subjects were given sulindac in the diet at a dose of 150 mg (2×/day) or a placebo for 6 months. Treatment with sulindac did not reduce the histologic grade or number of dysplastic lesions, nor did it reduce the median KI67 labeling index. The authors concluded that results from the trial did not warrant further Phase III testing of sulindac against lung cancer, and that investigations with agents that target specific cell signaling pathways is necessary for lung cancer chemoprevention.

There are several reports of the effects of budesonide on dysplastic lesions and pulmonary nodules in tobacco users at high risk for lung cancer. Again, Lam *et al.*[115] treated smokers with more than or equal to one site of bronchial dysplasia with inhaled budesonide at a dose of 800 μg twice daily for 6 months. The primary endpoint was change in the histologic grade of the dysplastic lesion on repeat biopsy after treatment. Budesonide had no effect on the histologic grade of bronchial dysplasia, although a significantly greater number of computerized tomography (CT)-detected peripheral lung nodules decreased in size after treatment. Based upon these results, Veronesi *et al.*[116] conducted a subsequent trial in current and former smokers with CT-detected peripheral lung nodules and evaluated the effects of inhaled budesonide on nodular size. Budesonide was administered at the dose used by Lam *et al.*[115] for a period of 1 year. The drug was well tolerated, however, budesonide treatment did not significantly affect nodular size. These same subjects were re-examined by low-dose CT 5 years after their 1-year treatment with budesonide.[117] CT results indicated that the diameter of non-solid nodules (less advanced nodules) was reduced significantly after 5 years. However, the size of the more advanced solid lesions did not change. In addition, the number of new lesions and of patients who ultimately developed lung cancer in the treated arm was not different from untreated controls. The authors concluded that the decrease in size of the less advanced non-solid nodules is of potential importance since some of these could progress to lung cancer. However, more advanced solid nodules do not appear to be affected by budesonide.

Although it had no effect on lung tumor development at the dose levels administered to NNK-treated A/J mice, the COX-2 selective inhibitor celecoxib (400 mg, 2×/day for 6 months) was evaluated in a Phase II trial involving former smokers.[118] The trial assessed the impact of celecoxib on cellular and molecular events associated with lung carcinogenesis, the primary endpoint was the bronchial Ki-67 labeling index (LI). Celecoxib significantly decreased the Ki-67 LI by 34% whereas the placebo increased the LI by 3.8%. It also reduced plasma biomarkers of inflammation such as C-reactive protein and IL-6 expression and increased 15(s)-hydroxyprostaglandin dehydrogenase expression in bronchoalveolar lavage samples. The authors concluded that these results support continued investigation of celecoxib for lung cancer chemoprevention in former smokers at low risk for cardiovascular disease.

4. Summary and Conclusions

This chapter describes studies to assess the efficacy of selected chemoprevention agents to inhibit the development of lung cancer in animals and in humans. The list of agents is not exhaustive in that, due to space limitations, only a portion of both animal and human studies could be described. Most of the animal studies have been conducted using mouse lung as the model system, and both NNK and BaP as the lung carcinogens. The agents tested in animals have been classified based upon their effects on lung tumor initiation and tumor promotion/progression. Multiple naturally occurring and synthetic agents have been quite effective in preventing lung cancer development in mice and a few of them have been effective in rat lung. Importantly, results from the animal studies have been used to select agent for testing in human clinical trials of lung cancer chemoprevention.

The human trials described here are a selected few of the clinical trials of lung cancer chemoprevention in tobacco smokers and former smokers. A more extensive description of the chemoprevention trials against lung cancer in humans is given by Greenberg *et al.*[119] Although some of the trials have promising results, to date, no single agent has yet been proven sufficiently effective in human trials. Perhaps this is not surprising in view of the multiple cellular and molecular events altered in lung cells by the complex mixture of compounds in tobacco smoke. Ongoing trials such as the one with metformin, the mTOR signaling pathway inhibitor, may prove to be more effective. Greenberg *et al.* have suggested multiple other agents known to influence oxidative stress, inflammation and various signaling pathways for further evaluation in lung cancer chemoprevention trials. Post-initiation studies in animals indicate that chemoprevention of lung cancer is likely to be more effective when targeting early lesions as opposed to advanced dysplasia or already developed cancer. The human trials conducted by Lam *et al.*[115] and Veronesi *et al.*[116,117] suggest the same for human lung cancer chemoprevention — focusing on early lesions is likely to be more effective. Successful chemoprevention of human lung cancer may also require the targeting of multiple pathways in cancer development, thus the use of agents in combination is likely to be more effective than single agents given alone. Finally, there could be a role for nutritional approaches to lung cancer chemoprevention, such as the evaluation of cruciferous vegetables high in ITCs or of tea and other polyphenol-rich foods high in antioxidants and anti-inflammatory agents. These foodstuffs could also be evaluated for effects when given in combination. In view of the relative lifespan of humans versus the animal models in which chemopreventive agents have been found to be effective against lung cancer, it is likely that long-term delivery of agents in humans will be required to observe substantial chemopreventive effects.

References

1. Siegel RL, Miller KD, Jemal A. Cancer statistics, 2020. *A Cancer J Clin* 2020;70(1):7–30. DOI: 10.3322/caac.21590.
2. International Agency for Research on Cancer. Tobacco Smoke and Involuntary Smoking. In *IARC Monographs on the Evaluation of Carcinogenic Risks to Humans*, vol 83. (Lyon, FR: IARC, 2004).
3. Hecht SS, Kassie F, Hatsukami DK. Chemoprevention of lung carcinogenesis in addicted smokers and ex-smokers. *Nat Rev Cancer* 2009;9(7):476–88. DOI: 10.1038/nrc2674.

4. Harris CC, Autrup H, Connor R, Barrett LA, McDowell EM, Trump BF. Interindividual variation in binding of benzo[a]pyrene to DNA in cultured human bronchi. *Science* 1976;194(4269):1067–9. DOI: 10.1126/science.982061.

5. Stoner GD, Harris CC, Autrup H, Trump BF, Kingsbury EW, Myers GA. Explant culture of human peripheral lung. I. Metabolism of benzo[alpha]pyrene. *Lab Investig; A J Tech Meth Pathol* 1978;38(6):685–92.

6. Castonguay A, Stoner GD, Schut HA, Hecht SS. Metabolism of tobacco-specific N-nitrosamines by cultured human tissues. *Proc Natl Acad Sci UnSA* 1983;80(21):6694–7. DOI: 10.1073/pnas.80.21.6694.

7. Liu C, Cui H, Gu D, *et al*. Genetic polymorphisms and lung cancer risk: Evidence from meta-analyses and genome-wide association studies. *Lung Cancer* 2017;113:18–29. DOI: 10.1016/j.lungcan.2017.08.026.

8. Mamdani H, Jalal SI. DNA repair in lung cancer: potential not yet reached. *Lung Cancer Management* 2016;5(1):5–8. DOI: 10.2217/lmt-2016-0004.

9. Warkentin MT, Morris D, Bebb G, Brenner DR. The role of DNA repair capacity in lung cancer risk among never-smokers: A systematic review of epidemiologic studies. *Cancer Treat Res Commun* 2017;13:13–24. DOI: https://doi.org/10.1016/j.ctarc.2017.08.001.

10. Doll R, Hill AB. Smoking and carcinoma of the lung; preliminary report. *Brit Med J* 1950;2(4682):739–48. DOI: 10.1136/bmj.2.4682.739.

11. Wynder EL, Graham EA. Tobacco smoking as a possible etiologic factor in bronchiogenic carcinoma; a study of 684 proved cases. *J Am Med Assoc* 1950;143(4):329–36. DOI: 10.1001/jama.1950.02910390001001.

12. Sporn MB, Dunlop NM, Newton DL, Smith JM. Prevention of chemical carcinogenesis by vitamin A and its synthetic analogs (retinoids). *Fed Proc* 1976;35(6):1332–8.

13. Greenwald P, Kelloff G, Burch-Whitman C, Kramer BS. Chemoprevention. *CA Cancer J Clin* 1995;45(1):31–49. DOI: 10.3322/canjclin.45.1.31.

14. Steele VE, Lubet RA. The use of animal models for cancer chemoprevention drug development. *Sem Oncol* 2010;37(4):327–38. DOI: 10.1053/j.seminoncol.2010.05.010.

15. Wattenberg LW. Chemoprevention of cancer. *Cancer Res* 1985;45(1):1–8.

16. Boone CW, Kelloff GJ, Malone WE. Identification of candidate cancer chemopreventive agents and their evaluation in animal models and human clinical trials: a review. *Cancer Res* 1990;50(1):2–9.

17. Morse MA, Stoner GD. Cancer chemoprevention: principles and prospects. *Carcinogenesis* 1993;14(9):1737–46. DOI: 10.1093/carcin/14.9.1737.

18. Strong LC. The establishment of the "A" strain of inbred mice. *J Heredity* 1936;27:21–4.

19. Shimkin MB, Stoner GD. Lung tumors in mice: Application to carcinogenesis bioassay. *Adv Cancer Res* 1975;21:1–58. DOI: 10.1016/s0065-230x (08)60970-7.

20. Stoner GD, Shimkin MB. Strain A mouse lung tumor bioassay. *J Am College Toxicol* 1982;1(1):145–169. DOI: 10.3109/10915818209013138.

21. Witschi H. A/J mouse as a model for lung tumorigenesis caused by tobacco smoke: strengths and weaknesses. *Exp Lung Res* 2005;31(1):3–18. DOI: 10.1080/01902140490494959.

22. Stoner GD, Kikkawa Y, Kniazeff AJ, Miya K, Wagner RM. Clonal isolation of epithelial cells from mouse lung adenoma. *Cancer Res* 1975;35:2177–85.

23. Gunning W, Goldblatt PJ, Stoner GD. Keratin expression in chemically induced mouse lung adenomas. *Am J Pathol* 1992;140(1):109–118.

24. Shimkin MB. Reaction of lungs in strain A mice to carcinogenic hydrocarbons. *Arch Pathol* 1940;29:239–55.

25. Stoner GD. Lung tumors in strain A mice as a bioassay for carcinogenicity of environmental chemicals. *Exp Lung Res* 1991;17:405–423.

26. Hecht SS. Approaches to chemoprevention of lung cancer based on carcinogens in tobacco smoke. *Environ Health Perspec* 1997;105 Suppl 4(Suppl 4):955–63. DOI: 10.1289/ehp.97105s4955.

27. You M, Candrian U, Maronpot RR, Stoner GD, Anderson MW. Activation of the Ki-ras protooncogene in spontaneously occurring and chemically induced lung tumors of the strain A mouse. *Proc Natl Acad Sci USA* 1989;86(9):3070–4. DOI: 10.1073/pnas.86.9.3070.

28. Vikis HG, Rymaszewski AL, Tichelaar JW. Mouse models of chemically-induced lung carcinogenesis. *Front Biosci* (Elite edition) 2013;5:939–46. DOI: 10.2741/e673.

29. Anandakumar P, Kamaraj S, Ramakrishnan G, Jagan S, Devaki T. Chemopreventive task of capsaicin against benzo(a)pyrene-induced lung cancer in Swiss albino mice. Basic & clinical pharmacology & toxicology 2009;104(5):360–5. DOI: 10.1111/j.1742-7843.2009.00387.x.

30. Stabile LP, Rothstein ME, Cunningham DE, *et al.* Prevention of tobacco carcinogen-induced lung cancer in female mice using antiestrogens. *Carcinogenesis* 2012;33(11):2181–9. DOI: 10.1093/carcin/bgs260.

31. Lubet RA, Zhang Z, Wang Y, You M. Chemoprevention of lung cancer in transgenic mice. *Chest* 2004;125(5 Suppl):144s–7s. DOI: 10.1378/chest.125.5_suppl.144s.

32. Hecht SS. Carcinogenicity studies of inhaled cigarette smoke in laboratory animals: Old and new. *Carcinogenesis* 2005;26(9):1488–92. DOI: 10.1093/carcin/bgi148.

33. Witschi H, Espiritu I, Peake JL, Wu K, Maronpot RR, Pinkerton KE. The carcinogenicity of environmental tobacco smoke. *Carcinogenesis* 1997;18(3):575–86. DOI: 10.1093/carcin/18.3.575.

34. Witschi H, Espiritu I, Maronpot RR, Pinkerton KE, Jones AD. The carcinogenic potential of the gas phase of environmental tobacco smoke. *Carcinogenesis* 1997;18(11):2035–42. DOI: 10.1093/carcin/18.11.2035.

35. Witschi H. Tobacco smoke as a mouse lung carcinogen. *Exp Lung Res* 1998;24(4):385–94. DOI: 10.3109/01902149809087375.

36. Finch GL, Nikula KJ, Belinsky SA, Barr EB, Stoner GD, Lechner JF. Failure of cigarette smoke to induce or promote lung cancer in the A/J mouse. *Cancer Lett* 1996;99(2):161–7. DOI: 10.1016/0304-3835(95)04059-5.

37. Witschi H, Uyeminami D, Moran D, Espiritu I. Chemoprevention of tobacco-smoke lung carcinogenesis in mice after cessation of smoke exposure. *Carcinogenesis* 2000;21(5):977–82. DOI: 10.1093/carcin/21.5.977.

38. Witschi H, Espiritu I, Yu M, Willits NH. The effects of phenethyl isothiocyanate, N-acetylcysteine and green tea on tobacco smoke-induced lung tumors in strain A/J mice. *Carcinogenesis* 1998;19(10):1789–94. DOI: 10.1093/carcin/19.10.1789.

39. Witschi H, Espiritu I, Uyeminami D. Chemoprevention of tobacco smoke-induced lung tumors in A/J strain mice with dietary myo-inositol and dexamethasone. *Carcinogenesis* 1999;20(7):1375–8. DOI: 10.1093/carcin/20.7.1375.

40. Roh JI, Lee HW. A *myo*-inositol diet for lung cancer prevention and beyond. *J Thoracic Dis* 2018;10(Suppl 33):S3919–21. DOI: 10.21037/jtd.2018.08.143.

41. Hutt JA, Vuillemenot BR, Barr EB, *et al*. Life-span inhalation exposure to mainstream cigarette smoke induces lung cancer in B6C3F1 mice through genetic and epigenetic pathways. *Carcinogenesis* 2005;26(11):1999–2009. DOI: 10.1093/carcin/bgi150.

42. Hecht SS, Chen CB, Hirota, N, Omaf RM, Tso TC, Hoffmann D. Tobacco-specific nitrosamines: formation by nitrosation of nicotine during curing of tobacco and carcinogenicity in strain A mice. *J Natl Cancer Inst* 1978;60:819–824.

43. Hecht SS. Lung carcinogenesis by tobacco smoke. *Int J Cancer* 2012;131(12):2724–32. DOI: 10.1002/ijc.27816.

44. Hecht SS. Biochemistry, biology, and carcinogenicity of tobacco-specific N-nitrosamines. *Chem Res Toxicol* 1998;11(6):559–603. DOI: 10.1021/tx980005y.

45. Carmella SG, Han S, Fristad A, Yang Y, Hecht SS. Analysis of total 4-(methylnitrosamino)-1-(3-pyridyl)-1-butanol (NNAL) in human urine. *Cancer Epidemiol, Biomarkers Prev* 2003;12(11 Pt 1):1257–61.

46. Ge GZ, Xu TR, Chen C. Tobacco carcinogen NNK-induced lung cancer animal models and associated carcinogenic mechanisms. *Acta biochimica et biophysica Sinica* 2015;47(7):477–87. DOI: 10.1093/abbs/gmv041.

47. Hecht SS, Morse MA, Amin S, *et al.* Rapid single-dose model for lung tumor induction in A/J mice by 4-(methylnitrosamino)-1-(3-pyridyl)-1-butanone and the effect of diet. *Carcinogenesis* 1989;10(10):1901–4. DOI: 10.1093/carcin/10.10.1901.

48. Juríková M, Danihel Ľ, Polák Š, Varga I. Ki67, PCNA, and MCM proteins: Markers of proliferation in the diagnosis of breast cancer. *Acta histochemica* 2016;118(5):544–52. DOI: 10.1016/j.acthis.2016.05.002.

49. Weidner N. Chapter 14. Measuring intratumoral microvessel density. *Meth Enzymol* 2008;444:305–23. DOI: 10.1016/s0076-6879(08)02814-0.

50. Kyrylkova K, Kyryachenko S, Leid M, Kioussi C. Detection of apoptosis by TUNEL assay. *Meth Molecular Biol* 2012;887:41–7. DOI: 10.1007/978-1-61779-860-3_5.

51. Khan N, Mukhtar H. Dietary agents for prevention and treatment of lung cancer. *Cancer Lett* 2015;359(2):155–64. DOI: 10.1016/j.canlet.2015.01.038.

52. Zheng HC, Takano Y. NNK-induced lung tumors: a review of animal model. *J Oncol* 2011;2011:635379. DOI: 10.1155/2011/635379.

53. Sones K, Heaney RK, Fenwick GR. An estimate of the mean daily intake of glucosinolates from cruciferous vegetables in the UK. *J Sci Food Agri* 1984;35(6):712–20. DOI: 10.1002/jsfa.2740350619.

54. Chung FL, Morse MA, Eklind KI, Lewis J. Quantitation of human uptake of the anticarcinogen phenethyl isothiocyanate after a watercress meal. *Cancer Epidemiol, Biomarkers Prev* 1992;1(5):383–8.

55. Morse MA, Eklind KI, Amin SG, Hecht SS, Chung FL. Effects of alkyl chain length on the inhibition of NNK-induced lung neoplasia in A/J mice by arylalkyl isothiocyanates. *Carcinogenesis* 1989;10(9):1757–9. DOI: 10.1093/carcin/10.9.1757.

56. Morse MA, Amin SG, Hecht SS, Chung FL. Effects of aromatic isothiocyanates on tumorigenicity, O^6-methylguanine formation, and metabolism of

the tobacco-specific nitrosamine 4-(methylnitrosamino)-1-(3-pyridyl)-1-butanone in A/J mouse lung. *Cancer Res* 1989;49(11):2894–7.

57. Hecht SS. Metabolic activation and detoxification of tobacco-specific nitrosamines — a model for cancer prevention strategies. *Drug Meta Rev* 1994;26(1–2):373–90. DOI: 10.3109/03602539409029803.

58. Smith TJ, Guo ZY, Thomas PE, *et al*. Metabolism of 4-(methylnitrosamino)-1-(3-pyridyl)-1-butanone in mouse lung microsomes and its inhibition by isothiocyanates. *Cancer Res* 1990;50(21):6817–22.

59. Wattenberg LW. Inhibitory effects of benzyl isothiocyanate administered shortly before diethylnitrosamine or benzo[a]pyrene on pulmonary and forestomach neoplasia in A/J mice. *Carcinogenesis* 1987;8(12):1971–3. DOI: 10.1093/carcin/8.12.1971.

60. Lin JM, Amin S, Trushin N, Hecht SS. Effects of isothiocyanates on tumorigenesis by benzo[a]pyrene in murine tumor models. *Cancer Lett* 1993;74(3):151–9. DOI: 10.1016/0304-3835(93)90237-4.

61. Hecht SS, Kenney PM, Wang M, Trushin N, Upadhyaya P. Effects of phenethyl isothiocyanate and benzyl isothiocyanate, individually and in combination, on lung tumorigenesis induced in A/J mice by benzo[a]pyrene and 4-(methylnitrosamino)-1-(3-pyridyl)-1-butanone. *Cancer Lett* 2000;150(1):49–56. DOI: 10.1016/s0304-3835(99)00373-0.

62. Conaway CC, Wang CX, Pittman B, *et al*. Phenethyl isothiocyanate and sulforaphane and their N-acetylcysteine conjugates inhibit malignant progression of lung adenomas induced by tobacco carcinogens in A/J mice. *Cancer Res* 2005;65(18):8548–57. DOI: 10.1158/0008-5472.can-05-0237.

63. Zhang Y, Kensler TW, Cho CG, Posner GH, Talalay P. Anticarcinogenic activities of sulforaphane and structurally related synthetic norbornyl isothiocyanates. *Proc Natl Acad Sci USA* 1994;91(8):3147–50. DOI: 10.1073/pnas.91.8.3147.

64. Clark LC, Alberts DS. Selenium and cancer: risk or protection? *J Natl Cancer Inst* 1995;87(7):473–5. DOI: 10.1093/jnci/87.7.473.

65. El-Bayoumy K, Upadhyaya P, Desai DH, Amin S, Hecht SS. Inhibition of 4-(methylnitrosamino)-1-(3-pyridyl)-1-butanone tumorigenicity in mouse lung by the synthetic organoselenium compound, 1,4-phenylenebis(methylene)selenocyanate. *Carcinogenesis* 1993;14(6):1111–3. DOI: 10.1093/carcin/14.6.1111.

66. Prokopczyk B, Cox JE, Upadhyaya P, *et al*. Effects of dietary 1,4-phenylenebis(methylene)selenocyanate on 4-(methylnitrosamino)-1-(3-pyridyl)-1-butanone-induced DNA adduct formation in lung and liver of

A/J mice and F344 rats. *Carcinogenesis* 1996;17(4):749–53. DOI: 10.1093/carcin/17.4.749.

67. Prokopczyk B, Amin S, Desai DH, Kurtzke C, Upadhyaya P, El-Bayoumy K. Effects of 1,4-phenylenebis(methylene)selenocyanate and selenomethionine on 4-(methylnitrosamino)-1-(3-pyridyl)-1-butanone-induced tumorigenesis in A/J mouse lung. *Carcinogenesis* 1997;18(9):1855–7. DOI: 10.1093/carcin/18.9.1855.

68. Yang CS, Ju J, Lu G, *et al.* Cancer prevention by tea and tea polyphenols. *Asia Pac J Clin Nutr* 2008;17 Suppl 1(Suppl 1):245–8.

69. Lu G, Liao J, Yang G, Reuhl KR, Hao X, Yang CS. Inhibition of adenoma progression in a 4-(methylnitrosamino)-1-(3-pryidyl)-1-butanone-induced lung tumorigenesis model in A/J mice by tea polyphenols and caffeine. *Cancer Res* 2006;66:11494–501.

70. Lu G, Xiao H, You H, *et al.* Synergistic inhibition of lung tumorigenesis by a combination of green tea polyphenols and atorvastatin. *Clin Cancer Res* 2008;14(15):4981–8. DOI: 10.1158/1078-0432.Ccr-07-1860.

71. Liao J, Yang GY, Park ES, *et al.* Inhibition of lung carcinogenesis and effects on angiogenesis and apoptosis in A/J mice by oral administration of green tea. *Nutr Cancer* 2004;48(1):44–53. DOI: 10.1207/s15327914nc4801_7.

72. Li GX, Chen YK, Hou Z, *et al.* Pro-oxidative activities and dose-response relationship of (-)-epigallocatechin-3-gallate in the inhibition of lung cancer cell growth: a comparative study in vivo and in vitro. *Carcinogenesis* 2010;31(5):902–10. DOI: 10.1093/carcin/bgq039.

73. Wang ZY, Hong JY, Huang MT, Reuhl KR, Conney AH, Yang CS. Inhibition of N-nitrosodiethylamine- and 4-(methylnitrosamino)-1-(3-pyridyl)-1-butanone-induced tumorigenesis in A/J mice by green tea and black tea. *Cancer Res* 1992;52(7):1943–7.

74. Morse MA, LaGreca SD, Amin SG, Chung FL. Effects of indole-3-carbinol on lung tumorigenesis and DNA methylation induced by 4-(methylnitrosamino)-1-(3-pyridyl)-1-butanone (NNK) and on the metabolism and disposition of NNK in A/J mice. *Cancer Res* 1990;50(9):2613–7.

75. Qian X, Melkamu T, Upadhyaya P, Kassie F. Indole-3-carbinol inhibited tobacco smoke carcinogen-induced lung adenocarcinoma in A/J mice when administered during the post-initiation or progression phase of lung tumorigenesis. *Cancer Lett* 2011;311(1):57–65. DOI: 10.1016/j.canlet.2011.06.023.

76. Dagne A, Melkamu T, Schutten MM, *et al.* Enhanced inhibition of lung adeno-carcinoma by combinatorial treatment with indole-3-carbinol and silibinin in A/J mice. *Carcinogenesis* 2011;32(4):561–7. DOI: 10.1093/carcin/bgr010.

77. Kassie F, Matise I, Negia M, Upadhyaya P, Hecht SS. Dose-dependent inhibition of tobacco smoke carcinogen-induced lung tumorigenesis in A/J mice by indole-3-carbinol. *Cancer Prev Res* 2008;1(7):568–76. DOI: 10.1158/1940-6207.Capr-08-0064.

78. Wattenberg LW, Estensen RD. Chemopreventive effects of myo-inositol and dexamethasone on benzo[a]pyrene and 4-(methylnitrosoamino)-1-(3-pyridyl)-1-butanone-induced pulmonary carcinogenesis in female A/J mice. *Cancer Res* 1996;56(22):5132-5.

79. Bauer AK, Dwyer-Nield LD, Malkinson AM. High cyclooxygenase 1 (COX-1) and cyclooxygenase 2 (COX-2) contents in mouse lung tumors. *Carcinogenesis* 2000;21(4):543–50. DOI: 10.1093/carcin/21.4.543.

80. Wardlaw SA, March TH, Belinsky SA. Cyclooxygenase-2 expression is abundant in alveolar type II cells in lung cancer-sensitive mouse strains and in premalignant lesions. *Carcinogenesis* 2000;21(7):1371–7.

81. Duperron C, Castonguay A. Chemopreventive efficacies of aspirin and sulindac against lung tumorigenesis in A/J mice. *Carcinogenesis* 1997;18(5):1001–6. DOI: 10.1093/carcin/18.5.1001.

82. Malkinson AM, Koski KM, Dwyer-Nield LD, *et al.* Inhibition of 4-(methylnitrosamino)-1-(3-pyridyl)-1-butanone-induced mouse lung tumor formation by FGN-1 (sulindac sulfone). *Carcinogenesis* 1998;19(8):1353–6. DOI: 10.1093/carcin/19.8.1353.

83. Kisley LR, Barrett BS, Dwyer-Nield LD, Bauer AK, Thompson DC, Malkinson AM. Celecoxib reduces pulmonary inflammation but not lung tumorigenesis in mice. *Carcinogenesis* 2002;23(10):1653–60. DOI: 10.1093/carcin/23.10.1653.

84. Memmott RM, Mercado JR, Maier CR, Kawabata S, Fox SD, Dennis PA. Metformin prevents tobacco carcinogen–induced lung tumorigenesis. *Cancer Prev Res* 2010;3(9):1066–76. DOI: 10.1158/1940-6207.Capr-10-0055.

85. Njatcha C, Farooqui M, Almotlak AA, Siegfried JM. Prevention of tobacco carcinogen-induced lung tumor development by a novel STAT3 decoy inhibitor. *Cancer Prev Res* 2020;13(9):735–46. DOI: 10.1158/1940-6207.Capr-20-0033.

86. Weinstein IB, Jeffrey AM, Jennette KW, *et al.* Benzo(a)pyrene diol epoxides as intermediates in nucleic acid binding in vitro and in vivo. *Science* 1976;193(4253):592–5. DOI: 10.1126/science.959820.

87. Autrup H, Harris CC, Trump BF, Jeffrey AM. Metabolism of benzo(a)pyr-ene and identification of the major benzo(a)pyrene-DNA adducts in cultured human colon. *Cancer Res* 1978;38(11 Pt 1):3689–96.

88. Kasala ER, Bodduluru LN, Barua CC, Sriram CS, Gogoi R. Benzo(a) pyrene induced lung cancer: Role of dietary phytochemicals in chemoprevention. *Pharmacol Rep* 2015;67(5):996–1009. DOI: 10.1016/j.pharep. 2015.03.004.

89. Adam-Rodwell G, Morse MA, Stoner GD. The effects of phenethyl isothiocyanate on benzo[a]pyrene-induced tumors and DNA adducts in A/J mouse lung. *Cancer Lett* 1993;71(1–3):35–42. DOI: 10.1016/ 0304-3835(93)90094-p.

90. Boysen G, Kenney PM, Upadhyaya P, Wang M, Hecht SS. Effects of benzyl isothiocyanate and 2-phenethyl isothiocyanate on benzo[a]pyrene and 4-(methylnitrosamino)-1-(3-pyridyl)-1-butanone metabolism in F-344 rats. *Carcinogenesis* 2003;24(3):517–25. DOI: 10.1093/carcin/24.3.517.

91. Yan Y, Wang Y, Tan Q, *et al.* Efficacy of polyphenon E, red ginseng, and rapamycin on benzo(a)pyrene-induced lung tumorigenesis in A/J mice. *Neoplasia* 2006;8(1):52–8. DOI: 10.1593/neo.05652.

92. Yun TK, Yun YS, Han IW. Anticarcinogenic effect of long-term oral administration of red ginseng on newborn mice exposed to various chemical carcinogens. *Cancer Detection Prev* 1983;6(6):515–25.

93. Anderson MW, Goodin C, Zhang Y, *et al.* Effect of dietary green tea extract and aerosolized difluoromethylornithine during lung tumor progression in A/J strain mice. *Carcinogenesis* 2008;29(8):1594–600. DOI: 10.1093/ carcin/bgn129.

94. Manna S, Mukherjee S, Roy A, Das S, Panda CK. Tea polyphenols can restrict benzo[a]pyrene-induced lung carcinogenesis by altered expression of p53-associated genes and H-ras, c-myc and cyclin D1. *The J Nutr Biochem* 2009;20(5):337–49. DOI: 10.1016/j.jnutbio.2008.04.001.

95. Zhang Z, Wang Y, Yao R, *et al.* Cancer chemopreventive activity of a mixture of Chinese herbs (antitumor B) in mouse lung tumor models. *Oncogene* 2004;23(21):3841–50. DOI: 10.1038/sj.onc.1207496.

96. Johnson TE, Hermanson D, Wang L, *et al.* Lung tumorigenesis suppressing effects of a commercial kava extract and its selected compounds in A/J mice. *The Am J Chin Med* 2011;39(4):727–42. DOI: 10.1142/ s0192415x11009202.

97. Carlton PS, Kresty LA, Stoner GD. Failure of dietary lyophilized strawberries to inhibit 4-(methylnitrosamino)-1-(3-pyridyl)-1-butanone-and benzo[a]pyrene-induced lung tumorigenesis in strain A/J mice. *Cancer Lett* 2000;159(2):113–7. DOI: 10.1016/s0304-3835(00)00464-x.

98. Carlton PS, Kresty LA, Siglin JC, Morgan C, Lu J, Stoner GD. Inhibition of *N*-nitrosomethylbenzylamine-induced tumorigenesis in the rat esophagus by dietary freeze-dried strawberries. *Carcinogenesis* 2001;22:441–6.

99. Pan P, Peiffer DS, Huang Y-W, Oshima K, Stoner GD, Wang LS. Inhibition of the development of N-nitrosomethylbenzylamine-induced esophageal tumors in rats by strawberries and aspirin, alone and in combination. *J Berry Res* 2018;8(2)137–46. DOI: 10.3233/JBR-170291.

100. Borges G, Roowi S, Rouanet JM, Duthie GG, Lean ME, Crozier A. The bioavailability of raspberry anthocyanins and ellagitannins in rats. *Mol Nutr Food Res* 2007;51(6):714–25. DOI: 10.1002/mnfr.200700024.

101. Wattenberg LW, Wiedmann TS, Estensen RD, Zimmerman CL, Steele VE, Kelloff GJ. Chemoprevention of pulmonary carcinogenesis by aerosolized budesonide in female A/J mice. *Cancer Res* 1997;57(24):5489–92.

102. Wattenberg LW, Wiedmann TS, Estensen RD, *et al*. Chemoprevention of pulmonary carcinogenesis by brief exposures to aerosolized budesonide or beclomethasone dipropionate and by the combination of aerosolized budesonide and dietary myo-inositol. *Carcinogenesis* 2000;21(2):179–82. DOI: 10.1093/carcin/21.2.179.

103. Yao R, Wang Y, Lemon WJ, Lubet RA, You M. Budesonide exerts its chemopreventive efficacy during mouse lung tumorigenesis by modulating gene expressions. *Oncogene* 2004;23(46):7746–52. DOI: 10.1038/sj.onc.1207985.

104. Galbraith AR, Seabloom DE, Wuertz BR, *et al*. Chemoprevention of lung carcinogenesis by dietary nicotinamide and inhaled budesonide. *Cancer Prev Res* 2019;12(2):69–78. DOI: 10.1158/1940-6207.Capr-17-0402.

105. Chung FL, Kelloff G, Steele V, *et al*. Chemopreventive efficacy of arylalkyl isothiocyanates and N-acetylcysteine for lung tumorigenesis in Fischer rats. *Cancer Res* 1996;56(4):772–8.

106. Chung FL, Wang M, Rivenson A, Iatropoulos MJ, Reinhardt JC, Pittman B, Ho CT, Amin SG. Inhibition of lung carcinogenesis by black tea in Fischer rats treated with a tobacco-specific carcinogen: Caffeine as an important constituent. *Cancer Res* 1998;58(18)4096–101.

107. Sikdar S, Mukherjee A, Khuda-Bukhsh AR. Ethanolic extract of marsdenia condurango ameliorates benzo[a]pyrene-induced lung cancer of rats: Condurango ameliorates bap-induced lung cancer in rats. *J Pharmacopuncture* 2014;17(2):7–17. DOI: 10.3831/kpi.2014.17.011.

108. Soria JC, Kim ES, Fayette J, Lantuejoul S, Deutsch E, Hong WK. Chemoprevention of lung cancer. *The Lancet Oncol* 2003;4(11):659–69. DOI: 10.1016/s1470-2045(03)01244-0.

109. Gray J, Mao JT, Szabo E, Kelley M, Kurie J, Bepler G. Lung cancer chemoprevention: ACCP evidence-based clinical practice guidelines (2nd Edition). *Chest* 2007;132(3 Suppl):56s–68s. DOI: 10.1378/chest.07-1348.

110. Yuan JM, Stepanov I, Murphy SE, *et al.* Clinical trial of 2-phenethyl isothiocyanate as an inhibitor of metabolic activation of a tobacco-specific lung carcinogen in cigarette smokers. *Cancer Prev Res* 2016;9(5):396–405. DOI: 10.1158/1940-6207.Capr-15-0380.

111. Lam S, McWilliams A, LeRiche J, MacAulay C, Wattenberg L, Szabo E. A phase I study of myo-inositol for lung cancer chemoprevention. *Cancer Epidemiol, Biomarkers Prev* 2006;15(8):1526–31. DOI: 10.1158/1055-9965.Epi-06-0128.

112. Lam S, Mandrekar SJ, Gesthalter Y, *et al.* A Randomized Phase IIb Trial of myo-Inositol in Smokers with Bronchial Dysplasia. *Cancer Prev Res* 2016;9(12):906–914. DOI: 10.1158/1940-6207.Capr-15-0254.

113. Lambert JD. Does tea prevent cancer? Evidence from laboratory and human intervention studies. *The Am J Clin Nutr* 2013;98(6 Suppl):1667s–75s. DOI: 10.3945/ajcn.113.059352.

114. Limburg PJ, Mandrekar SJ, Aubry MC, *et al.* Randomized phase II trial of sulindac for lung cancer chemoprevention. *Lung Cancer* 2013;79(3):254–61. DOI: 10.1016/j.lungcan.2012.11.011.

115. Lam S, leRiche JC, McWilliams A, *et al.* A randomized phase IIb trial of pulmicort turbuhaler (budesonide) in people with dysplasia of the bronchial epithelium. *Clin Cancer Res: J Am Assoc Cancer Res* 2004;10(19):6502–11. DOI: 10.1158/1078-0432.Ccr-04-0686.

116. Veronesi G, Szabo E, Decensi A, *et al.* Randomized phase II trial of inhaled budesonide versus placebo in high-risk individuals with CT screen-detected lung nodules. *Cancer Prev Res* 2011;4(1):34–42. DOI: 10.1158/1940-6207. Capr-10-0182.

117. Veronesi G, Lazzeroni M, Szabo E, *et al.* Long-term effects of inhaled budesonide on screening-detected lung nodules. *Ann Oncology: J Eur Soc Med Oncol* 2015;26(5):1025–30. DOI: 10.1093/annonc/mdv064.

118. Mao JT, Roth MD, Fishbein MC, *et al.* Lung cancer chemoprevention with celecoxib in former smokers. *Cancer Prev Res* 2011;4(7):984–93. DOI: 10.1158/1940-6207.Capr-11-0078.

119. Greenberg AK, Tsay JC, Tchou-Wong KM, Jorgensen A, Rom WN. Chemoprevention of lung cancer: prospects and disappointments in human clinical trials. *Cancers* 2013;5(1):131–48. DOI: 10.3390/cancers5010131.

https://doi.org/10.1142/9789811239533_0011

Chapter 11

Epidemiology of Smoking and Cancer, Recent Trends, and Benefits of Quitting

Terry Frank Pechacek*

Key Points

- Smoking and use of tobacco products cause cancer:[1–4]
  - There is no safe tobacco product, but combustible products (cigarettes, cigars, pipes, bidi and kreteks) are most lethal.[4]
  - Among the combustible tobacco products, cigarettes are the most widely used worldwide.[3]
- Preventing cancers caused by tobacco use:
  - Never start using tobacco products.[4,5]
  - For tobacco users, quit completely as early in life as possible.[6,7]
  - Using daily and more frequently increases risk.[8,9]
  - Reducing amount used later in life may not reduce risk.[9]

---

1. Epidemiology of Smoking and Cancer

Chapter 2 provided the background on the epidemiology of smoking and cancer. While the risk of lung cancer from inhaling tobacco smoke is most

---

*Health Policy and Behavioral Sciences, School of Public Health, Georgia State University, Atlanta, Georgia, USA. tpechacek@gsu.edu

widely known, smoking can cause cancer almost anywhere in your body: bladder, blood (acute myeloid leukemia), cervix, colon and rectum (colorectal), esophagus, kidney and ureter, larynx, liver, oropharynx (includes parts of the throat, tongue, soft palate, and the tonsils), pancreas, stomach, and trachea, bronchus, and lung.[4] Smoking also increases the risk of dying from cancer and other diseases in cancer patients and survivors who have cancers not known to be smoking-related.[4] Smoking cessation reduces the risk of premature death and can add as much as a decade to life expectancy.[10] Smoking cessation reduces the risk of many diseases, including the 12 cancer sites most linked to smoking (see Figure 1).[10] If nobody smoked, one of every three cancer deaths in the United States would not happen.[4]

In the understanding of individual- or population-level risk and prevalence for smoking-related diseases, particularly multiple cancers, cardiovascular disease, and chronic obstructive pulmonary diseases (see

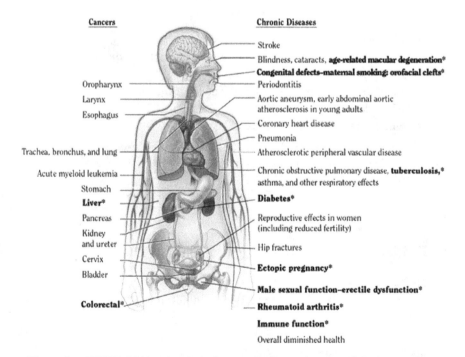

Figure 1:   USSGR 2014 estimation of anatomic sites and cancers linked to smoking.
Source: Adapted from US Department of Health and Human Services (2014).

Figure 1), it is important to understand several key domains of data on patterns of tobacco use:

- *Who* are the current and past users,
- *What* products have been and are currently used,
- *How Much* of the product has been and is currently used,
- *How Long* were the products used, and
- *Other Risk Factors* such as use of alcohol, BMI, and other lifestyle factors.

The full discussion of these domains, for each of the multiple combustible and non-combustible tobacco products, and for individual countries or WHO regions is available in other publications and comprehensive review documents.[1–7,10–15] This chapter will consider some key and common aspects of these domains as they relate to the ongoing burden of cancer caused by smoking. Some global examples will be provided, but this overview will primarily use evidence from the US.[4–6,16–19]

2. Smoking Causes Cancer

Tobacco use is the leading preventable cause of cancer worldwide. An estimated 1.3 billion people use tobacco products worldwide. The majority (about 1.2 billion) use smoked tobacco products, chiefly as manufactured or hand rolled cigarettes. Other smoked products include pipes, cigars, bidi, hookah, and/or kreteks (see The Cancer Atlas https://canceratlas.cancer.org/).[20]

Several key reviews provide the details on the links between use of tobacco products, and particularly cigarettes, and specific cancers.[2–4,13,20–24] A detailed review or summary of these extensive data is beyond the scope of this chapter. Other chapters in this book, however, provide more details on the specific aspects of the cancer risks from using tobacco products (see Chapters 2, 5, and 9).

There are no safe tobacco products; however, combustible tobacco products, particularly cigarettes, are the most lethal.[3,4,13,24] Other combustible products such as cigars, pipes, and hookah also have been shown to increase cancer risks.[3,4,22,24,25] However, this chapter will review the evidence primarily on cigarettes.

The global burden of cancers caused by tobacco use has been documented.[1,3,13–15,26] Lung cancer continues to be the leading cause of cancer deaths worldwide.[1,13,15] Lung cancer death rates vary about 20-fold across regions and countries (see data on individual countries in The Cancer Atlas https://canceratlas.cancer.org/the-burden/lung-cancer/).[20]

Assessing the disease burden attributable to tobacco use requires both the surveillance of cancer incidence and mortality,[1,12–14] along with national and international surveillance surveys of current or past use of tobacco products.[12,13,21,27] These surveys optimally are maintained consistently over time, assess patterns of current and past use of tobacco products, and typically report their data by multiple demographic subgroups (such as by age categories, male/female, and income and education levels). Following the epidemiological linkage between tobacco use and cancer (see Chapter 2), annual surveillance surveys were established in many developed countries.[2,3,21,27–29] For example, the National Health Interview Survey (NHIS) has been conducted annually in the United States since 1965 (see detailed history of this survey in the 2014 *The Health Consequences of Smoking — 50 Years of Progress*).[4,28]

Since 1965, the NHIS has provided annual estimates of the percentage of adults aged 18 years or older who reported ever, currently, or formerly using tobacco products in a household nationally representative survey of the non-institutionalized US civilian population.[4,17] Since 1993, the prevalence of cigarette smoking has been estimated for use "every day" or "some days." The range of tobacco products assessed has varied over time, as products commercially available have changed. In 2019, the NHIS reported current tobacco use by eight categories of tobacco product use: (1) Any tobacco product, (2) Any combustible product, (3) Cigarettes, (4) Cigars/Cigarillos/Filtered Little Cigars, (5) Regular Pipe/Water pipe/Hookah, (6) E-cigarettes, (7) Smokeless tobacco, and (8) Two or more tobacco products.[17]

The "who" defined by the NHIS are the ever, current, and former tobacco users. The NHIS reports data for multiple demographic subgroups, which have varied somewhat over the decades. In the Morbidity and Mortality Weekly Report (MMWR) in 2020, the NHIS reported tobacco use data for the eleven categories of socio-demographic and policy-related characteristics shown in the box.[17] With tobacco use reported by the eight categories listed above (that is, the "what"), the MMWR reported data in a complex table of 39 rows and eight columns which provided data on how tobacco use varies across the adult population in the United States.

2019 NHIS Selected Socio-Demographic Characteristics

- Overall
- Sex (Male and Female)
- Age Groups (18–24, 25–44, 45–64, 65 and older)
- Race/Ethnicity (White, non-Hispanic; Black, non-Hispanic; Asian, non-Hispanic; American Indian/Alaska Native, non-Hispanic; Hispanic; and Other, non-Hispanic)
- U.S. Census region (Northeast, Midwest, South, West)
- Education (adults aged 25 years or older) (0–12 years, no diploma; General Educational Development; High School diploma; Some college, no diploma; Associate degree [academic or technical/vocational]; Undergraduate degree [bachelor's]; Graduate degree [master's, professional, or doctoral])
- Marital status (Married/living with partner; Divorced/Separated/Widowed; Single/Never Married/Not living with partner)
- Annual household income ($) (less than 35,000, 35,000–74,999, 75,000–99,999, 100,000 or more)
- Sexual orientation (Heterosexual/Straight; Lesbian, Gay, or Bisexual)
- Health Insurance coverage (Private insurance; Medicaid, Medicare only (aged 65 and older); Other public insurance; Uninsured
- Disability (Yes, No)

These detailed data by socio-demographic and policy-related characteristics are reported to enable patterns of disparities in tobacco product use to be observed annually and over time.[11,30–32] For example, in 2019 the annual estimates for current use of tobacco products among adults in the US indicated that there were large and policy relevant disparities across sub-categories within several socio-demographic characteristics. Table 1 provides data from the 2019 NHIS report *Tobacco Product Use Among Adults — United States, 2019.*[17] These patterns of disparities in tobacco product use can provide important insights into national tobacco-related diseases, including cancer rates.[33,34] It has been noted that greater

Table 1:   Percentage of adults aged 18 years and older who reported tobacco product use "every day" or "some days", by tobacco product and for selected characteristics — NHIS, United States, 2019.

Characteristic	Any tobacco product	Any combustible product	Cigarettes	E-cigarettes
Overall	20.8	16.7	14.0	4.5
Sex				
Male	26.7	20.1	15.3	5.5
Female	15.7	13.6	12.7	3.5
Race/Ethnicity				
White, non-Hispanic	23.3	18.3	15.5	5.1
Black, non-Hispanic	20.7	18.6	14.9	3.4
Asian, non-Hispanic	11.0	8.6	7.2	2.7
American Indian/ Alaska Native, non-Hispanic	29.3	22.3	20.9	—
Hispanic	13.2	11.2	8.8	2.8
Other, non-Hispanic	28.1	22.0	19.7	9.3
Annual household income ($)				
Less than 35,000	27.0	23.2	21.4	5.0
35,000–74,999	22.0	18.1	15.7	4.5
75,000–99,999	18.8	14.3	11.4	4.6
100,000 or more	15.1	10.8	7.1	3.8
Sexual orientation				
Heterosexual/straight	20.5	16.5	13.8	4.2
Lesbian, Gay, or Bisexual	29.9	22.7	19.2	11.5

Source: Selected data from full table (MMWR 2020).[17]

emphasis on these types of disparities in smoking is needed to achieve more progress in cancer prevention in the US (see Chapter 9).[11,15,30–33,35]

The current and past patterns of tobacco use, and particularly cigarette smoking, among ethnic/racial populations (as shown in Table 1) must be considered when analyzing population patterns of smoking-related cancer, such as lung cancer. Public health researchers have documented and continued to study the higher rates of lung cancer among African–American males compared to non-Hispanic white males, as noted in Chapter 9.[4,30,35–38] Historical patterns of cigarette smoking can explain some of this difference, but there remain important issues under study, including systemic racism in access and quality of medical treatment.[31,32,35,39]

Disparity in current cigarette smoking by annual household income is another very important characteristic to consider.[11,31] The current pattern seen in the US of increased smoking being more concentrated among the less educated, lower-income segments of our society is being observed in many parts of the world.[21] Historically, in the early stages of the smoking epidemic, smoking rates were high among the affluent and smoking was viewed as a high-status behavior.[4,40,41] However, in recent decades, smoking and tobacco use patterns have become more concentrated in less-educated, lower-income populations (Table 1). Not shown in data selected for Table 1, in the 2019 NHIS, the highest prevalence of smoking was seen among adults in the US with a General Educational Development (GED) education. These GED individuals who typically are high school dropouts reported a current smoking prevalence of 35.3% as compared to adults with a graduate degree, who reported 4.0%. As has been noted in other reports, education and household income are showing some of the largest disparities in smoking and tobacco use.[4,31,32] Both in the US and globally, disparities in tobacco use by education and annual income are increasingly being reflected in changing patterns of smoking-related cancer rates.[1,21]

Another disparity in current smoking rates which has been getting more attention in recent decades is by sexual orientation.[42–44] In many parts of the world, social/cultural biases prevent the collection of data on sexual orientation. However, as more attention is focused on this disparity, varying patterns of tobacco product use by sexual orientation are being observed where such data are allowed to be collected. For example, in the 2019 NHIS survey in the US, one of the largest disparities observed for current use of e-cigarettes is between Heterosexual/straight (4.2%) and Lesbian/Gay/Bisexual (11.5%) adults.

Other characteristics measured in the 2019 NHIS survey also are relevant to identify vulnerable populations for smoking-related disease and death. For example, rates of current smoking among adults aged 18–64 who are covered by Medicaid (24.9%) and the uninsured (22.5%) are higher than among adults covered by private insurance (10.7%). As with disparities by education and annual income, higher smoking rates among these vulnerable populations are important in our analysis of population patterns in cancer rates.[4,11,31] Finally, other data suggest that the rates of smoking among the homeless[45,46] and those experiencing mental illness[47] are important disparities in the United States.[31]

3. Understanding Male/Female Differences in Lung Cancer

In the US and globally, cancer rates related to current and past use of tobacco products have varied greatly between males and females.[1,4,13,21] However, to fully understand the history of these patterns of cancer risk and prevalence of cancers, the changing patterns of smoking prevalence between males and females requires the careful analysis of several key factors, including the significant differences in social/cultural norms, and history of tobacco industry advertising campaigns (as covered in Chapter 1).[4,21,40,48]

In the US, the prevalence of current daily smoking has been steadily decreasing among both males and females in recent decades, with the prevalence of smoking among men remaining somewhat higher than among women (like the 2019 difference shown in Table 1). However, in earlier decades, the prevalence among males in the US was much higher than for women. In the initial 1965 NHIS survey, 51.9% of men were current smokers compared with 33.9% of women.[4] Rates among men declined sharply from 1965 to 1985 (from 51.9% to 32.6%) but declined less for women (from 33.9% to 27.9%). Since then, rates of cigarette smoking have been declining at a similar rate for men and women in the US.[18,49] Thus, the analyses of the population patterns of lung cancer among males and females in the US has needed to consider these historical patterns of smoking.[4] Consistent with these patterns of smoking, the

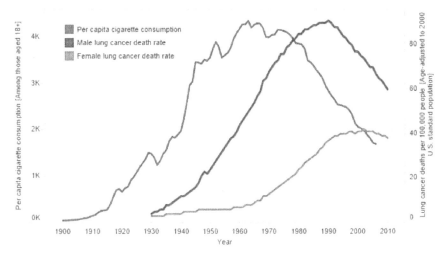

Figure 2:   Lung cancer death rates, by sex in USA: Compared with per capita cigarette smoking consumption overall 1900–2010. Trends in per capita cigarette consumption and age-standardized lung cancer death rates in the US.

Source: Adapted from American Cancer Society (2013).[7]

epidemic of lung cancer began earlier in men in the US, with the rapid increase in lung cancer starting later among women, as shown in Figure 2. As this comparison with the pattern of per capita cigarette consumption shows, lung cancer rates lag behind the population-wide adoption of regular smoking.[4,6,7] These types of links between per capita cigarette consumption and trends in smoking-related diseases, particularly lung cancer, have been observed in many other countries.[2,27,29]

Similar to the US, throughout the world, men also smoke more than women (see Figure 3). Research indicates that these differences between men and women are due to many social and cultural factors, as well as tobacco industry advertising and promotional campaigns. As shown on the left side of the graph, this is particularly true for Asian and African countries (for example, in Tunisia, China, and Indonesia very few women smoke while a very high percentage of men smoke). While the percentage of men who smoke in many countries is substantially higher than the percentage of women who smoke, in some developed countries the difference between men and women is much smaller. For example, the prevalence of

Figure 3:   Smoking in men vs. women, 2016.

Source: https://ourworldindata.org/who-smokes-more-men-or-women.

smoking is almost equal between men and women in Australia and Sweden.

As in the US, the prevalence of smoking has been declining among both men and women in most countries. However, the rate of decline is not always similar between men and women. An example of how patterns of daily smoking prevalence among males and females have changed around the world from 1990 to 2015 is shown in Figure 4. Note that in most developed countries, the prevalence has declined significantly among both males and females. However, in some Asian countries, like South Korea, female smoking prevalence has *increased* while male smoking prevalence rates have sharply decreased. Even more disturbing for future cancer rates, in other developing countries, the prevalence of current smoking has been increasing among both males and females (e.g., in Montenegro, Macedonia, Chile, and Cyprus).

Consistent with these patterns of smoking by men and women, smoking-related cancers globally differ significantly, with the rates

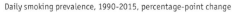

What a drag

Daily smoking prevalence, 1990-2015, percentage-point change

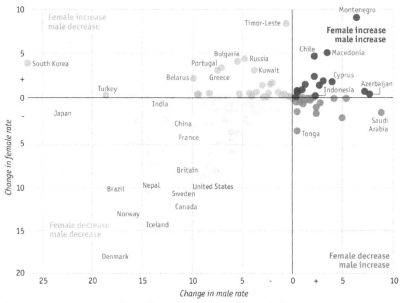

Source: "Smoking prevalence and attributable disease burden in 195 countries and territories, 1990–2015: a systematic analysis from the Global Burden of Disease Study 2015", the *Lancet*, 2017

Figure 4:   Daily smoking prevalence, male and female 1990–2015 (percentage-point change).

Source: © The Economist Group Limited, London (2017), used with permission. https://www.economist.com/graphic-detail/2017/04/06/a-global-decline-in-smoking-masks-regional-variations-between-the-sexes.

among men being much higher than among women.[1,13,14,26,50] Thus, while Figures 3 and 4 give two snapshots of these global patterns of difference in smoking between men and women, more detailed analyses of longer-term trends show that the prevalence of smoking over time is a very reliable indicator of national trends in smoking-related cancers, particularly lung cancer.[1,13,26,27] As in the US, as per capita cigarette consumption increased in other countries around the world, lung cancer rates increased.[2,7,27,29] But also like the pattern shown in Figure 2 for the US, as the per capita cigarette consumption overall started to decline in countries around the world due to declines in the prevalence of current smoking among both men and women, lung cancer death rates also have been declining.[1–4,13,27]

Lung cancer incidence rates continue to remain much higher for men compared to women globally (see Figure 5).[1,13,26,50] Global monitoring of cancer incidence and deaths typically show that lung cancer trends in

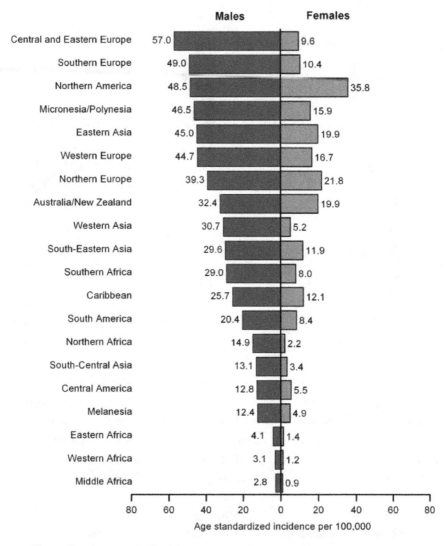

Figure 5: Age-standardized lung cancer incidence rates by sex and world area.

Source: GLOBOCAN 2008. Reproduced from Ref. 26 by permission of Wiley Periodicals, Inc.

women tend to lag a decade or more behind men, primarily since women began smoking at higher rates later than among men. The wide variability of lung cancer incidence rates globally shown in Figure 5 reflects the great variability in how tobacco use has been adopted in various parts of the world.[12,16,27]

4. WHAT Tobacco Product Used Is Important

In the history of the smoking epidemic, which resulted in the 20th century being labeled the Cigarette Century, the highly addictive cigarette overtook all other forms of tobacco use in almost all parts of the world, including the US.[40,41] Thus, major attention in cancer prevention and control was focused on the cigarette. However, the "cigarette" has not remained the same over these decades.[4,40,41] The "cigarette" used around the world varies greatly, from hand-rolled shredded tobacco leaf, to highly engineered drug delivery devices in the developed world.[3,4,21] These significant differences in the type of cigarette smoked have important implications for cancer risks.[4,24] For example, as the tobacco industry responded to health concerns among smokers following the 1964 Surgeon General Report[51] by adding filters, then manufacturing and promoting the "low tar" cigarettes,[52] the types of lung cancer caused by cigarette smoking changed.[4,24]

In the last decades of the 20th century, tobacco product use primarily was combustible products (that is, cigarettes, cigars, and pipes).[4,25,40,41,53] However, in the 21st century, the patterns of tobacco product use have shifted, with the expansion of new and alternative forms of nicotine delivery.[19,53] While historically, smokers sometimes did use other forms of tobacco in conjunction with their smoking of cigarettes, in recent years, particularly among young adults, patterns of poly-tobacco product use have become very common.[4,5,19,53] More recently in the US, the cigarette-like small cigars became popular after the 2009 federal tax created a lower price for these cigarette-like products (also called cigarillos) in comparison to the traditional cigarette.[54–57] Due to the increased use of these products since 2009, the US estimates of current smoking now emphasize the prevalence of any combustible product (in 2019, the prevalence was 16.7% compared with cigarettes at 14%). Additionally, in recent years, the poly-tobacco patterns have included more of the non-combustible products.[53,58] In the 2019 NHIS, the prevalence of using any tobacco product was 20.8%. Thus, while the prevalence of cigarette smoking has been continuing to decline in the US, overall rates of use of any tobacco product have been declining less, particularly among young adults.[53] The full implications of these emerging patterns on cancer risk are just now being studied.[59–62]

Among youth and young adults, the prevalence of current smoking has been declining sharply in the US and other developed countries.[5,19,21,53] The role of the new vaping and electronic products in these trends is being closely monitored.[19,53,62–64] Major national surveys have shown that the prevalence of current cigarette smoking among youth is reaching historically low levels, as the rates of vaping (or e-cigarette) use has dramatically increased. For example, in the 2020 NYTS survey of middle school students in the US, only 1.6% of middle school students reported current use (past 30-day prevalence) of cigarettes versus 4.7% for e-cigarettes.[19] For high school students, where cigarette smoking rates typically are much higher, only 5.0% reported current use (past 30-day prevalence) for cigarettes, but 19.6% for e-cigarettes. The 5.0% prevalence of current smoking among US high school students is a dramatic drop from the 36.4% prevalence in 1997.[5]

Other surveys of youth in the US are showing similar downward trends in current (past 30-day prevalence) and daily use of cigarettes, but higher prevalence of vaping or use of e-cigarettes.[53] The annual Monitoring the Future survey[65] conducted since the late 1970s among students in the 8th, 10th, and 12th grades has observed that current cigarette smoking (defined as any smoking in the past 30 days) has declined since the 1990s, from 21.0% in 1996 to 2.2% in 2020 among 8th graders, and from 36.5% in 1997 to 7.5% in 2020 among 12th graders.[66] Daily cigarette smoking rates are now at historical lows: 0.8% among 8th graders, 1.2% among 10th graders, 3.1% among 12th graders. While cigarette smoking rates have been declining, rates of vaping (any in the past 30 days) have been increasing: for example, from 16.3% in 2015 to 28.2% in 2020 among 12th graders.

While the specific cancer risks of long-term use of these newer, noncombustible products are still being studied,[53,60,67,68] there is the expectation that these sharp declines in youth cigarette smoking will have significant impact on future cancer rates.[53,59,61,69–71]

Around the world, the impact of new and emerging nicotine delivery products is being carefully monitored.[63,72–75] While some forms of non-combustible tobacco products (such as snus and other forms of smokeless tobacco) have been common in many parts of the world,[12,76] the markets for these newer forms such as e-cigarettes and heated tobacco systems are expanding.[17,62,65,77–80] Thus, the impact of *what* product is being used on international cancer rates continues to be important. Traditionally, global comparisons of the prevalence of daily cigarette smoking (see Figure 3) provided a simple but good metric for assessing current and future cancer patterns.[13,29]

5. Amount Smoked Is Important

How much you smoke dramatically affects your risk of developing a smoking-related cancer.[1,13,26] Lung cancer is the most widely known and studied of these smoking-related cancers. Figure 6 shows the significantly increasing relative risk of developing lung cancer among smokers compared with life-long never smokers, by amount smoked. This graph is

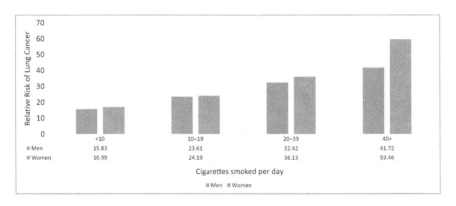

Figure 6: Relative risk of lung cancer by amount smoked, current smokers versus never smokers. Adapted from *New Engl J Med*, M.J. Thun *et al.*, 50 year trends in smoking mortality in the U.S., 368,351–364. Copyright © 2013 Massachusetts Medical Society. Reprinted with permission from Massachusetts Medical Society.

Notes: The *relative risk*, compares the *risk* of lung cancer among current smokers with the *risk* among life-long never smokers. This is computed by dividing the rate per 100,000 of dying from lung cancer during the study follow-up among the cohort of smokers with the rate among life-long never smokers in the cohort.

based upon large cohorts of adults in the US (two historical cohorts and five pooled contemporary cohort studies).[4,23] The relative risk (i.e., comparison of rates of having lung cancer among smokers versus life-long never smokers) are shown for men (aged 55–74) and women (aged 60–74).

The US NHIS has tracked the amount used of each tobacco product in the annual survey.[16] For cigarettes, the reported amounts smoked have declined over time.[4] Fewer smokers have reported higher levels of daily consumption, while the proportion of current smokers reporting levels under 20 cigarettes/day (such as 1–9, 10–19 cigarettes/day) has been growing, as has the proportion of current smokers who report smoking on "some days".[4] In addition to the declines in the prevalence of smoking in the US discussed above, this pattern of decline in amount smoked daily per smoker has also contributed to the decline in per capita annual cigarette consumption and in rates of smoking-related cancers.[4] Similar patterns of decline are being observed in other developed countries.[2,3,21]

In Section 6, the duration of smoking will be discussed, since this has a very large impact on cancer risk. Both self-reported amount smoked and duration of smoking (years since starting to smoke regularly) have been combined to give an estimated profile of lung cancer risk that has been used in screening smokers (such as in the National Lung Cancer Screening Trial).[81] This estimate, called pack-years, can be used to show the high risk of continuing to smoke large numbers of cigarettes for many years. (*For example, typically smoking a pack-a-day for 20 years = 20 pack-years, as does typically smoking two packs-a-day for 10 years = 20 pack-years.*) However, epidemiologists caution about the use of this measure beyond simple clinical screening for risk.[82]

6. Number of Years Smoked Is Even More important

As noted above, amount smoked dramatically impacts cancer risk. In the past, when the rates of smoking cessation were much lower, this metric (amount smoked) and the related "pack-years" were used more clinically to advise individuals about the risk of smoking. However, as more adults were quitting, and longer-term epidemiological studies were completed, there has been a greater emphasis on *duration* of smoking.[6] Basically, the cancer risks due to smoking increase sharply in the decades after middle-age, and duration of smoking becomes much more predictive of lung cancer risk than amount smoked.[4,6] Quitting earlier in life lowers the risks and increases the benefits of quitting. The NHIS survey has tracked quit rates, and the increasing proportion of ever smokers who have become former smokers.[4,10,18] Public health experts now put much more emphasis on this relationship: namely, focusing on the fact that younger smokers can avoid over 90% of the long-term risks, like lung cancer and overall premature death, by quitting by the age of 35.[4,6,10] Note the graphic in the upper left side of Figure 7. The curves showing observed rate of death up to age 80 among *never smokers* and smokers who quit before age 35 are virtually overlapping.

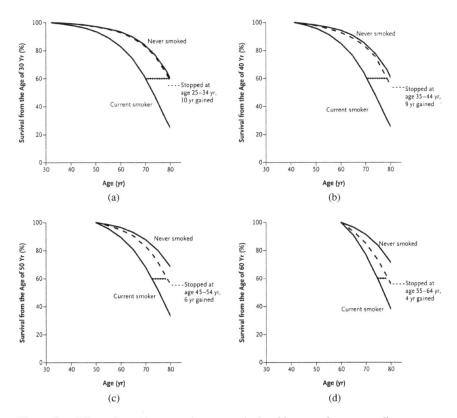

Figure 7: Effect of smoking cessation on survival to 80 years of age, according to age at the time of quitting. Reproduced from Ref. 6. Copyright © 2013 Massachusetts Medical Society. Reprinted with permission from Massachusetts Medical Society.

The pattern of benefits from quitting shown in Figure 7 encourages smokers to quit as early in life as possible. The benefits of quitting are well documented.[10] Thus, the public health message is clear: *quit smoking completely as early in life as possible.* Recent patterns of product use have made this message even more important. Other chapters (see Chapters 12, 13, and 15) in this book discuss smoking cessation and strategies to increase the success in trying to quit.

As noted above, the section on *what* products are used highlighted the increasing pattern of using vaping or e-cigarette products.[19,53] There is a significant policy debate about the benefits of switching to such products. However, one of the most significant findings of current surveillance of tobacco products is that a large proportion (up 70% or more) of those smokers who are using these new products are continuing to smoke cigarettes.[59,62,83–87] This raises two significant questions:

- Are these smokers reducing the number of cigarettes they smoke per day?
- Even if they are reducing the number of cigarettes smoked, are they delaying quitting completely (i.e., increasing their duration of smoking)?

First, duration of smoking is critically important (as shown in Figure 7). Smoking heavily (such as 20–30 or more cigarettes/day) for many decades and then reducing amount smoked by 50% or more (such as from 20 cigarettes/day down to 10/day) has been shown to result in little benefit on overall patterns of premature death, particularly from cardiovascular death.[4,8,9] The benefits on reduced risk of lung cancer are somewhat better than for cardiovascular death but the benefits are still small compared with complete cessation. More sustained reductions in amount smoked (i.e., reducing for 10 years or more) can have somewhat greater benefits; however, the overall relative risk of premature death, in comparison to never smokers, is still large.[8] As shown in Figure 7, quitting *completely* earlier in life results in death rates among these former smokers which are virtually the same as among never smokers.[6] So, bottom line, cutting down on amount smoked appears to reduce the smoker's risk somewhat for lung cancer, but little reduction has been observed for cardiovascular disease so quitting is the best route to take.

Overall population patterns in almost all developed countries are showing that the prevalence of lower smoking rates per day, and particularly the proportion of smokers who are not smoking every day (termed non-daily smokers) has been increasing.[4] The most recent research is documenting that these lifelong non-daily smokers have substantially lower risk for lung cancer and premature death compared with lifelong daily smokers.[8,9] However, their risk of lung cancer has been estimated to be 5.6 times higher than lifelong never smokers. While this level of risk is much lower than lifelong daily smokers (see Figure 6), it certainly still is of concern.

These new studies are continuing to raise caution about how the emerging pattern of use of the alternative forms of nicotine delivery products will impact future cancer rates.[53,62,67,69,75,88,89] If reducing the number of cigarettes smoked per day, and even changing from daily to non-daily smoking patterns later in life, rather than quitting completely, appears to result in sustained and elevated risk for premature death and smoking-related cancer, then the pattern of how these products are typically being used (i.e., to substitute for smoking cigarettes at certain times, but still smoking cigarettes in most other situations and times) may not substantially reduce population cancer rates. Thus, population-level surveillance of patterns of tobacco product use and how these may impact cancer risk are getting significant public health attention.[64,69,70,90,91]

Among the more positive new data related to lifelong smoking risk, recent research has shown that the age of smoking initiation among youth has been significantly increasing.[92] This research estimates that the proportion of young adult ever cigarette smokers in the US who started smoking after age 18 increased from 21% in 2002 up to 43% in 2018. Additionally, as noted above, the overall rates of smoking among youth and young adults have been declining. Given the importance of duration of smoking on lifelong risk of cancer and premature death (see Figure 7), these trends suggest that smoking-related cancer rates will decline in the future.

7. Other Risk Factors for Cancer

This chapter focuses on the epidemiology of smoking and cancer. However, to understand the patterns of smoking-related cancers, it is important to remember the synergistic role of other lifestyle patterns (particularly alcohol use and body mass index) on specific smoking-related cancer sites.[2,4,23] For example, alcohol consumption is very important in the study of cancer in oropharynx, larynx, and esophagus.[4] Multivariate estimates of smoking risk for lung cancer typically adjust for these types of other risk factors (e.g., as in data shown in Figure 6). The full discussion of these other risk factors is beyond the scope of this chapter.

8. Summary

It is worth repeating the following: if nobody smoked, one of every three cancer deaths in the US would not happen.[4,6] While smoking and tobacco use patterns vary significantly worldwide, cancer death rates in most developed countries would similarly decline sharply if nobody smoked.[2,3,13,20,21] Prevention of cancer worldwide will require sustained emphasis on reducing the uptake and use of tobacco products globally (see Chapter 13 for worldwide tobacco control efforts).[2,3,21]

The key takeaways from this overview of the epidemiology of smoking and cancer are as follows:

- Smoking and use of tobacco products cause cancer[1-4]
  - o There is no safe tobacco product, but combustible products (cigarettes, cigars, pipes, bidi and kreteks) are most lethal[4]
  - o Among the combustible tobacco products, cigarettes are the most widely used worldwide[3]
- Preventing cancers caused by tobacco use:
  - o Never start using tobacco products[4,5]
  - o For tobacco users, quit completely as early in life as possible[6,7]
  - o Using daily and more frequently increases risk[8,9]
  - o Reducing amount used later in life may not reduce risk[9]

Acknowledgments

Preparation of this chapter was supported in part by the National Cancer Institute of the National Institutes of Health (NIH) and US Food and Drug Administration (FDA) Center for Tobacco Products (CTP) under Award

Number R01CA235719. The content is solely the responsibility of the author and does not necessarily represent the official views of the NIH or the FDA.

References

1. Torre LA, Bray F, Siegel RL, Ferlay J, Lortet-Tieulent J, Jemal A. Global cancer statistics, 2012. *CA Cancer J Clin* 2015;65(2):87–108.
2. Jha P. Avoidable global cancer deaths and total deaths from smoking. *Nat Rev Cancer* 2009;9(9):655–64.
3. Samet JM. Tobacco smoking: The leading cause of preventable disease worldwide. *Thorac Surg Clin* 2013;23(2):103–12.
4. U.S. Department of Health and Human Services. *The Health Consequences of Smoking — 50 Years of Progress. A Report of the Surgeon General* (Atlanta, GA: U.S. Dept. of Health and Human Services, Centers for Disease Control and Prevention, National Center for Chronic Disease Prevention and Health Promotion, Office on Smoking and Health, 2014).
5. U.S. Department of Health and Human Services. *Preventing Tobacco Use Among Youth and Young Adults: A Report of the Surgeon General* (Atlanta, GA: U.S. Dept. of Health and Human Services, Centers for Disease Control and Prevention, National Center for Chronic Disease Prevention and Health Promotion, Office on Smoking and Health, 2012).
6. Jha P, Ramasundarahettige C, Landsman V, *et al.* 21st-century hazards of smoking and benefits of cessation in the United States. *N Engl J Med* 2013;368(4):341–50.
7. Jha P. The hazards of smoking and the benefits of cessation: A critical summation of the epidemiological evidence in high-income countries. *Elife* 2020;9. DOI: 10.7554/eLife.49979
8. Inoue-Choi M, Christensen CH, Rostron BL, *et al.* Dose-response association of low-intensity and nondaily smoking with mortality in the United States. *JAMA Netw Open* 2020;3(6):e206436.
9. Chang JT, Anic GM, Rostron BL, Tanwar M, Chang CM. Cigarette smoking reduction and health risks: A systematic review and meta-analysis. *Nicotine Tobacco Res* 2021;23(4):635–42.
10. U.S. Department of Health and Human Services. *Smoking Cessation: A Report of the Surgeon General* (Atlanta, GA: U.S. Dept. of Health and Human Services, Centers for Disease Control and Prevention, National Center for Chronic Disease Prevention and Health Promotion, Office on Smoking and Health, 2020).

11. U.S. Department of Health and Human Services. Healthy People 2020: Disparities (Washington, DC: U.S. Dept. of Health and Human Services, Office of Disease Prevention and Health Promotion, 2010).

12. Giovino GA, Mirza SA, Samet JM, *et al*. Tobacco use in 3 billion individuals from 16 countries: An analysis of nationally representative cross-sectional household surveys. *Lancet* 2012;380(9842):668–79.

13. Smoking prevalence and attributable disease burden in 195 countries and territories, 1990-2015: A systematic analysis from the Global Burden of Disease Study 2015. *Lancet* 2017;389(10082):1885–906.

14. Torre LA, Siegel RL, Ward EM, Jemal A. Global cancer incidence and mortality rates and trends — an update. *Cancer Epidemiol Biomarkers Prev* 2016;25(1):16–27.

15. Siegel RL, Miller KD, Jemal A. Cancer statistics, 2019. *CA Cancer J Clin* 2019;69(1):7–34.

16. Vital signs: Current cigarette smoking among adults aged ≥18 years — United States, 2005–2010. *MMWR Morb Mortal Wkly Rep* 2011;60(35):1207–12.

17. Cornelius ME, Wang TW, Jamal A, Loretan CG, Neff LJ. Tobacco product use among adults — United States, 2019. *MMWR Morb Mortal Wkly Rep* 2020;69(46):1736–42.

18. Babb S, Malarcher A, Schauer G, Asman K, Jamal A. Quitting smoking among adults — United States, 2000–2015. *MMWR Morb Mortal Wkly Rep* 2017;65(52):1457–64.

19. Gentzke AS, Wang TW, Jamal A, *et al*. Tobacco product use among middle and high school students — United States, 2020. *MMWR Morb Mortal Wkly Rep* 2020;69(50):1881–8.

20. Printz C. ACS publishes 2nd edition of Cancer Atlas. *Cancer.* 2015;121(11):1723.

21. Eriksen MP, Mackay J, Schluger N, Gomeshtapeh FI, Drope J. *The Tobacco Atlas* (American Cancer Society, Inc. World Lung Foundation; 2015).

22. Chang CM, Corey CG, Rostron BL, Apelberg BJ. Systematic review of cigar smoking and all cause and smoking related mortality. *BMC Public Health* 2015;15(1):390.

23. Thun MJ, Carter BD, Feskanich D, *et al*. 50-year trends in smoking-related mortality in the United States. *N Engl J Med* 2013;368(4):351–64.

24. Samet JM. Carcinogenesis and lung cancer: 70 years of progress and more to come. *Carcinogenesis* 2020;41(10):1309–17.

25. Christensen CH, Rostron B, Cosgrove C, *et al*. Association of Cigarette, Cigar, and Pipe Use With Mortality Risk in the US Population. *JAMA Int Med* 2018;178(4):469–76.

26. Jemal A, Bray F, Center MM, Ferlay J, Ward E, Forman D. Global cancer statistics. *CA Cancer J Clin* 2011;61(2):69–90.
27. Ng M, Freeman MK, Fleming TD, *et al.* Smoking prevalence and cigarette consumption in 187 countries, 1980–2012. *Jama.* 2014;311(2):183–192.
28. Garfinkel L. Trends in cigarette smoking in the United States. *Prev Med* 1997;26(4):447–50.
29. Peto R, Lopez AD, Boreham J, Thun M, Heath C, Jr. Mortality from tobacco in developed countries: Indirect estimation from national vital statistics. *Lancet* 1992;339(8804):1268–78.
30. DeSantis C, Naishadham D, Jemal A. Cancer statistics for African Americans, 2013. *CA: A Cancer J Clin* 2013;63(3):151–66.
31. Drope J, Liber AC, Cahn Z, *et al.* Who's still smoking? Disparities in adult cigarette smoking prevalence in the United States. *CA Cancer J Clin* 2018;68(2):106–15.
32. Garrett BE, Dube SR, Babb S. Addressing the social determinants of health to reduce tobacco-related disparities. *Nicotine Tobacco Res* 2015;17:892–7.
33. Ward E, Jemal A, Cokkinides V. Cancer disparities by race/ethnicity and socioeconomic status. *CA Cancer J Clin* 2004;54(2):78–93.
34. O'Keefe EB, Meltzer JP, Bethea TN. Health disparities and cancer: Racial disparities in cancer mortality in the United States, 2000–2010. *Front Public Health* 2015;3:51.
35. Meza R, Meernik C, Jeon J, Cote ML. Lung cancer incidence trends by gender, race and histology in the United States, 1973–2010. *PloS One* 2015;10(3):e0121323.
36. Garrett BE, Gardiner PS, Wright LT, Pechacek TF. The African American youth smoking experience: An overview. *Nicotine Tobacco Res* 2016;18 Suppl 1:S11–5.
37. Jemal A, Center MM, Ward E. The convergence of lung cancer rates between blacks and whites under the age of 40, United States. *Cancer Epidemiol Biomarkers Prev.* 2009;18(12):3349–52.
38. Haiman CA, Stram DO, Wilkens LR, *et al.* Ethnic and racial differences in the smoking-related risk of lung cancer. *N Engl J Med.* 2006;354(4):333–342.
39. Jamal A, Dube SR, King BA. Tobacco use screening and counseling during hospital outpatient visits among US adults, 2005–2010. *Prev Chronic Disease.* 2015;12:E132.
40. Proctor R. *Golden Holocaust: Origins of the Cigarette Catastrophe and the Case for Abolition* (Berkeley: University of California Press; 2011).

41. Brandt AM. *The Cigarette Century: The Rise, Fall, and Deadly Persistence of the Product that Defined America* (New York: Basic Books; 2007).

42. Azagba S, Shan L, Latham K, Qeadan F. Disparities in adult cigarette smoking and smokeless tobacco use by sexual identity. *Drug Alcohol Depend.* 2020;206:107684.

43. Harlow AF, Lundberg D, Raifman JR, *et al.* Association of coming out as lesbian, gay, and bisexual+ and risk of cigarette smoking in a nationally representative sample of youth and young adults. *JAMA Pediatr* 2021;175(1):56–63.

44. Li J, Berg CJ, Weber AA, *et al.* Tobacco use at the intersection of sex and sexual identity in the U.S., 2007–2020: A meta-analysis. *Am J Prev Med* 2021;60(3):415–24.

45. Baggett TP, Tobey ML, Rigotti NA. Tobacco use among homeless people-addressing the neglected addiction. *N Engl J Med* 2013;369(3):201–4.

46. Agrawal P, Taing M, Chen TA, *et al.* Understanding the associations between smoking-related risk perception, interest in quitting smoking, and interest in lung cancer screening among homeless adult smokers. *Int J Environ Res Public Health.* 2020;17(23):8817.

47. Spears CA, Jones DM, Pechacek TF, Ashley DL. Use of other combustible tobacco products among priority populations of smokers: Implications for U.S. tobacco regulatory policy. *Addict Behav.* 2019;93:194–197.

48. Stroup DF. Women and smoking: A report of the Surgeon General. Executive summary. *Public Health Rep* 2002;51(Rr-12):i–iv; 1–13.

49. Ten great public health achievements — United States, 1900–1999. *MMWR Morb Mortal Wkly Rep.* 1999;48(12):241–3.

50. Torre LA, Islami F, Siegel RL, Ward EM, Jemal A. Global cancer in women: Burden and trends. *Cancer Epidemiol Biomarkers Prev.* 2017;26(4):444–57.

51. U.S. Department of Health, Education, and Welfare. *Smoking and Health. Report of the Advisory Committee to the Surgeon General of the Public Health Service* (Washington, DC: U.S. Department of Health, Education, and Welfare. Public Health Service, 1964).

52. U.S. Department of Health and Human Services. *Reducing the Health Consequences of Smoking: 25 Years of Progress. A Report of the Surgeon General* (Rockville, MD: U.S. Department of Health and Human Services, Public Health Service, Centers for Disease Control, Center for Chronic Disease Prevention and Health Promotion, Office on Smoking and Health., 1989).

53. U.S. Department of Health and Human Services. *E-Cigarette Use Among Youth and Young Adults. A Report of the Surgeon General* (Atlanta, GA: U.S. Department of Health and Human Services, Centers for Disease Control and Prevention, National Center for Chronic Disease Prevention and Health Promotion, Office on Smoking and Health, 2016).

54. Corey CG, King BA, Coleman BN, *et al.* Little filtered cigar, cigarillo, and premium cigar smoking among adults — United States, 2012–2013. *Morb Mortal Wkly Rep.* 2014;63(30):650–4.

55. Messer K, White MM, Strong DR, *et al.* Trends in use of little cigars or cigarillos and cigarettes among U.S. smokers, 2002–2011. *Nicotine Tobacco Res* 2015;17(5):515–23.

56. Richardson A, Rath J, Ganz O, Xiao H, Vallone D. Primary and dual users of little cigars/cigarillos and large cigars: Demographic and tobacco use profiles. *Nicotine Tobacco Res* 2013;15(10):1729–36.

57. Cohn A, Cobb CO, Niaura RS, Richardson A. The other combustible products: Prevalence and correlates of little cigar/cigarillo use among cigarette smokers. *Nicotine Tobacco Res* 2015;17(12):1473–81.

58. Corey CG, King BA, Coleman BN, *et al.* Little filtered cigar, cigarillo, and premium cigar smoking among adults–United States, 2012–2013. *MMWR Morbidity and Mortality Weekly Report.* 2014;63(30):650–4.

59. Levy DT, Cummings KM, Villanti AC, *et al.* A framework for evaluating the public health impact of e-cigarettes and other vaporized nicotine products. *Addiction* 2017;112(1): 8–17.

60. Rigotti NA. Balancing the benefits and harms of e-cigarettes: A national academies of science, engineering, and medicine report. *Ann Intern Med* 2018;168(9):666–7.

61. Institute of Medicine Committee to Assess the Science Base for Tobacco Harm Reduction. *Clearing the Smoke: Assessing the Science Base for Tobacco Harm Reduction.* Stratton K, Shetty P, Wallace R, Bondurant S, eds. (Washington, DC: Institute of Medicine, National Academy Press, 2001).

62. National Academies of Sciences, Engineering, and Medicine, Health and Medicine Division. *Public Health Consequences of E-Cigarettes.* Eaton DL, Kwan LY, Stratton K, eds. (Washington, DC: National Academies Press, 2018).

63. Walton KM, Abrams DB, Bailey WC, *et al.* NIH electronic cigarette workshop: Developing a research agenda. *Nicotine Tobacco Res* 2015;17(2): 259–69.

64. Glantz SA, Bareham DW. E-Cigarettes: Use, effects on smoking, risks, and policy implications. *Annu Rev Public Health* 2018;39:215–35.

65. Meza R, Jimenez-Mendoza E, Levy DT. Trends in tobacco use among adolescents by grade, sex, and race, 1991–2019. *JAMA Netw Open.* 2020; 3(12):e2027465.

66. Miech R, Leventhal A, Johnston L, O'Malley PM, Patrick ME, Barrington-Trimis J. Trends in use and perceptions of nicotine vaping among US youth from 2017 to 2020. *JAMA Pediatr* 2021;175(2):185–90.

67. Vugrin ED, Rostron BL, Verzi SJ, *et al.* Modeling the potential effects of new tobacco products and policies: A dynamic population model for multiple product use and harm. *PloS One* 2015;10(3):e0121008.

68. Mravec B, Tibensky M, Horvathova L, Babal P. E-cigarettes and cancer risk. *Cancer Prev Res* 2020;13(2):137–44.

69. Abrams DB. Promise and peril of e-cigarettes: Can disruptive technology make cigarettes obsolete? *JAMA* 2014;311(2):135–6.

70. Cobb NK, Abrams DB. The FDA, e-cigarettes, and the demise of combusted tobacco. *N Engl J Med* 2014;371(16):1469–71.

71. Niaura RS, Glynn TJ, Abrams DB. Youth experimentation with e-cigarettes: Another interpretation of the data. *JAMA* 2014;312(6):641–2.

72. Coleman B, Rostron B, Johnson SE, *et al.* Transitions in electronic cigarette use among adults in the population assessment of tobacco and health (PATH) study, waves 1 and 2 (2013–2015). *Tob Control* 2019;28(1):50–9.

73. Fagerstrom K, Etter J-F, Unger JB. E-cigarettes: A disruptive technology that revolutionizes our field? *Nicotine Tobacco Res* 2015;17(2):125–6.

74. The Lancet. E-cigarettes: Public Health England's evidence-based confusion. *The Lancet* 2015;386(9996):829.

75. Fairchild AL. Is Good enough good enough? e-cigarettes, evidence, and policy. *American J Public Health* 2021;111(2):221–3.

76. Rodu B, Godshall WT. Tobacco harm reduction: An alternative cessation strategy for inveterate smokers. *Harm Reduct J* 2006;3:37.

77. Biener L, Roman AM, Mc Inerney SA, *et al.* Snus use and rejection in the USA. *Tob Control* 2016;25(4):386–92.

78. Kozlowski L, Sweanor D. Withholding differential risk information on legal consumer nicotine/tobacco products: The public health ethics of health information quarantines. *Int J Drug Policy* 2016;32:17–23.

79. Agaku IT, Alpert HR. Trends in annual sales and current use of cigarettes, cigars, roll-your-own tobacco, pipes, and smokeless tobacco among US adults, 2002–2012. *Tob Control* 2016;25(4):451–7.

80. Caputi TL. Heat-not-burn tobacco products are about to reach their boiling point. *Tob Control* 2017;26:609–610.
81. Hoffman RM, Sanchez R. Lung cancer screening. *Med Clin North Am* 2017;101(4):769–85.
82. Peto J. That the effects of smoking should be measured in pack-years: Misconceptions 4. *Br J Cancer* 2012;107(3):406–7.
83. Weaver SR, Majeed BA, Pechacek TF, Nyman AL, Gregory KR, Eriksen MP. Use of electronic nicotine delivery systems and other tobacco products among USA adults, 2014: Results from a national survey. *Int J Public Health* 2016;61(2):177–88.
84. Weaver SR, Huang J, Pechacek TF, Heath SJ, Ashley DL, Eriksen MP. Are electronic nicotine delivery systems helping cigarette smokers quit? Evidence from a prospective cohort study of U.S. adult smokers, 2015–2016. *PLoS One.* 2018 Jul 9;13(7):e0198047. doi: 10.1371/journal.pone.0198047. eCollection 2018.
85. Barrington-Trimis JL, Urman R, Berhane K, *et al.* E-cigarettes and future cigarette use. *Pediatrics* 2016;138(1):e20160379.
86. Wills TA, Knight R, Williams RJ, Pagano I, Sargent JD. Risk factors for exclusive e-cigarette use and dual e-cigarette use and tobacco use in adolescents. *Pediatric* 2015;135(1):e43–51.
87. Cataldo JK, Petersen AB, Hunter M, Wang J, Sheon N. E-cigarette marketing and older smokers: Road to renormalization. *Am J Health Behav* 2015;39(3):361–71.
88. Levy DT, Cummings KM, Villanti AC, *et al.* A framework for evaluating the public health impact of e-cigarettes and other vaporized nicotine products. *Addiction* 2017;112(1):8–17.
89. Committee on the Public Health Implications of Raising the Minimum Age for Purchasing Tobacco Products, Institute of Medicine Board on Population Health and Public Health Practice. *Public Health Implications of Raising the Minimum Age of Legal Access to Tobacco Products.* Bonnie RJ, Stratton K, Kwan LY, eds. (Washington, DC: National Academies Press, 2015).
90. Grana R, Benowitz N, Glantz SA. E-cigarettes: A scientific review. *Circulation* 2014;129(19):1972–86.
91. Fairchild AL, Bayer R. Public health. Smoke and fire over e-cigarettes. *Science* 2015;347(6220):375–6.
92. Barrington-Trimis JL, Braymiller JL, Unger JB, *et al.* Trends in the age of cigarette smoking initiation among young adults in the US From 2002 to 2018. *JAMA Netw Open* 2020;3(10):e2019022.

Chapter 12

Nicotine Addiction and Its Treatment

Judith J. Prochaska* and Neal L. Benowitz[†]

1. Introduction

Nicotine is the addicting agent in cigarettes.[1] Tobacco products uniquely contain and deliver nicotine, a potent drug with a variety of physiological effects.[2] One of the main reasons people smoke is to experience the physiological effects of nicotine on the human system.[3]

These statements from the 1950s, 1970s, and 1980s were made by researchers working for the tobacco industry. Yet, despite extensive knowledge of the pharmacologic effects of nicotine in cigarettes, tobacco industry executives have, for many decades, publicly denied and distorted the truth as to the addictive nature of cigarettes.[4] In 1994, testifying before Congress, the seven chief executives of the leading US tobacco manufacturers each denied that nicotine in cigarettes was addictive.[5]

The drug nicotine acts on similar reward pathways in the brain as cocaine and heroin.[6,7] Nicotine establishes and maintains tobacco addiction by complex actions that affect the brain's structure and functioning and leads to the development of tolerance, withdrawal, and dependence.[8]

---

* Stanford Prevention Research Center, Department of Medicine, Stanford University, USA. jpro@stanford.edu
[†]Program in Clinical Pharmacology, Division of Cardiology, and the Center for Tobacco Control Research and Education, Department of Medicine, University of California San Francisco, USA.

This chapter reviews nicotine's effects on the brain; indicators of nicotine addiction; tobacco product design features that initiate and sustain nicotine addiction; failure to quit tobacco use; and evidence-based tobacco cessation treatments, pharmacologic and behavioral. The chapter closes with specific attention to efforts aimed at integrating tobacco treatment into cancer care.

2. Nicotine's Effects on the Brain

The speed at which a drug reaches the brain influences a drug's abuse liability.[9] Inhaled nicotine (such as with smoking or vaping) reaches the brain quickly via the lungs and arterial blood.[8] The modern-day US combustible cigarette, through a shift from air-curing to predominantly flue-curing of tobacco, has been designed to be easily inhalable (pH 5.5–6) delivering nicotine to the brain within only 15–20 s.[9] Rapid delivery not only results in higher nicotine concentrations reaching the brain, but also rapid reinforcement of behavior and the ability for minute-to-minute dose titration. Rapid delivery of nicotine to the brain reinforces and perpetuates the tobacco use behavior. In contrast, dependence on nicotine from cessation medications (e.g., nicotine patches, gum, lozenge) that deliver nicotine slowly, appears to be low.

Nicotine diffuses readily into brain tissue, where it binds to nicotinic acetylcholine receptors (nAChRs), triggering rewarding effects on mood, cognition, stress, and anxiety.[8] Many subtypes of nAChRs are present in the brain and throughout the body, each comprised of five subunits. In the brain, eleven nAChR subunits are expressed including $\alpha 2$–$\alpha 7$, $\alpha 9$, $\alpha 10$, and $\beta 2$–$\beta 4$.[10] Nicotinic receptors can be heteromeric, with α and β subunits, or homomeric, with five $\alpha 7$ subunits. The most abundant nAChRs in the brain are $\alpha 4\beta 2$ and $\alpha 7$. The $\alpha 4\beta 2$ nAChR also can contain $\alpha 5$ and/or $\alpha 6$ subunits, which alter receptor physiology and contribute to differences in susceptibility to nicotine dependence.

Activation of nAChRs results in facilitation of the release of various neurotransmitters, including the following:

- dopamine, the feel good hormone released by all drugs of abuse;
- norepinephrine and acetylcholine, which enhance vigilance and cognitive function;

- glutamate, which enhances memory and learning;
- serotonin, which improves mood;
- gamma-amino butyric acid (GABA) and endorphins, which ameliorate stress and anxiety.

Regular daily tobacco use exposes the brain to nicotine throughout the day and night. With prolonged exposure to nicotine, structural changes occur in the brain. Most notably, the presence of nicotine causes upregulation, or an increase, in the number of nAChRs in brain cells, creating a physical need for nicotine in order to maintain normal brain functioning.

Nicotine's rewarding effects, however, are short-lived. The half-life of nicotine is about 2 h. Each cigarette produces a spike of arterial nicotine concentration, followed by a rapid decline. When nicotine levels decline, brain function is disrupted, withdrawal symptoms develop, reversing nicotine's positive effects. An abstinent smoker may feel anxious, irritable, agitated, and depressed; have disturbed sleep and problems concentrating; and experience hunger with weight gain. Headache and constipation also are common. Thus, nicotine addiction is sustained both by positive effects of pleasure and arousal (i.e., positive reinforcement) combined with continued use to avoid the unpleasant effects of nicotine withdrawal (i.e., negative reinforcement). Although not life-threatening, nicotine dependence and withdrawal promote continuous and prolonged daily and often heavy tobacco use that leads to disease and death.

Not all smokers become regular, daily, addicted users. The younger the age of smoking initiation — and nine in 10 individuals who smoke as adults started by the age of 18 — the greater the risk of stronger physiological addiction to nicotine. Adolescence is a critical window for brain development, with the brain not reaching full maturity until the mid-20s; hence, state and federal policy efforts have sought to restrict the sale of tobacco to people age 21 and older. In adolescence, the brain areas responsible for adult-level judgment and impulse control (i.e., prefrontal cortical regions) are still developing;[11] hence, adolescents are especially vulnerable to drug experimentation and addiction.[12] Nicotine exposure in adolescence may have sustained adverse neurologic consequences. In animals, nicotine exposure in adolescence causes permanent changes in brain structure and function, delaying maturation of the prefrontal cortex and including enhanced self-administration of nicotine and other drugs as adults.[13] In humans, adolescents experience dependence symptoms at lower nicotine exposure levels than adults.[14,15] Earlier age of onset of daily smoking is associated with higher nicotine dependence scores[16] and chronic, heavier smoking careers compared to late onset smokers.[17,18] Smoking as a teen, as opposed to in one's 20s or later, predicts becoming a life-long smoker.[19–21] In a study of 1,200 individuals, initiating smoking before age 13 predicted the lowest likelihood of quitting, followed by initiating between ages 14 and 17, while initiating at age 18 or later predicted the highest likelihood of quitting,[22] consistent with other studies.[23]

Functional magnetic resonance imaging (fMRI) examining the neural circuitry involved in nicotine craving and addiction in adolescent smokers has documented smaller neural responses in the ventral striatum and midbrain in anticipation of financial reward in adolescent smokers (age 14 years) compared to matched non-smoking controls.[24] The reduced response showed a clear-cut relationship with smoking frequency. Findings support that adolescent smokers display a hypo-responsivity to the anticipation of non-drug reward (i.e., financial reward) relative to non-smokers, and this hypo-responsivity becomes more severe with increased smoking. There also is evidence that adolescents who smoke 5 or fewer cigarettes per day display attenuated responses to other non-drug rewards, including pleasurable food images, relative to non-smokers, in areas including the insula and inferior frontal region.[25] The implication of both these studies is that the use of extremely rewarding drugs, such as nicotine, decreases the perception of the pleasure obtained from non-drug rewards. Demonstration in young and light smoking teens indicates that such changes in the brain occur in the early phases of smoking. Initial symptoms of nicotine dependence occur, in some teens, within days to weeks of onset of use. Describing the process from youth experimentation to addiction, a Philip Morris 1969 draft report titled *Why One Smokes* noted, "Smoking a cigarette for the beginner is a symbolic act... 'I am no longer my mother's child, I'm tough, I am an adventurer, I'm not square.' ... As the force from the psychological symbolism subsides, the pharmacological effect takes over to sustain the habit."[26]

3. Indicators of Nicotine Addiction

An important aspect of addiction is the development of tolerance, defined as diminished effects with continued use of the same amount of drug or greater amounts of the drug needed to achieve the desired effect.[9] With repeated exposures, tolerance develops to many of the effects of nicotine. The nausea and dizziness typically experienced by a novice smoker abate after repeated intake with the development of tolerance. Tolerance in a regular smoker also occurs throughout a typical day as nicotine levels rise in the blood.[8] After smoking the first cigarette of the day, individuals experience notable drug effects, particularly arousal. This is because overnight abstinence leads to resensitization to drug responses (i.e., loss of tolerance). For this reason, many people describe the first cigarette as the most important one of the day. The latency in time from waking to smoking is a measure of physical dependence to nicotine, presumably reflecting the intensity of withdrawal symptoms after overnight abstinence.

Shortly after the initial cigarette of the day, tolerance begins to develop, and the threshold levels for both pleasure/arousal and abstinence rise progressively. With continued smoking throughout the day, nicotine accumulates leading to an even greater degree of tolerance. Most dependent smokers tend to smoke a certain number of cigarettes per day (usually >10) and tend to consume 10–40 mg of nicotine per day to achieve the desired effects of cigarette smoking and to minimize withdrawal.[27] The number of cigarettes smoked per day is a measure both of daily nicotine intake and the frequency of nicotine self-administration.

In a prospective study, time to first cigarette and cigarettes per day were the most robust predictors of smoking cessation.[28] The 2-item Heaviness of Smoking Index (HSI), a widely used measure of nicotine dependence severity, assesses cigarettes per day and time to first cigarette.[29] Figure 1 shows the items and scoring of the HSI. Sum scores of 0–2 are rated as low dependence, 3-4 as moderate dependence, and 5-6 as high dependence. HSI scores predict difficulty with quitting smoking[30] and the likelihood of developing tobacco-related diseases, such as heart and lung disease and lung cancer.[31–33] Both cigarettes per day and time to

How soon after you wake up do you smoke your first cigarette?
- Within 5 min (3 points)
- 6–30 min (2 points)
- 31–60 min (1 point)
- After 60 min (0 points)

How many cigarettes a day do you smoke?
- 10 or less (0 points)
- 11–20 (1 point)
- 21–30 (2 points)
- 31 or more (3 points)

Sum scores: 0–2 low, 3–4 moderate, 5–6 high dependence

Figure 1:   Heaviness of Smoking Index.

first cigarette are used for dosing nicotine replacement therapy (NRT) medications, discussed below, with higher doses for heavier smokers and those who smoke within 30 min of waking. The two items of the HSI have been found to be the most important factors correlating with biomarkers of exposure.[34] Smoking affects gene expression,[35] and in genomic research, number of cigarettes smoked per day and time to first cigarette have shown an association with candidate genes that include those previously associated with cocaine addiction, alcohol dependence, and heroin addiction.[36] The rate of nicotine metabolism, that is, the speed by which the body breaks down and eliminates nicotine, also correlates significantly with HSI.[37] Faster metabolizers tend to smoke more cigarettes per day (presumably to titrate desirable nicotine levels in the blood).[38] HSI scores also are associated with smoking-induced deprivation, measured as prioritization of cigarettes over household essentials such as food.[39]

With repeated nicotine exposure, the brain adapts and becomes hypersensitive ("sensitized") to nicotine and, through associative learning, to tobacco-associated stimuli in the environment. Via conditioning to the drug nicotine, sensorimotor factors associated with the act of using tobacco become reinforcing (e.g., the smell, taste, and feel of the tobacco or the smoke; handling of the tobacco product; the hit to the throat) as do specific daily behaviors (e.g., drinking coffee or alcohol, driving a car, after meals) that become conditioned cues, contributing to maintained tobacco use. Exposure to tobacco advertising, particularly prevalent in the retail environment and in popular media (e.g., movies, TV, music) and exposure to others' tobacco use also can elicit craving.[40–42] When a person quits tobacco, cravings persist long after nicotine withdrawal symptoms have resolved.[43]

With repeated drug exposure and sensitization of brain mesolimbic systems (reward pathways in the brain), physical and psychological "wanting" of a drug increases over time as an individual becomes addicted.[44] What starts as an experimental curiosity or social activity, becomes a compulsion to use. In this regard, nicotine addiction comes to constrain free choice. That is, repeated exposure to nicotine changes the reward, motivation/drive, memory, and control circuits of the brain.[45] These changes are long-lasting and result in an enhanced saliency value for the drug, in the loss of inhibitory control, and in the drive for compulsive drug administration.[46] This loss of free choice with nicotine addiction is exhibited in preoccupation with maintaining a steady supply of product and regular, frequent opportunities to use, and in prioritizing spending on tobacco over other basic needs.[47] The mindshare dedicated to managing dosing of nicotine can impair attention and performance. In the workplace, tobacco use is associated with significant worker productivity loss due to distraction and preoccupation, termed "presenteeism."[48] Interrupted sleep to use tobacco at night is an observable indicator of the physiological drive to use the drug, which overrides the body's need for sleep. Use of the drug becomes more important than other survival functions. A 1969 presentation to the Philip Morris Board of Directors noted, "… the cigarette will even preempt food in times of scarcity on the smoker's priority list."[49] In what appears to be irrational decision-making to the non-user, the addicted tobacco user prioritizes money, time, and physical well-being to maintain a steady tobacco dosing to deliver nicotine to the brain.[39]

In 1988, the Surgeon General's Report[50] concluded that (1) cigarettes and other forms of tobacco are addicting; (2) nicotine is the drug in tobacco that causes addiction; and (3) the pharmacologic and behavioral processes that determine tobacco addiction are similar to those that determine addiction to drugs such as heroin and cocaine.[6] Today, leading national and international organizations recognize nicotine in tobacco as addictive. These include the World Health Organization (WHO),[51] the Centers for Disease Control and Prevention, the National Institute on Drug Abuse,[7] the American Medical Association, the American Psychiatric Association,[52] the American Psychological Association, the American

Society of Addiction Medicine, and the Society for Research on Nicotine and Tobacco. Further, as a policy intervention with clinical and public health implications, the WHO has recommended that countries with strong tobacco control policies consider limiting the sale of combustible tobacco products to brands with a nicotine content that is insufficient for developing and maintaining addiction, the basis for which is discussed further in Section 4.[53]

4. Tobacco Product Design Features that Initiate and Sustain Addiction

All commercially available tobacco products (e.g., cigarettes, cigars, smokeless tobacco) sold in the US contain the drug nicotine. Cigarettes contain about 10–15 mg of nicotine, of which about 10% is systemically absorbed when smoked; that is, on average, a smoker absorbs 1–1.5 mg of nicotine per cigarette.[54] There are a number of processes available for removing nicotine from tobacco to render the product minimally addictive or non-addictive. The methods date from the mid-1800s to the present and include plant breeding; use of solvents, steam, microbes, and gases; super-critical extraction (an adaptation of a patented process to decaffeinate coffee beans that Philip Morris acquired in 1985, when it purchased General Foods);[55,56] and most recently, genetic modifications of tobacco to block nicotine biosynthesis. In 1986, Philip Morris identified over 100 patents for the denicotinization of tobacco[57] with the ability to achieve substantial reductions, in the range of 80–98%.

Yet, as early as the 1950s, the tobacco industry also was aware that to lower nicotine too much "...might end in destroying the nicotine habit in a large number of consumers and prevent it ever being acquired by new smokers."[58] In his 1972 paper titled *Motives and Incentives in Cigarette Smoking*, William Dunn, Jr of the Philip Morris Research Center wrote "Nicotine is the active constituent of cigarette smoke" and "...without nicotine ... there would be no smoking."[59] A 1980 Lorillard internal memo stated, "Goal — Determine the minimum level of nicotine that will allow continued smoking. We hypothesize satisfaction cannot be compensated for by psychological satisfaction. At this point smokers will quit, or return to higher T&N [tar and nicotine] brands."[60]

In 1994, Benowitz and Henningfield proposed the idea of federal regulation of the nicotine content of cigarettes to reduce levels over time, resulting in lower intake of nicotine, and a lower level of nicotine dependence.[61] The proposal was a maximum level of 0.5 mg of nicotine per gram of tobacco (0.5 mg/g) in a cigarette, of which 0.05 mg/cigarette (10%) would be absorbed by a smoker. Hence, a pack of cigarettes would yield about 1 mg in total, as opposed to about 20 mg, which is about a 95% reduction. In the US, the Food and Drug Administration (FDA) is barred from completely removing nicotine from cigarettes but is allowed to reduce the amount of nicotine in cigarettes to very low levels.[62] Initiated in March 2018, the FDA is now going through the lengthy regulatory rulemaking processes required in pursuit of a product standard to reduce nicotine in combustible cigarettes to minimally or non-addictive levels.[63] The tobacco industry could make this change voluntarily.

The tobacco industry has been aware of consumer interest in a low nicotine cigarette product since at least as early as the 1980s.[57] Interest was in a product that would be healthier; "a way to quit smoking;" and "would allow smokers to cut down or quit."[64,65] More recent opinion poll surveys show support among US adults (47% in support in 2010[66] and 76% in 2011[67]) for a federally regulated nicotine reduction product standard.

Cigarettes marketed by the tobacco industry as "light" or "ultralight," in practice yielded nicotine levels similar to regular "full-flavor" cigarettes when ventilation holes in the filter, which resulted in lower machine determined nicotine and tar yields, were blocked or with deeper inhaling.[8] In contrast, very low nicotine content cigarettes (VLNCs) are engineered to have reduced yields of nicotine in the tobacco contained in the cigarette rod and deliver much lower nicotine levels than standard cigarettes.[61] Randomized trials examining use behavior with VLNCs in comparison with standard nicotine cigarettes have shown reductions in smoking and dependence and increases in quit attempts.[68] A 6-week trial found decreases in nicotine levels and dependence for VLNCs, less craving during abstinence from smoking, and reductions in the number of cigarettes smoked without significantly increasing levels of expired carbon monoxide or total puff volume, which suggests minimal compensation behavior.[69] In a randomized, parallel-arm, semi-blinded study of adult cigarette smokers, those receiving 0.05 mg/g cigarettes had greater relief of withdrawal from usual-brand cigarettes than the nicotine lozenge; greater abstinence at the 6-week follow-up than the 0.3 mg/g cigarette; and a similar rate of cessation as the nicotine lozenge.[70] In another study, any beneficial effects from smoking reduced nicotine content cigarettes were not sustained at 12-month follow-up.[71] In clinical trials, particularly after the VLNCs are no longer provided, relapse is in part a function of the easy availability of conventional cigarettes in the current regulatory environment.[72,73] Combining VLNCs with nicotine patches may increase adherence, but doing so was not found to improve long-term quit rates. If nicotine in all cigarettes was reduced to make them minimally or non-addictive, either through regulation or by the tobacco industry's own initiative, then problems with compliance could be less of an issue and the ability to sustain abstinence from smoking could be higher. The availability of non-combusted nicotine products, in the form of NRT or e-cigarettes, also would counter arguments about nicotine prohibition and concerns about the development of an illicit market for cigarettes with high nicotine levels.[74]

In research funded by the FDA, a simulation model quantified the potential public health effects of enacting regulation to reduce nicotine in cigarettes to minimally or non-addictive levels.[75] Model inputs were informed by empirical evidence and expert opinion; outputs included tobacco use prevalence, tobacco-related mortality, and gains in life-years. The statistical model found that reducing nicotine levels to "minimally addictive levels" could bring the smoking prevalence down to as low as 1.4% and substantially reduce tobacco-related deaths. The researchers estimated that reduction in nicotine in cigarettes to minimally or non-addictive levels "could save millions of lives and tens of millions of life-years over the next several decades."

Manipulation of the pH level of cigarette smoke also affects the addictiveness and resulting harm of cigarettes. Commercial US cigarettes today have an acidic pH of about 5.5–6.[76] As early as the 1970s, researchers noted that the irritation and harshness of smoke at higher pH made it more difficult for smokers to inhale the smoke into the lungs.[77] Raising the pH of cigarettes to 8 or more (its level prior to 20th century methods of cigarette manufacturing) would make cigarettes harder to inhale.[78] A more acrid smoke that cannot easily be drawn deep into the lungs could reduce both smoking initiation and lung cancer and other lung diseases, resulting in a less harmful way to smoke.[79]

Though designed to deliver nicotine efficiently into the lungs at addictive levels, to this day still, in the US, none of the mandated health warnings for cigarette packs or ads acknowledge addiction. Efforts by the FDA to update labeling with inclusion of a health warning of the addictive nature of cigarettes were thwarted by the tobacco industry through litigation in 2012.[80] The corrective statements, which include truthful statements on the addictiveness of nicotine and the design of cigarettes to create and sustain addiction, were held up in litigation by the tobacco industry for over a decade, finally released at the end of 2017.[81] Judge Kessler's Final Opinion in US vs. Philip Morris USA, Inc. stated that for over 50 years, the tobacco industry "publicly, vehemently, and repeatedly denied the addictiveness of smoking and nicotine's central role in smoking."[4] Further, Judge Kessler's conclusions stated that the tobacco industry's denial "misled the public about why quitting smoking is so difficult, exactly how difficult it is, and about why failure to quit is not simply a function of personal weakness or lack of willpower."[4] The next section summarizes the epidemiology of tobacco quit attempts in the US and covers evidence-based pharmacologic and behavioral cessation treatments.

5. Failure to Quit Tobacco Use

Most attempts to quit tobacco use fail. Relapse is a hallmark of nicotine addiction: it is common and expected. The most recent data, for 2019, indicate that declines in the US adult smoking prevalence have stalled since 2017, with 14% of US adults continuing to smoke (34.1 million).[82] Further, there are more adults in the US today who use tobacco products (50.6 million) than in 2017 (47.4 million). About seven in 10 US adults who smoke want to quit, and over half quit for 24 h in a given year (many more people attempt to quit smoking but are unable to make it a full day);[83] 60% of those who quit for a day, relapse within a week.[43] Today, despite the availability of evidence-based treatments, only seven in 100 quit attempts (7%) are sustained for 6 months or more; of which about

45% end in relapse.[83] Over 90% of people who smoke have tried to quit and most make multiple quit attempts, averaging about one per year.[84] About half of people who ever smoked ultimately are successful in achieving long-term abstinence, with most not achieving abstinence from cigarettes until after age 30.[43] Success with quitting smoking is greater for non-daily and light (i.e., fewer than 5 cigarettes/day) smokers relative to daily, heavier, addicted smokers.

6. Evidence-Based Tobacco Cessation Treatments

Addiction to nicotine and the conditioned behavioral habit compel chronic use of tobacco. Hence, to maximize treatment effectiveness, US tobacco treatment clinical practice guidelines recommend a multi-pronged approach.[85] FDA-approved cessation medications treat the physical dependence aspect of smoking, while behavioral approaches address the conditioned habit. Tobacco cessation treatment models have historically used an "opt-in" approach, whereby patients have to request or accept a referral from their health care providers. As an alternative, in an "opt-out" model, all patients who use tobacco are automatically referred for evidence-based tobacco cessation treatment, with the option to opt-out from engaging in care. The opt-out model has increased patient reach and engagement,[86] and quit rates.[87] "Opt-out" models for tobacco treatment have proven feasible in inpatient and outpatient care settings.[88,89] Further, to encourage quit attempts and support sustained abstinence, policy interventions can promote tobacco-free environments.

Our review of evidence-based tobacco cessation interventions centers on treating cigarette smoking in adults. In young people, smoking cessation efforts have been particularly challenging, and the literature largely consists of failed smoking cessation trials.[90] Further, there are no trials yet published on e-cigarette cessation in adolescents or adults.

6.1. *Pharmacologic treatments*

The US Public Health Service and the National Cancer Center Network recommend smoking cessation medications for all adults who smoke daily where feasible and safe.[85,91] In general, medications alleviate the discomfort of nicotine withdrawal while individuals learn to cope with daily cues/triggers and life stressors without smoking. Cessation medications can facilitate quitting smoking by three main mechanisms: (1) reducing nicotine withdrawal symptoms; (2) blocking or desensitizing nicotine receptors, thereby reducing the rewarding effects of nicotine from smoking; and/or (3) supplying nicotine with the desired pharmacologic effects previously achieved from smoking. Medications can be considered for non-daily smokers too, although few clinical trials inform treatment in this group. The mechanism of benefit would be reduced reward from smoking by nAChR desensitization or antagonism, as discussed below. Most cessation medications are recommended for 8–12 weeks, while use out to 6 months or longer may be needed to avoid relapse.

The FDA-approved cessation medications, including dosing guidelines, advantages, disadvantages, side effects, and precautions, are summarized in Table 1, with additional details provided below. FDA-approved medications are varenicline; bupropion; and NRT in the form of gum, patches, lozenge, nasal spray, and inhaler. In the US, nicotine gums, lozenges and patches are available over-the-counter, while the nicotine nasal spray, nicotine inhaler, varenicline, and bupropion are by prescription only. Outside of the US, nicotine mouth spray is available and found to be acceptable and efficacious, including with minimal behavioral support.[92] Cessation medication protocols with the strongest evidence are varenicline as a mono-therapy and the combined use of the nicotine patch with nicotine gum, lozenge, inhaler, or nasal spray (i.e., combination NRT).

Varenicline is a partial agonist at the nicotinic α4β2 receptor, the major receptor mediating nicotine addiction. Varenicline activates (~50% of the maximal effect of nicotine) and blocks nicotine's effects on the α4β2 receptor;[93] thereby both reducing withdrawal symptoms, while also reducing the rewarding effects of nicotine from smoking. Treatment with varenicline prior to quitting often reduces smoking, presumably because cigarettes are less satisfying, an effect that can ultimately support cessation.

Varenicline is more effective than bupropion or nicotine patch alone in promoting smoking cessation and comparably effective to combined NRT.[94] The EAGLES trial, conducted with 8000 adults, compared varenicline, bupropion, nicotine patch, and placebo for treating smoking.

Table 1: Pharmacologist product guide: FDA-approved medications for smoking cessation.

	Nicotine Replacement Therapy (NRT) Formulations					Bupropion SR	Varenicline
	Gum	Lozenge	Transdermal patch	Nasal spray	Oral inhaler		
Product	**Nicorette[a], Generic** OTC 2 mg, 4 mg original, cinnamon, fruit, mint (various)	**Nicorette[a], Generic Nicorette[a] Mini** OTC 2 mg, 4 mg; cinnamon, cherry, mint	**Habitrol[b], NicoDerm CQ[a], Generic** OTC 7 mg, 14 mg, 21 mg (24-hr release)	**Nicotrol NS[c]** Rx Metered spray 10 mg/mL nicotine solution	**Nicotrol Inhaler[c]** Rx 10 mg cartridge delivers 4 mg inhaled vapor	**Generic** (formerly Zyban) Rx 150 mg sustained-release tablet	**Chantix[c]** Rx 0.5 mg, 1 mg tablet
Precautions	▪ Recent (≤ 2 weeks) myocardial infarction ▪ Serious underlying arrhythmias ▪ Serious or worsening angina pectoris ▪ Temporomandibular joint disease ▪ Pregnancy[d] and breastfeeding ▪ Adolescents (<18 years)	▪ Recent (≤ 2 weeks) myocardial infarction ▪ Serious underlying arrhythmias ▪ Serious or worsening angina pectoris ▪ Pregnancy[d] and breastfeeding ▪ Adolescents (<18 years)	▪ Recent (≤ 2 weeks) myocardial infarction ▪ Serious underlying arrhythmias ▪ Serious or worsening angina pectoris ▪ Pregnancy[d] and breastfeeding ▪ Adolescents (<18 years)	▪ Recent (≤ 2 weeks) myocardial infarction ▪ Serious underlying arrhythmias ▪ Serious or worsening angina pectoris ▪ Underlying chronic nasal disorders (rhinitis, nasal polyps, sinusitis) ▪ Severe reactive airway disease	▪ Recent (≤ 2 weeks) myocardial infarction ▪ Serious underlying arrhythmias ▪ Serious or worsening angina pectoris ▪ Bronchospastic disease ▪ Pregnancy[d] and breastfeeding ▪ Adolescents (<18 years)	▪ Concomitant therapy with medications/conditions known to lower the seizure threshold ▪ Hepatic impairment ▪ Pregnancy[d] and breastfeeding ▪ Adolescents (<18 years) ▪ Treatment-emergent neuropsychiatric symptoms[e] **Contraindications:** ▪ Seizure disorder ▪ Concomitant bupropion (e.g., Wellbutrin) therapy ▪ Current or prior diagnosis of bulimia or anorexia nervosa ▪ Simultaneous abrupt discontinuation of alcohol or sedatives/benzodiazepines	▪ Severe renal impairment (dosage adjustment is necessary) ▪ Pregnancy[d] and breastfeeding ▪ Adolescents (<18 years) ▪ Treatment-emergent neuropsychiatric symptoms[e]

				■ Pregnancy[d] and breastfeeding ■ Adolescents (<18 years)		■ MAO inhibitors in preceding 14 days; concurrent use of reversible MAO inhibitors	
Dosing	■ 1st cigarette ≤30 minutes after waking: 4 mg ■ 1st cigarette >30 minutes after waking: 2 mg Weeks 1–6: ■ 1 piece q 1–2 hours* Weeks 7–9: ■ 1 piece q 2–4 hours* Weeks 10–12: ■ 1 piece q 4–8 hours* *while awake ■ Maximum, 24 pieces/day ■ During initial 6 weeks of treatment, use at least 9 pieces/day ■ Chew each piece slowly ■ Park between cheek and gum when peppery or tingling sensation appears (~15–30 chews) ■ Resume chewing when tingle fades	■ 1st cigarette ≤30 minutes after waking: 4 mg ■ 1st cigarette >30 minutes after waking: 2 mg Weeks 1–6: ■ 1 lozenge q 1–2 hours* Weeks 7–9: ■ 1 lozenge q 2–4 hours* Weeks 10–12: ■ 1 lozenge q 4–8 hours* *while awake ■ Maximum, 20 lozenges/day ■ During initial 6 weeks of treatment, use at least 9 lozenges/day ■ Allow to dissolve slowly (20–30 minutes) ■ Nicotine release may cause a warm, tingling sensation	≥10 cigarettes/day: ■ 21 mg/day × 4–6 weeks ■ 14 mg/day × 2 weeks ■ 7 mg/day × 2 weeks ≤10 cigarettes/day: ■ 14 mg/day × 6 weeks ■ 7 mg/day × 2 weeks ■ Rotate patch application site daily; do not apply a new patch to the same skin site for at least one week ■ May wear patch for 16 hours if patient experiences sleep disturbances (remove at bedtime); rule	■ 1–2 doses/hour* (8–40 doses/day) ■ One dose = 2 sprays (one in each nostril): each spray delivers 0.5 mg of nicotine to the nasal mucosa *while awake ■ Maximum – 5 doses/ hour or – 40 doses/day ■ During intial 6–8 weeks of treatment, use at least 8 doses/day ■ Gradually reduce daily dosage over an additional 4–6 weeks	■ 6–16 cartridges/day ■ Individualize dosing; initially use 1 cartridge q 1–2 hours* *while awake ■ Best effects with continuous puffing for 20 minutes ■ During initial 6 weeks of treatment use at least 6 cartridges/day ■ Gradually reduce daily dosage over the following 6–12 weeks ■ Nicotine in cartridge is depleted after 20 minutes of active puffing ■ Inhale into back of throat or puff in short breaths	■ 150 mg po q AM × 3 days, then 150 mg po bid ■ Do not exceed 300 mg/day ■ Begin therapy 1–2 weeks **prior** to quit date ■ Allow at least 8 hours between doses ■ Avoid bedtime dosing to minimize insomnia ■ Dose tapering is not necessary ■ Duration: 7–12 weeks, with maintenance up to 6 months in selected patients	■ Days 1–3: 0.5 mg po q AM ■ Days 4–7: 0.5 mg po bid ■ Weeks 2–12: 1 mg po bid ■ Begin therapy 1 week **prior** to quit date ■ Take dose after eating and with a full glass of water ■ Dose tapering is not necessary ■ Dosing adjustment is necessary for patients with severe renal impairment ■ Duration: 12 weeks; an additional 12-week course may be used in selected patients

(Continued)

Table 1:   *(Continued)*

	Nicotine Replacement Therapy (NRT) Formulations						
	Gum	**Lozenge**	**Transdermal patch**	**Nasal spray**	**Oral inhaler**	**Bupropion SR**	**Varenicline**
	■ Repeat chew/park steps until most of the nicotine is gone (tingle does not return; generally 30 min) ■ Park in different areas of mouth ■ No food or beverages 15 minutes before or during use ■ Duration: up to 12 weeks	■ Do not chew or swallow ■ Occasionally rotate to different areas of the mouth ■ No food or beverages 15 minutes before or during use ■ Duration: up to 12 weeks	out other factors first, e.g., caffeine/tobacco smoke drug interaction, other medications, and lifestyle factors ■ Duration: 8–10 weeks	■ Do not sniff, swallow, or inhale through the nose as the spray is being administered ■ Duration: 12 weeks	■ Do NOT inhale into the lungs (like a cigarette) but "puff" as if lighting a pipe ■ Open cartridge retains potency for 24 hours ■ No food or beverages 15 minutes before or during use ■ Duration: 3–6 months		■ May initiate up to 35 days before target quit date OR may reduce smoking over a 12-week period of treatment prior to quitting and continue treatment for an additional 12 weeks
Adverse Effects	■ Mouth and throat irritation ■ Jaw muscle soreness ■ Hiccups ■ GI complaints (dyspepsia, nausea) ■ May stick to dental work	■ Mouth and throat irritation ■ Hiccups ■ GI complaints (dyspepsia, nausea)	■ Local skin reactions (erythema, pruritus, burning) ■ Sleep disturbances (abnormal or vivid dreams, insomnia); associated with nocturnal nicotine absorption	■ Nasal and/or throat irritation (hot, peppery, or burning sensation) ■ Ocular irritation/tearing ■ Sneezing ■ Cough	■ Mouth and/or throat irritation ■ Cough ■ Hiccups ■ GI complaints (dyspepsia, nausea)	■ Insomnia ■ Dry mouth ■ Nausea ■ Anxiety/difficulty concentrating ■ Constipation ■ Tremor ■ Rash ■ Seizures (risk is 0.15%) ■ Neuropsychiatric symptoms (rare; see PRECAUTIONS)	■ Nausea ■ Sleep disturbances (insomnia, abnormal/vivid dreams) ■ Headache ■ Flatulence ■ Constipation ■ Taste alteration ■ Neuropsychiatric symptoms (rare; see PRECAUTIONS)

Adverse effects more commonly experienced when chewing the lozenge or using incorrect gum chewing technique (due to rapid nicotine release):
– Lightheadedness/dizziness
– Nausea/vomiting
– Hiccups
– Mouth and throat irritation

Advantages	■ Might serve as an oral substitute for tobacco ■ Might delay weight gain ■ Can be titrated to manage withdrawal symptoms ■ Can be used in combination with other agents to manage situational urges ■ Relatively inexpensive	■ Might serve as an oral substitute for tobacco ■ Might delay weight gain ■ Can be titrated to manage withdrawal symptoms ■ Can be used in combination with other agents to manage situational urges ■ Relatively inexpensive	■ Once-daily dosing associated with fewer adherence problems ■ Of all NRT products, its use is least obvious to others ■ Can be used in combination with other agents; delivers consistent nicotine levels over 24 hours ■ Relatively inexpensive	■ Can be titrated to rapidly manage withdrawal symptoms ■ Can be used in combination with other agents to manage situational urges	■ Might serve as an oral substitute for tobacco ■ Can be titrated to manage withdrawal symptoms ■ Mimics hand-to-mouth ritual of smoking ■ Can be used in combination with other agents to manage situational urges	■ Twice-daily oral dosing is simple and associated with fewer adherence problems ■ Might delay weight gain ■ Might be beneficial in patients with depression ■ Can be used in combination with NRT agents ■ Relatively inexpensive (generic formulations)	■ Twice-daily oral dosing is simple and associated with fewer adherence problems ■ Offers a different mechanism of action for patients who have failed other agents ■ Most effective cessation agent when used as monotherapy
Disadvantages	■ Need for frequent dosing can compromise adherence ■ Might be problematic for patients with significant dental work ■ Proper chewing technique is necessary for effectiveness and to minimize adverse effects ■ Gum chewing might not be acceptable or desirable for some patients	■ Need for frequent dosing can compromise adherence ■ Gastrointestinal side effects (nausea, hiccups, heartburn) might be bothersome	■ When used as monotherapy, cannot be titrated to acutely manage withdrawal symptoms ■ Not recommended for use by patients with dermatologic conditions (e.g., psoriasis, eczema, atopic dermatitis)	■ Need for frequent dosing can compromise adherence ■ Nasal administration might not be acceptable or desirable for some patients; nasal irritation often problematic	■ Need for frequent dosing can compromise adherence ■ Cartridges might be less effective in cold environments (≤60°F) ■ Cost of treatment	■ Seizure risk is increased ■ Several contraindications and precautions preclude use in some patients (see PRECAUTIONS) ■ Patients should be monitored for potential neuropsychiatric symptoms[d] (see PRECAUTIONS)	■ Patients should be monitored for potential neuropsychiatric symptoms[d] (see PRECAUTIONS) ■ Cost of treatment

(Continued)

Table 1:   *(Continued)*

	Nicotine Replacement Therapy (NRT) Formulations					Bupropion SR	Varenicline
	Gum	Lozenge	Transdermal patch	Nasal spray	Oral inhaler		
				■ Not recommended for use by patients with chronic nasal disorders or severe reactive airway disease ■ Cost of treatment			
Cost/Day[a]	2 mg or 4 mg: $1.90–$5.49 (9 pieces)	2 mg or 4 mg: $2.97–$4.23 (9 pieces)	$1.52–$3.49 (1 patch)	$9.64 (8 doses)	$16.38 (6 cartridges)	$0.72 (2 tables)	$17.20 (2 tablets)

[a]Marketed by GlaxoSmithKline.

[b]Marketed by Dr. Reddy's.

[c]Marketed by Pfizer.

[d]The U.S. Clinical Practice Guideline states that pregnant smokers should be encouraged to quit without medication based on insufficient evidence of effectiveness and theoretical concerns with safety. Pregnant smokers should be offered behavioral counseling interventions that exceed minimal advice to quit.

[e]In July 2009, the FDA mandated that the prescribing information for all bupropion- and varenicline-containing products include a black-boxed warning highlighting the risk of serious neuropsychiatric symptoms, including changes in behavior, hostility, agitation, depressed mood, suicidal thoughts and behavior, and attempted suicide. Clinicians should advise patients to stop taking varenicline or bupropion SR and contact a health care provider immediately if they experience agitation, depressed mood, or any changes in behavior that are not typical of nicotine withdrawal, or if they experience suicidal thoughts or behavior. If treatment is stopped due to neuropsychiatric symptoms, patients should be monitored until the symptoms resolve. Based on results of a mandated clinical trial, the FDA removed this boxed warning in December 2016.

[f]Approximate cost based on the recommended initial dosing for each agent and the wholesale acquisition cost from Red Book Online. Thomson Reuters, January 2021.

Abbreviations: MAO, monoamine oxidase; NRT, nicotine replacement therapy; OTC, over-the-counter (nonprescription product); Ex, prescription product.

For complete prescribing information and a comprehensive listing of warnings and precautions, please refer to the manufacturers' package inserts.

Source: Updated January 15, 2021.

Varenicline achieved the highest quit rates; bupropion and nicotine patch had similar quit rates to each other and outperformed placebo.[95] EAGLES compared treatment effects for smokers with and without mental health diagnoses. Quit rates were higher in those without mental health diagnoses, but the relative treatment effects were similar. Use of varenicline for 6 months increases sustained abstinence relative to the standard 12-week treatment.[96]

Neuropsychiatric adverse effects of varenicline, including depression, psychosis, and suicide, were reported after FDA approval, prompting a box warning in the label after the drug was marketed (for both varenicline and bupropion). In the EAGLES trial, however, neuropsychiatric adverse events for varenicline and bupropion were not significantly greater relative to nicotine patch or placebo, in smokers with or without psychiatric illness, and in 2016 the box warnings were removed for both medications.[95] In patients with cardiovascular disease, varenicline enhances smoking cessation,[97,98] and several meta-analyses, a large cohort study, and clinical trials in smokers with cardiovascular disease, as well as the EAGLES trial, showed no increase in cardiovascular risk.[99,100] Varenicline also has been found efficacious for quitting smokeless tobacco use.[101]

Bupropion, originally marketed as an antidepressant, is a stimulant that blocks neuronal reuptake of norepinephrine and dopamine thereby increasing their availability in the brain. Bupropion also has antagonist activity on the $\alpha4\beta2$ nicotinic receptor, simulating the effects of nicotine. In a Cochrane meta-analysis of bupropion for quitting smoking high-certainty evidence from 45 randomized controlled trials confirmed the benefit of bupropion as a single pharmacotherapy for smoking cessation; treatment effects of bupropion for quitting smoking were comparable for participants with psychiatric conditions, such as depression and schizophrenia; bupropion had comparable efficacy to NRT and inferior efficacy than varenicline; and adding bupropion to NRT or varenicline did not appear to provide additional benefit compared to treatment with NRT or varenicline alone, respectively.[102] The usual duration of bupropion treatment is 12 weeks, although use for a year achieved higher sustained quit rates.[103] With lower quit rates than combination NRT or varenicline, bupropion is considered to be second-line.

NRTs provide purified nicotine to alleviate dependence and withdrawal symptoms when quitting smoking. Delivering nicotine slowly through the skin, nicotine patches relieve nicotine withdrawal symptoms without providing much if any of the pleasure/arousal effects. Faster acting than the patch, nicotine gums, lozenges, inhalers, and nasal and mouth sprays provide some acute nicotine effects that may serve as a substitute for smoking. Combining a short acting (nicotine gum, lozenge, inhaler, or spray) with a long acting (nicotine patch) NRT results in superior quit rates compared to a single form of NRT, is comparable to varenicline, and is recommended as a first-line treatment.[104]

NRT products come in different strengths, with higher doses recommended for more dependent smokers based on time to first cigarette upon waking or the number of cigarettes smoked daily. In more highly dependent smokers, the 4-mg gum is more effective than the 2-mg gum, while the 21-mg patch is more effective than the 14-mg patch in general.[104] Clinical trials do not demonstrate superiority of double-patch dosing (42 mg) to the standard 21-mg nicotine patch; however, some clinicians use high dose patch for smokers with particularly severe withdrawal symptoms. Tapering of nicotine patch dose is an option but does not appear to affect outcome.

All forms of NRT show similar efficacy in clinical trials,[104] increasing abstinence by 50% to 100% compared to behavioral treatment alone. For the NRTs, compliance is greatest with the patch, lower with gum and lozenge, and lowest with the nasal spray and inhaler. Nicotine patches are usually placed on the skin in the morning and deliver nicotine over 16–24 h. If patch-related insomnia and/or abnormal dreams occur, removal of the patch at bedtime is recommended. The nicotine gum, lozenge, and inhaler deliver relatively low doses of nicotine over 15–30 min with regular use every 1–2 h providing the best treatment response. The nicotine inhaler is a plastic device that provides a hand-to-mouth experience similar to smoking a cigarette but delivers nicotine to the oropharyngeal area rather than to the lungs, which explains its slow absorption. All oral NRTs have an alkaline pH, with a high proportion of nicotine in the free base form that is rapidly absorbed across mucous membranes. The nicotine nasal spray most closely resembles a cigarette with respect to speed of nicotine absorption, which is faster than the other rapid release products (e.g., nicotine gum, lozenge), and may be particularly useful for more highly dependent smokers.

Combining varenicline and nicotine patch has had mixed results,[105] with unclear mechanism, though appears to be safe and can be considered in a smoker who does not quit with dual NRT or varenicline.

Though most smokers would like to quit, they may not be immediately prepared to commit when advised by a medical provider. Starting nicotine patches or varenicline while still smoking without setting a specific quit date has been studied (i.e., preloading or flexible quit) and has evidence of efficacy.[104,106] The idea is to reduce withdrawal symptoms between cigarettes, reduce satisfaction from smoking, and decrease the number of cigarettes smoked per day. A small trial of heavy smokers with chronic obstructive pulmonary disease (COPD), all initially unprepared to quit, prescribed varenicline without a fixed quit date; by 18 months, most had quit smoking.[107] Another approach with evidence of benefit is reduce-to-quit, that is, prescribing varenicline with instructions to reduce cigarettes per day by 50% at 4 weeks, 75% at 8 weeks, and 100% by 12 weeks.[108]

In medicine generally, to optimize outcomes, there is interest in using individual patient characteristics to guide treatment selection. For tobacco addiction, a promising approach involves matching treatment based on an individual's rate of nicotine metabolism, which can be measured using a nicotine metabolite-derived biomarker (called the nicotine metabolite ratio) that can be measured in blood, urine, or saliva. Compared to slower metabolizers of nicotine, faster metabolizers tend to be heavier smokers[38] and experience more severe withdrawal symptoms when not smoking.[109] In a clinical trial, varenicline and nicotine patch were equally effective in slow metabolizers, but in normal metabolizers, varenicline was twice as effective; additionally, slow metabolizers had greater side effects with varenicline.[110] Though further confirmation is needed, the findings would support varenicline for normal metabolizers and the use of patch for slow metabolizers, which is less costly and to minimize side effects. Personalized NRT dosing also is being examined as a way to optimize existing medications.[111]

With slower nicotine absorption, NRT medications are less satisfying than smoking and quit rates are modest. Nicotine delivery from electronic cigarettes (i.e., e-cigarettes), however, now can resemble that of a cigarette and tends to be much more satisfying than NRT. e-Cigarettes produce an inhalable aerosol from a liquid that typically contains nicotine without generating products of tobacco combustion.

e-Cigarettes, with a very different path of entry to the US market than NRT, are considered tobacco products in the US. No e-cigarette has FDA approval as a therapeutic aid, though they have been marketed as "switching" devices, and as a less-harmful alternative to combustible cigarettes. Research is accumulating on the efficacy of e-cigarettes for smoking cessation. A meta-analysis of 50 studies, of which 26 were randomized controlled trials, found moderate evidence that nicotine e-cigarettes increase quit rates compared to nicotine-free (placebo) e-cigarettes and NRT.[112] Side effects of the nicotine e-cigarettes were low with no clear evidence of harm; however, the longest follow-up was 2 years. The largest randomized clinical trial of e-cigarettes, conducted with 886 smokers treated in the UK's National Health Service, compared a second-generation e-cigarette refillable tank type device to patients' choice of NRT.[113] The treatments were provided by the study for 3 months with counseling support. At 12 months, smoking quit rates were 18% for the e-cigarette condition and 10% for the NRT arm, although 80% of those randomized to the e-cigarette arm who quit smoking were still using e-cigarettes at 12-month compared to 9% of those randomized to NRT. The long-term health risks of chronic e-cigarette use are unknown. During the trial, side effects were minor in severity and showed greater throat or mouth irritation in the e-cigarette group, and more nausea in the NRT group. In the UK's National Health Service, e-cigarette use is associated with greater numbers of sustained quitting than NRT or other medications.[114] In the US, given epidemic levels of e-cigarette use among youth,[115] some public health professionals have warned that the potential benefits of e-cigarettes for quitting smoking in adults are outweighed by the risks to young people.

Cytisine is the oldest known smoking cessation aid, with use dating back more than 50 years in Eastern and Central European countries. Cytisine is an alkaloid extracted from the seeds of the golden rain or golden chain plant (*Cytisus laburnum*), which is common in Central and

Southern Europe. Similar to varenicline, cytisine acts on the α4β2 nAChR as a partial agonist with nicotine-like effects. Cytisine has been found to have superior effects relative to placebo[116] and NRT[117] and comparable effects to varenicline.[118] The recommended treatment is 25 days, which is shorter than most other smoking cessation medications and less costly. Cytisine's most common side effects are nausea, vomiting, dyspepsia, and dry mouth. Clinical trials show fewer adverse effects reported for cytisine relative to varenicline[118] but more than for NRT.[117] Cytisine is currently undergoing clinical trials in the US.

Nortriptyline (an antidepressant) and *clonidine* (a sedative and antihypertensive), though not FDA-approved, have demonstrated efficacy for smoking cessation in clinical trials[119,120] and are considered second-line treatments. Both drugs primarily are used by specialists with smokers who have failed other treatments, and clonidine appears most useful in those with anxiety as a major withdrawal symptom.

6.2. *Behavioral treatments*

Tobacco cessation behavioral treatment approaches are directed at helping patients successfully prepare to quit and maintain abstinence. Treatment can vary in duration and frequency of contact and may include building and supporting motivation, education on the harms of tobacco use and benefits of quitting, strategies for overcoming barriers to quitting, encouragement of proper use and adherence to medication regimens, and cognitive-behavioral cessation and relapse prevention strategies.

Brief cessation advice increases the likelihood of a successful quit[121] and has a "Grade A" recommendation from the US Preventive Services Task Force (USPSTF).[122] Counseling by non-physician health providers, including nurses,[123] dental professionals,[124] and pharmacists,[125] also increases quit rates. With evidence of increased patient treatment engagement, quit attempts, and tobacco abstinence,[126] the National Cancer Institute's (NCI) 5-As framework is to do the following: (1) Ask all patients about all forms of tobacco use; (2) Advise tobacco users to quit; (3) Assess readiness to quit; (4) Assist with counseling, cessation medications, and referrals; and (5) Arrange follow-up. When time is limited, an alternate approach with evidence is Ask-Advise-Refer (AAR), referring patients to outside services for assistance and follow-up, like the tobacco quitline (1-800-QUIT-NOW).[127,128] Further adaptation is Ask-Advise-Connect (AAC) with referral provided in the form of a direct connection, such as a fax or other electronic referral.[129] Comparison of AAR to the 5-A's delivered in dental clinics found comparable quit rates, with both approaches better than usual care, though sustained quit rates were under 4% in all three study arms.[128] A standard of care, brief provider advice is effective for encouraging quitting;[85] more intensive interventions, however, are needed to increase sustained abstinence.

Intensive cessation counseling, provided individually or in groups, is recommended by clinical practice guidelines.[85] Counseling may be provided by a trained clinician or tobacco treatment specialist in clinical, behavioral, or community settings or via telemedicine. The counseling framework tends to be cognitive behavioral and motivational, although increasingly other clinical approaches (e.g., mindfulness, acceptance and commitment therapy) are being incorporated. A systematic review of 49 randomized trials with 19,000 participants concluded that intensive counseling only (without medications) delivered individually by a cessation counselor was more effective than minimal contact (i.e., brief advice, self-help materials); greater effects were found when combined with cessation medications.[130] Intensive counseling treatments, individual and group-based, also are effective in workplace settings.[131] Access to intensive counseling may be challenged by distance, schedule, cost, or privacy concerns. Tobacco quitlines aim to improve the accessibility and reach of cessation counseling treatment.

Tobacco quitlines provide health education, self-help materials, individual counseling, local referrals, and may provide limited supplies of free cessation medications. Tobacco quitlines have demonstrated strong evidence of efficacy[132] and are available free-of-charge in the US accessed via a toll-free national portal (1-800-QUIT-NOW or 1-855-DÉJELO-YA). Based on callers' area code, the centralized number links to their state quitline. Most state quitlines provide at least one counseling session, and many states provide multiple sessions with reactive and proactive calls. The former relies upon smokers to initiate the contact, whereas the latter makes outbound calls to engage tobacco users. Better outcomes are achieved with multi-call versus single-call protocols[132] and with proactive versus reactive calls.[133]

Despite their convenience and being provided at no cost, on average, quitlines in most states reach only 1% of smokers annually.[134] The Centers for Disease Control and Prevention's (CDC) *Tips From Former Smokers*® (*Tips*®) media campaign, conducted annually since 2012, has generated hundreds of thousands of calls to state quitlines.[135] To further expand reach, some state quitlines incorporate mobile technologies.

Mobile health technologies utilizing the internet, chat, texting, and smart phone applications (apps) can be scaled with broad reach potential. Internet-delivered tobacco cessation interventions have existed for over 25 years with expanded sophistication, interaction, and functionality, and improved treatment efficacy. The Community Preventive Services Task Force (CPSTF) found adequate evidence to recommend internet-based tobacco treatment interventions. A 2016 review found internet-based quit smoking interventions superior in efficacy relative to print materials and equivalent in efficacy to telephone and in-person counseling.[136] In the US, internet-delivered tobacco cessation interventions have 27 times greater reach than quitlines (annually 11 million for internet vs. 400,000 for quitlines)[134] and at a lower cost-per-quit (e.g., $291 for internet vs. $900 for quitlines).[137]

The NCI's Smokefree.gov is a model internet-delivered tobacco cessation program that combines evidence-based guidelines, tailored to readiness to quit, with professional assistance available via telephone (1-877-44U-QUIT) and instant messaging. The site has tailored offerings for older adults (60+), women, adolescents, Spanish-speaking smokers, and veterans. SmokefreeTXT is a mobile service that provides encouragement, advice, and tips for young adults to quit smoking. Smokefree's smartphone app (quitSTART) has motivational reminders, trackers, tips for quitting (with functionality allowing the user to drop pins in high-risk locations and then receive tips when they approach those settings), badges for reaching milestones, and links to social media for sharing progress. The Smokefree.gov site had 3.6 million visitors in 2016[137] with high user satisfaction ratings.[138] Randomized trial evidence supports Smokefree.gov as a population-based intervention for smoking cessation.[137,139]

The CPSTF also recommends mobile text tobacco cessation interventions.[140] Texting is the most widely and frequently used application on smartphones, with 97% of Americans texting at least once a day.[141] Trials in New Zealand and the UK found that text messages sent daily up to the quit day that tapered to a maintenance phase outperformed a no-text control group; the texts were educational and motivational, provided quitting advice, and distraction strategies.[142,143] A later review of text-based quit smoking interventions found significant short-term effects that were not sustained long-term.[144] More intensive extended interventions may be needed to address the chronic, relapsing nature of tobacco dependence.

Quit smoking apps have the potential for greater interaction and can be downloaded for use on smartphones, tablets, and other handheld devices. Apps overcome many barriers in remote and resource-poor settings and can be provided at low or no-cost to the user with images and video for enhanced health literacy. In 2019, about 80% of White, Black and Latino adults owned a smartphone.[145] In a 2015 survey, 58% of mobile phone owners reported downloading a health app.[146] A 2014 search identified 546 quit smoking apps in the Apple Store and on Google Play that were downloaded 3.2 million times in the US and 20 million times worldwide.[147] A 2015 review of 225 Android apps for quitting smoking found most provided only simplistic tools (e.g., trackers, calculators); tailoring was limited, although positively related to app popularity and quality ratings.[148] A 2015 systematic review of the literature identified six tobacco cessation apps having evidence of scientific support, of which three (50%) were available in an app store.[149] In contrast, of the top 50 apps recommended by the leading app stores, only two (4%) had any scientific support. Evaluation of app intervention effects on quitting smoking is greatly needed. Of note, one randomized trial found a simpler, direct texting program outperformed a quit smoking app.[150]

Social media platforms are being examined for delivering tobacco cessation treatment. In the US, 74% of online adults use social media, 80% of whom seek health information, and many access the sites daily (74% for Facebook, 42% for Twitter).[151] Preliminary evidence of social media use for quitting smoking indicates good acceptability and efficacy; however, sustaining engagement is key and can be challenging.[152,153] Using Twitter, small, private peer support groups of 20 smokers, interacting for

100-days, have been studied. The intervention (Tweet2Quit) seeds the groups with twice-daily tweets to encourage group support and sharing. In a randomized trial, Tweet2Quit Twitter groups added to Smokefree.gov and the nicotine patch significantly doubled the likelihood of sustained abstinence relative to the website and patch alone.[154] Similar efforts were developed on Facebook, with a focus on young adult smokers. In a randomized trial, a novel Facebook intervention increased tobacco abstinence at the end of treatment although effects were not sustained at 12-month follow-up.[155]

Social media offers the possibility of anonymity, which may be appealing. Having failed to quit smoking in the past, people may hesitate publicizing quit attempts with their family and friends.[156] Social media sites that are un-curated or expert moderated, however, may carry inaccurate information or promote non-evidence-based treatments (e.g., lasers or herbs for quitting smoking).[152] With social media applications for smoking cessation still emerging, knowledge gaps remain regarding their efficacy.

Monetary incentives that reward engagement in tobacco cessation treatment and/or quitting smoking have been evaluated in 33 trials, with a meta-analysis finding increased abstinence that persisted after the incentives ceased.[157] Incentives ranged from zero (self-deposits) to between $45 and $1185, with no clear difference by level of incentive. Conditional incentives outperformed non-conditional incentives. Trials of incentives with smokers with substance use problems were consistent with the overall analysis, and trials with pregnant smokers reported an over 2-fold greater odds of abstinence at up to 24 weeks post-partum. Smoking brings substantial harms in the perinatal period, and currently there is no other effective cessation treatment for pregnant smokers.

Policy interventions can encourage quit attempts and support cessation, including legislation for tobacco-free worksites, housing, and public areas (e.g., parks, beaches); excise taxation on tobacco products; and expanded healthcare coverage for tobacco cessation treatment. Insurance coverage for tobacco treatment in the US remains inconsistent and often non-comprehensive, creating access challenges for patients. While the Affordable Care Act and other federal laws require most health insurance plans to cover some tobacco treatment, policymakers may not enforce these requirements.[158] Other population-based interventions to reduce tobacco use have faced challenges in the US at the federal (e.g., pictorial warnings on products, regulation of advertising and promotion at point-of-sale) and state level (e.g., California's tobacco flavor ban). As detailed earlier, the FDA has opened and invited public commenting to their proposal to reduce the amount of nicotine in cigarettes to minimize its addictiveness.

7. Integrating Tobacco Treatment into Cancer Care

Approximately 30% of cancer deaths in the US are attributed to smoking.[159] Patients diagnosed with cancer who smoke report higher motivation to quit relative to the general population; however, success with quitting is no higher.[160,161] About half of patients who smoked prior to a cancer diagnosis continued to smoke during treatment.[162] Continued smoking after a cancer diagnosis can complicate cancer treatments via medication interactions, increasing the risk of treatment side-effects, and by decreasing wound healing time.[163–166] Quitting smoking avoids these complications and decreases the risks of cancer recurrence and second primary tumors, thereby improving survival.[167,168] Hence, treating tobacco use is recommended as a standard component of cancer care.[169]

The National Comprehensive Cancer Network's (NCCN) guidelines for treating tobacco dependence in cancer care recommend repeated interventions (even as brief as 3 min) to encourage engagement in tobacco treatment, including counseling and the use of cessation medications.[169,170] Despite the promotion of NCCN guidelines for effective tobacco cessation strategies, system wide adoption of comprehensive tobacco treatment in cancer settings has been low. In a survey of NCI-designated comprehensive cancer centers, 40% reported not having any tobacco treatment available for patients.[171] System-level barriers to care include lack of organizational prioritization, inadequate staff training, poor clarity in roles and responsibilities, and few resources for treating tobacco.[171,172] In a survey of 1,101 members of the American Society of Clinical Oncology, 80% of responding clinicians reported they always ask about tobacco use at the initial visit, 58% always advised patients who use tobacco to quit, and 38% reported re-assessing tobacco at follow-up.[173] Barriers to routinely addressing tobacco were perceiving patients as resistant to tobacco treatment (74%) and inadequate training (38%).

Despite the known harms of tobacco use and the recommended need for tobacco cessation treatment in the oncology setting, the clinical trial evidence is weak with regard to outcomes. A meta-analysis of 21 smoking cessation studies with cancer survivors reported a non-significant treatment effect.[174] Subgroup analyses of specific behavior change techniques (e.g., general encouragement and enhancing self-efficacy), found to be effective in other patient populations (e.g., patients with COPD and surgical patients), also were non-significant. Novel approaches appear warranted and particularly with consideration of the unique aspects of cancer care systems and cancer survivorship. A more recent randomized controlled trial found that relative to 4 weeks of counseling and medication advice, extended counseling (i.e., the addition of 4 biweekly and 3 monthly telephone counseling sessions) plus free cessation medication resulted in significantly higher 6-month biochemically confirmed quit rates.[175]

Aimed at building the evidence base for accessible tobacco treatment that is consistent with NCCN guidelines and integrated into cancer care, NCI created the Cancer Center Cessation Initiative (C3I) with funding to 52 comprehensive cancer centers across the US.[176] The C3I aims to increase participation of patients with cancer in tobacco cessation treatment and improve the effectiveness of cancer treatment, preventing cancer recurrence. The initiative supports quality improvement (QI) projects at the participating cancer centers, with data coordination across sites, and with attention to outcomes and cost-effectiveness. Conducted in clinical settings with real-world patient populations, the C3I optimizes external validity or generalizability of project findings and is responsive to calls for "practice-based production."[177] Funded sites commit to the following: (1) identifying every patient treated for cancer in their center who smokes, urging cessation, offering evidence-based cessation treatment, and tracking treatment outcomes; (2) taking a systems-based approach, integrating evidence-based tobacco-dependence treatment into cancer care workflows and using EHR technology to facilitate such integration; and (3) supporting the program after NCI funding ends to ensure sustainability. A potential collateral benefit is expansion of the tobacco treatment service to other medical specialties. Patient outcomes are tracked out to 6-month follow-up and reported twice annually to the C3I coordinating center.

As part of the C3I initiative, the QI effort at the Stanford Cancer Center adopted an opt-out model, whereby patients identified in clinic as tobacco users are automatically referred to the tobacco treatment service. The service's tobacco treatment specialist calls all identified patients and offers a menu of tobacco cessation treatment options including individual, family, or group counseling provided in-person or via telemedicine, given that many patients live at a distance. The counseling services are provided to patients at no charge as a covered benefit. Additionally, telemedicine medication consultations are available with the service's physicians, and partnership with a virtual pharmacy provides direct-to-home medication delivery. Patients also receive referrals to California's quitline and NCI's smokefree.gov web and text services.

Initial QI efforts started with an assessment of clinic workflows and a 9-month pilot in three clinics identified as having higher patient smoking prevalence and staff interest. Evaluation demonstrated an increase in tobacco screening rates to 99% (from 95%); referrals to 100% (from <10%); with 74% of patients reached by phone; 33% of those reached engaging in treatment; and 20% of those engaged in treatment reporting abstinence from all tobacco products at 6-month follow-up.[178] Findings were reported back to the pilot sites and leadership before scaling the tobacco treatment service across the entire Stanford Cancer Center. Patient engagement has been higher than other comprehensive tobacco treatment services within oncology settings,[179,180] which tend to be about 20%. With regard to abstinence, the University of Texas MD Anderson Cancer Center, which provides a comprehensive approach to tobacco treatment, has reported a 9-month abstinence rate of 38% among 2779 individuals treated from 2006–2013. Automatic referral systems that identify current tobacco users or recent quitters at clinical or preclinical evaluations have been found to dramatically increase participation in tobacco treatment in cancer care.[161,179]

8. Summary

Nicotine addiction is a chronic brain disorder making quitting tobacco extremely difficult.[181] The tobacco industry designed cigarettes to create and sustain addiction. In 1982, RJ Reynolds scientist Claude Teague wrote, "Most of those who have smoked for any significant time would like to stop... we cannot ever be comfortable selling a product which most of our customers would stop using if they could... if the exit gate from our market should suddenly open, we could be out of business almost overnight."[182]

Though most smokers want to quit, relatively few quit attempts are successful. To address the substantial morbidity and mortality caused by tobacco — at nearly half a million preventable deaths annually in the US — a number of treatment approaches have been developed.[183] Smoking cessation treatments with evidence in adults include seven FDA-approved cessation medications, individual and group counseling, quitlines and other mobile technologies. Most efficacious are combinations of medication and behavioral treatments leveraged in an environment with strong tobacco control policies (Chapter 13). Current collaborative efforts funded by NCI are developing practice-based evidence for integrating tobacco cessation treatment into cancer care on a national scale with relevance for other medical specialties.

Given the modest efficacy of available tobacco cessation treatment approaches, attention has turned to policy interventions and regulatory actions. One concept, proposed more than 25 years ago, is to require a product standard for nicotine levels that would render cigarettes to be minimally or non-addictive, thereby helping smokers reduce their consumption, aid quitting, and prevent young people who experiment with tobacco from transitioning to regular, daily, addicted use. The public deserves an exit gate from nicotine addiction that is well illuminated and open.

Acknowledgment

Moonshot Supplements to the National Cancer Institute grant numbers P30CA 124435-1S2 and P30CA 1244351-13S2. Drs. Prochaska and Benowitz have served as expert witnesses in lawsuits against the tobacco companies and have provided consultation to pharmaceutical (Pfizer, Achieve Life Sciences) and technology companies that make medications and other treatments for quitting smoking.

References

1. Mellman AJ. Project recommendations. Product Design MSA Collection; 1983: Bates No. 514110006-9.
2. Teague Jr. C. Research planning memorandum on the nature of the tobacco business and the crucial role of nicotine therein. Philip Morris Records; Master Settlement Agreement; 1996: Bates No. 2072555994-7.
3. Wakeham H. An Opinion on Cigarette Smoking and Cancer. Philip Morris Records; Master Settlement Agreement; 1959: Bates No. 1005039423-4.
4. Kessler G. United States of America v. Philip Morris USA, Inc., *et al.*, Civil Action no. 99–2496, Final Opinion, 2006
5. Hilts PJ. Tobacco chiefs say cigarettes aren't addictive. *New York Times* 1994 April 15;Sect. 1.
6. U.S. Department of Health and Human Services. *The Health Consequences of Smoking: Nicotine Addiction.* A Report of the Surgeon General. (Washington, DC: U.S. Department of Health and Human Services, Centers for Disease Control, Center for Health Promotion and Education, Office on Smoking and Health, 1988).
7. Cigarettes and other tobacco products DrugFacts. 2020. https://www. drugabuse.gov/publications/drugfacts/cigarettes-other-tobacco-products, accessed January 4, 2021.
8. Benowitz NL. Nicotine addiction. *New Eng J Med* 2010;362:2295–303.
9. Koob GF, Volkow ND. Neurocircuitry of addiction. *Neuropsychopharmacology* 2010;35:217–38.
10. Fowler CD, Turner JR, Imad Damaj M. Molecular mechanisms associated with nicotine pharmacology and dependence. *Handb Exp Pharmacol* 2020;258:373–393.
11. Giedd JN, Blumenthal J, Jeffries NO, *et al.* Brain development during childhood and adolescence: A longitudinal MRI study. *Nature Neurosci* 1999;2:861–3.
12. U.S. Department of Health and Human Services. *Preventing Tobacco Use Among Youth and Young Adults: A Report of the Surgeon General.* (Atlanta, GA: U.S. Dept. of Health and Human Services, Centers for Disease Control and Prevention, National Center for Chronic Disease Prevention and Health Promotion, Office on Smoking and Health, 2012).
13. Yuan M, Cross SJ, Loughlin SE, Leslie FM. Nicotine and the adolescent brain. *J Physiol* 2015;593:3397–412.
14. O'Loughlin J, DiFranza J, Tyndale RF, *et al.* Nicotine-dependence symptoms are associated with smoking frequency in adolescents. *Am J Prev Med* 2003;25:219–25.

15. Kandel DB, Chen K. Extent of smoking and nicotine dependence in the United States: 1991–1993. *Nicotine Tobacco Res* 2000;2:263–74.

16. Robinson ML, Berlin I, Moolchan ET. Tobacco smoking trajectory and associated ethnic differences among adolescent smokers seeking cessation treatment. *J Adolescent Health* 2004;35:217–24.

17. Grant BF. Age at smoking onset and its association with alcohol consumption and DSM-IV alcohol abuse and dependence: Results from the national longitudinal alcohol epidemiologic survey. *J Substance Abuse* 1998; 10:59–73.

18. Taioli E, Wynder EL. Effect of the age at which smoking begins on frequency of smoking in adulthood. *New Eng J Med* 1991;325:968–9.

19. Dierker L, Swendsen J, Rose J, He J, Merikangas K, Network TTER. Transitions to regular smoking and nicotine dependence in the Adolescent National Comorbidity Survey (NCS-A). *Ann Behav Med* 2012;43: 394–401.

20. Hu M-C, Griesler PC, Schaffran C, Wall MM, Kandel DB. Trajectories of criteria of nicotine dependence from adolescence to early adulthood. *Drug Alcohol Depend* 2012;125:283–9.

21. Volkow N. Altered pathways: Drug abuse and age of onset. *Addict Prof* 2006;26:29.

22. Breslau N, Peterson EL. Smoking cessation in young adults: Age at initiation of cigarette smoking and other suspected influences. *Am J Public Health* 1996;86:214.

23. Chassin L, Presson CC, Rose JS, Sherman SJ. The natural history of cigarette smoking from adolescence to adulthood: Demographic predictors of continuity and change. *Health Psychol* 1996;15:478–84.

24. Peters J, Bromberg U, Schneider S, *et al.* Lower ventral striatal activation during reward anticipation in adolescent smokers. *The Am J Psych* 2011;168:540–9.

25. Rubinstein ML, Luks TL, Dryden WY, Rait MA, Simpson GV. Adolescent smokers show decreased brain responses to pleasurable food images compared with nonsmokers. *Nicotine Tob Res* 2011;13:751–5.

26. Why one smokes. Philip Morris Records; Master Settlement Agreement; 1969: Bates No.1003287836-48.

27. Benowitz NL. Cigarette smoking and nicotine addiction. *Med Clin North Am* 1992;76:415–37.

28. Hymowitz N, Cummings KM, Hyland A, Lynn WR, Pechacek TF, Hartwell TD. Predictors of smoking cessation in a cohort of adult smokers followed for five years. *Tobacco Control* 1997;6 Suppl 2:S57–62.

29. Heatherton TF, Kozlowski LT, Frecker RC, Rickert W, Robinson J. Measuring the heaviness of smoking: Using self-reported time to the first cigarette of the day and number of cigarettes smoked per day. *British J Add.* 1989;84:791–800.

30. Baker TB, Piper ME, McCarthy DE, *et al.* Time to first cigarette in the morning as an index of ability to quit smoking: Implications for nicotine dependence. *Nicotine Tobacco Res* 2007;9 Suppl 4:S555–70.

31. Schnoll RA, Goren A, Annunziata K, Suaya JA. The prevalence, predictors and associated health outcomes of high nicotine dependence using three measures among US smokers. *Addiction* 2013;108:1989–2000.

32. Baker TB, Breslau N, Covey L, Shiffman S. DSM criteria for tobacco use disorder and tobacco withdrawal: A critique and proposed revisions for DSM-5. *Addiction* 2012;107:263–75.

33. Gu F, Cheung LC, Freedman ND, Katki HA, Caporaso NE. Potential impact of including time to first cigarette in risk models for selecting ever-smokers for lung cancer screening. *J Thoracic Oncol* 2017;12:1646–53.

34. Muhammad-Kah RS, Hayden AD, Liang Q, Frost-Pineda K, Sarkar M. The relationship between nicotine dependence scores and biomarkers of exposure in adult cigarette smokers. *Reg Toxicol Pharmacol* 2011;60:79–83.

35. Kopa PN, Pawliczak R. Effect of smoking on gene expression profile — overall mechanism, impact on respiratory system function, and reference to electronic cigarettes. *Toxicol Mech Meth* 2018;28:397–409.

36. Chen J, Loukola A, Gillespie NA, *et al.* Genome-wide meta-analyses of FTND and TTFC phenotypes. *Nicotine Tob Res* 2020;22(6):900–909.

37. Schnoll RA, George TP, Hawk L, Cinciripini P, Wileyto P, Tyndale RF. The relationship between the nicotine metabolite ratio and three self-report measures of nicotine dependence across sex and race. *Psychopharmacology (Berl)* 2014;231:2515–23.

38. Allenby CE, Boylan KA, Lerman C, Falcone M. Precision medicine for tobacco dependence: Development and validation of the nicotine metabolite ratio. *J Neuro Pharmacol* 2016;11:471–83.

39. Siahpush M, Borland R, Yong HH. Sociodemographic and psychosocial correlates of smoking-induced deprivation and its effect on quitting: Findings from the International Tobacco Control Policy Evaluation Survey. *Tobacco Control* 2007;16:e2.

40. Siahpush M, Shaikh RA, Cummings KM, *et al.* The association of point-of-sale cigarette marketing with cravings to smoke: results from a cross-sectional population-based study. *Tobacco Control* 2016;25:402–5.

41. Nonnemaker J, Kim A, Shafer P, *et al*. Influence of point-of-sale tobacco displays and plain black and white cigarette packaging and advertisements on adults: Evidence from a virtual store experimental study. *Addictive Behav* 2016;56:15–22.

42. Shmueli D, Prochaska JJ, Glantz SA. Effect of smoking scenes in films on immediate smoking: A randomized controlled study. *Am J Prev Med* 2010;38:351–8.

43. American Psychiatric Association. *Diagnostic and Statistical Manual of Mental Disorders*. 5th edn. (Arlington,VA: American Psychiatric Association, 2013).

44. Berridge KC, Robinson TE. Liking, wanting, and the incentive-sensitization theory of addiction. *Am Psychol* 2016;71:670–9.

45. Leshner AI. Drug abuse and addiction are biomedical problems. (Bethesda, MD: National Institute on Drug Abuse, National Institutes of Health, 1997).

46. Volkow ND, Fowler JS, Wang GJ. The addicted human brain: Insights from imaging studies. *J Clin Invest* 2003;111:1444–51.

47. Prochaska JJ, Michalek AK, Brown-Johnson C, *et al*. Likelihood of unemployed smokers vs nonsmokers attaining reemployment in a one-year observational study. *JAMA Int Med* 2016;176:662–70.

48. Baker CL, Flores NM, Zou KH, Bruno M, Harrison VJ. Benefits of quitting smoking on work productivity and activity impairment in the United States, the European Union and China. *Int J Clin Pract* 2017;71.

49. Wakeham HRR, Ph.D. *Smoker Psychology Research*. Product Design MSA Collection, 1969: Bates No. 1000273741-71.

50. U.S. Department of Health and Human Services. *The Health Consequences of Smoking: Nicotine Addiction. A Report of the Surgeon General*. (Washington, DC: U.S. Department of Health and Human Services, Centers for Disease Control, Center for Health Promotion and Education, Office on Smoking and Health, 1988).

51. World Health Organization. Tobacco. 2021. https://www.who.int/health-topics/tobacco#tab=tab_1.

52. APA Workgroup on Tobacco Use Disorder, Council on Addiction Psychiatry. *Position Statement on Tobacco Use Disorder* (American Psychiatric Association, 2015).

53. World Health Organization. *Advisory Note: Global Nicotine Reduction Strategy: WHO Study Group on Tobacco Product Regulation* (Switzerland: World Health Organization, 2015).

54. Benowitz NL. Clinical pharmacology of nicotine: Implications for under-standing, preventing, and treating tobacco addiction. *Clin Pharmacol Therap* 2008;83:531–41.

55. Philip Morris Developments. *The Denicotinized Tobacco Story*. Philip Morris Records; Master Settlement Agreement, 1990: Bates No. 2078425524-40.

56. Alkaloid Reduced Tobacco (ART) Program. Product Design MSA Collection; 1994: Bates No. 2057908259-91.

57. Dunsby J, Bero L. A nicotine delivery device without the nicotine? Tobacco industry development of low nicotine cigarettes. *Tobacco Control* 2004;13:362–9

58. RDW. *Complexity of the PA5A Machine and Variables Pool*. British American Tobacco Records. Truth Tobacco Industry Documents, UCSF, 1959.

59. Dunn Jr. WL. *Motives and Incentives in Cigarette Smoking*. Lorillard Records; Master Settlement Agreement, 1973: Bates No. 85873686-703.

60. Smith RE. *RT Information Task Force Goal*. Marketing to Youth MSA Collection; 1980: Bates No. 01394380-1Exhibit101.

61. Benowitz NL, Henningfield JE. Establishing a nicotine threshold for addiction. The implications for tobacco regulation. *New Eng J Med* 1994;331:123–5.

62. Food and Drug Administration. Family Smoking Prevention and Tobacco Control Act. In: Food and Drug Administration (FDA), ed. Silver Spring, MD2012.

63. Gottlieb S. Statement from FDA Commissioner Scott Gottlieb, M.D., on pivotal public health step to dramatically reduce smoking rates by lowering nicotine in combustible cigarettes to minimally or non-addictive levels. U.S. Food and Drug Administration; 2018.

64. Bamundo Qualitative Research. *A Qualitative Exploration Designed to Gain Insights Into the Appeal of a 97 Percent Nicotine-free Cigarette*. Philip Morris Records; Master Settlement Agreement, 1987: Bates No. 2023087252-83.

65. Leo Burnett Agency, Philip Morris, Bonhomme J, Lalley C, Levy C, Stamel N. *Marketing Research Department Report Qualitative Research on Art*. Philip Morris Records; Master Settlement Agreement, 1988: Bates No. 2023088868-71.

66. Pearson JL, Abrams DB, Niaura RS, Richardson A, Vallone DM. Public support for mandated nicotine reduction in cigarettes. *Am J Public Health* 2013;103:562–7.

67. Bolcic-Jankovic D, Biener L. Public opinion about FDA regulation of menthol and nicotine. *Tobacco Control* 2015;24:e241–5.
68. Berman ML, Glasser AM. Nicotine reduction in cigarettes: Literature review and gap analysis. *Nicotine Tobacco Res* 2019;21:S133–S44.
69. Donny EC, Denlinger RL, Tidey JW, *et al.* Randomized trial of reduced-nicotine standards for cigarettes. *New Eng J Med* 2015;373:1340–9.
70. Hatsukami DK, Kotlyar M, Hertsgaard LA, *et al.* Reduced nicotine content cigarettes: Effects on toxicant exposure, dependence and cessation. Addiction 2010;105:343–55.
71. Benowitz NL, Nardone N, Dains KM, *et al.* Effect of reducing the nicotine content of cigarettes on cigarette smoking behavior and tobacco smoke toxicant exposure: 2-year follow up. *Addiction* 2015;110:1667–75.
72. Nardone N, Donny EC, Hatsukami DK, *et al.* Estimations and predictors of non-compliance in switchers to reduced nicotine content cigarettes. *Addiction* 2016;111:2208–16.
73. Mercincavage M, Wileyto EP, Saddleson ML, Lochbuehler K, Donny EC, Strasser AA. Attrition during a randomized controlled trial of reduced nicotine content cigarettes as a proxy for understanding acceptability of nicotine product standards. *Addiction* 2017;112:1095–103.
74. Benowitz NL, Donny EC, Hatsukami DK. Reduced nicotine content cigarettes, e-cigarettes and the cigarette end game. *Addiction* 2017;112:6–7.
75. Apelberg BJ, Feirman SP, Salazar E, *et al.* Potential public health effects of reducing nicotine levels in cigarettes in the United States. *N Engl J Med* 2018;378:1725–33.
76. Prochaska JJ, Benowitz NL. Current advances in research in treatment and recovery: Nicotine addiction. *Sci Adv* 2019;5:eaay9763.
77. Brunnemann KD, Hoffmann D. The pH of tobacco smoke. *Food Cosmet Toxicol* 1974;12:115–24.
78. Proctor RN. *Golden Holocaust: Origins of the Cigarette Catastrophe and a Case for Abolition* (California: University of California Press, 2011).
79. Chang CM, Corey CG, Rostron BL, Apelberg BJ. Systematic review of cigar smoking and all cause and smoking related mortality. *BMC Public Health* 2015;15:390.
80. Ingram D, Yukhananov A. *U.S. Court Strikes Down Graphic Warnings on Cigarettes* (Reuters: Reuters, 2012).
81. Fox M. Big tobacco finally tells the truth in court-ordered ad campaign. *NBC News*, 2017.

82. Cornelius ME, Wang TW, Jamal A, Loretan CG, Neff LJ. Tobacco product use among adults — United States. *MMWR Morb Mortal Wkly Rep* 2020:1736–472.

83. Babb S, Malarcher A, Schauer G, Asman K, Jamal A. Quitting smoking among adults — United States, 2000–2015. *MMWR Morb Mortal Wkly Rep* 2017:1457–64.

84. Borland R, Partos TR, Yong HH, Cummings KM, Hyland A. How much unsuccessful quitting activity is going on among adult smokers? Data from the International Tobacco Control Four Country cohort survey. *Addiction* 2012;107:673–82.

85. Fiore MC, Jaén CR, Baker TB, *et al. Treating Tobacco use and Dependence: 2008 Update. U.S. Public Health Service Clinical Practice Guideline* (Rockville (MD): U.S. Department of Health and Human Services, 2008).

86. Richter KP, Ellerbeck EF. It's time to change the default for tobacco treatment. *Addiction* 2015;110:381–6.

87. Amato KA, Reid ME, Ochs-Balcom HM, *et al.* Evaluation of a dedicated tobacco cessation support service for thoracic cancer center patients. *J Public Health Manage Pract* 2018;24:E12.

88. Nahhas GJ, Wilson D, Talbot V, *et al.* Feasibility of implementing a hospital-based "opt-out" tobacco-cessation service. *Nicotine Tobacco Res* 2017;19:937–43.

89. Nolan M, Ridgeway JL, Ghosh K, Martin D, Warner DO. Design, implementation, and evaluation of an intervention to improve referral to smoking cessation services in breast cancer patients. *Supp Care Cancer* 2019;27:2153–8.

90. Fanshawe TR, Halliwell W, Lindson N, Aveyard P, Livingstone-Banks J, Hartmann-Boyce J. Tobacco cessation interventions for young people. *Cochrane Database Syst Rev* 2017;11(11):CD003289.

91. Shields P, Bierut L, Herbst R, *et al.* NCCN guidelines: Smoking cessation, version 2.2019. *J Natl Comp Cancer Netw* 2019.

92. Nides M, Danielsson T, Saunders F, *et al.* Efficacy and safety of a nicotine mouth spray for smoking cessation: A randomized, multicenter, controlled study in a naturalistic setting. *Nicotine Tob Res* 2020;22(3):339–345.

93. Rollema H, Coe JW, Chambers LK, Hurst RS, Stahl SM, Williams KE. Rationale, pharmacology and clinical efficacy of partial agonists of alpha-4beta2 nACh receptors for smoking cessation. *Trends Pharmacol Sci* 2007;28:316–25.

94. Cahill K, Stevens S, Perera R, Lancaster T. Pharmacological interventions for smoking cessation: An overview and network meta-analysis. *Cochrane Database Syst Rev* 2013:Cd009329.

95. Anthenelli RM, Benowitz NL, West R, *et al*. Neuropsychiatric safety and efficacy of varenicline, bupropion, and nicotine patch in smokers with and without psychiatric disorders (EAGLES): A double-blind, randomised, placebo-controlled clinical trial. *Lancet* 2016;387:2507–20.

96. Tonstad S, Tonnesen P, Hajek P, Williams KE, Billing CB, Reeves KR. Effect of maintenance therapy with varenicline on smoking cessation: A randomized controlled trial. *JAMA* 2006;296:64–71.

97. Eisenberg MJ, Windle SB, Roy N, *et al*. Varenicline for smoking cessation in hospitalized patients with acute coronary syndrome. *Circulation* 2016;133:21–30.

98. Rigotti NA, Pipe AL, Benowitz NL, Arteaga C, Garza D, Tonstad S. Efficacy and safety of varenicline for smoking cessation in patients with cardiovascular disease: A randomized trial. *Circulation* 2010;121:221–9.

99. Benowitz NL, Pipe A, West R, *et al*. Cardiovascular safety of varenicline, bupropion, and nicotine patch in smokers: A randomized clinical trial. *JAMA Int Med* 2018;178:622–31.

100. Sterling LH, Windle SB, Filion KB, Touma L, Eisenberg MJ. Varenicline and adverse cardiovascular events: A systematic review and meta-analysis of randomized controlled trials. *J Am Heart Assoc* 2016;5.

101. Ebbert JO, Elrashidi MY, Stead LF. Interventions for smokeless tobacco use cessation. *Cochrane Database Syst Rev* 2015:Cd004306.

102. Howes S, Hartmann-Boyce J, Livingstone-Banks J, Hong B, Lindson N. Antidepressants for smoking cessation. *Cochrane Database Syst Rev* 2020;4:Cd000031.

103. Hays JT, Hurt RD, Rigotti NA, *et al*. Sustained-release bupropion for pharmacologic relapse prevention after smoking cessation. A randomized, controlled trial. *Ann Int Med* 2001;135:423–33.

104. Lindson N, Chepkin SC, Ye W, Fanshawe TR, Bullen C, Hartmann-Boyce J. Different doses, durations and modes of delivery of nicotine replacement therapy for smoking cessation. *Cochrane Database Syst Rev* 2019;4(4): CD013308.

105. Chang PH, Chiang CH, Ho WC, Wu PZ, Tsai JS, Guo FR. Combination therapy of varenicline with nicotine replacement therapy is better than varenicline alone: A systematic review and meta-analysis of randomized controlled trials. *BMC Public Health* 2015;15:689.

106. Rennard S, Hughes J, Cinciripini PM, *et al*. A randomized placebo-controlled trial of varenicline for smoking cessation allowing flexible quit dates. *Nicotine Tobacco Res* 2012;14:343–50.

107. Sansores RH, Ramirez-Venegas A, Arellano-Rocha R, *et al*. Use of varenicline for more than 12 months for smoking cessation in heavy chronic obstructive pulmonary disease smokers unmotivated to quit: A pilot study. *Therap Adv Resp Dis* 2016;10:383–90.

108. Ebbert JO, Hughes JR, West RJ, *et al*. Effect of varenicline on smoking cessation through smoking reduction: A randomized clinical trial. *JAMA* 2015;313:687–94.

109. Liakoni E, Edwards KC, St Helen G, *et al*. Effects of nicotine metabolic rate on withdrawal symptoms and response to cigarette smoking after abstinence. *Clin Pharmacol Therap* 2019;105:641–51.

110. Lerman C, Schnoll RA, Hawk LW, Jr., *et al*. Use of the nicotine metabolite ratio as a genetically informed biomarker of response to nicotine patch or varenicline for smoking cessation: A randomised, double-blind placebo-controlled trial. *Lancet Resp Med* 2015;3:131–8.

111. Zawertailo L, Hendershot CS, Tyndale RF, *et al*. Personalized dosing of nicotine replacement therapy versus standard dosing for the treatment of individuals with tobacco dependence: Study protocol for a randomized placebo-controlled trial. *Trials* 2020;21:592.

112. Hartmann-Boyce J, McRobbie H, Lindson N, *et al*. Electronic cigarettes for smoking cessation. *Cochrane Database Syst Rev* 2020;10:Cd010216.

113. Hajek P, Phillips-Waller A, Przulj D, *et al*. A randomized trial of e-cigarettes versus nicotine-replacement therapy. *New Eng J Med* 2019;380:629–37.

114. McNeill A, Brose LS, Calder R, Bauld L, Robson D. *Evidence Review of e-cigarettes and Heated Tobacco Products 2018*. A report commissioned by Public Health England (London: Public Health England, 2018).

115. Wang TW, Neff LJ, Park-Lee E, Ren C, Cullen KA, King BA. E-cigarette use among middle and high school students — United States, 2020. *MMWR Morb Mortal Wkly Rep* 2020;69:1310–2.

116. Tutka P, Vinnikov D, Courtney RJ, Benowitz NL. Cytisine for nicotine addiction treatment: A review of pharmacology, therapeutics and an update of clinical trial evidence for smoking cessation. *Addiction* 2019;114(11): 1951–1969.

117. Walker N, Howe C, Glover M, *et al*. Cytisine versus nicotine for smoking cessation. *New Eng J Med* 2014;371:2353–62.

118. Achieve announces successful results from the investigator-initiated RAUORA head-to-head non-inferiority clinical trial comparing Cytisinicline and Chantix (varenicline) as a treatment to quit smoking. *Achieve Life Sciences*, 2020.

119. Gourlay SG, Stead LF, Benowitz NL. Clonidine for smoking cessation. *Cochrane Database Syst Rev* 2004:Cd000058.

120. Hughes JR, Stead LF, Lancaster T. Nortriptyline for smoking cessation: a review. *Nicotine Tobacco Res* 2005;7:491–9.

121. Stead LF, Buitrago D, Preciado N, Sanchez G, Hartmann-Boyce J, Lancaster T. Physician advice for smoking cessation. *Cochrane Database Syst Rev* 2013;2013(5):CD000165.

122. Final Update Summary: *Tobacco Smoking Cessation in Adults, Including Pregnant Women: Behavioral and Pharmacotherapy Interventions*. U.S. Preventive Services Task Force. 2015. https://www.uspreventiveservicestaskforce.org/Page/Document/UpdateSummaryFinal/tobacco-use-in-adults-and-pregnant-women-counseling-and-interventions, accessed July 31, 2019.

123. Rice VH, Heath L, Livingstone-Banks J, Hartmann-Boyce J. Nursing interventions for smoking cessation. *Cochrane Database Syst Rev* 2017;12:Cd001188.

124. Carr AB, Ebbert J. Interventions for tobacco cessation in the dental setting. *Cochrane Database Syst Rev* 2012:Cd005084.

125. Augustine JM, Taylor AM, Pelger M, Schiefer D, Warholak TL. Smoking quit rates among patients receiving pharmacist-provided pharmacotherapy and telephonic smoking cessation counseling. *J Am Pharm Assoc* 2016;56:129–36.

126. Quinn VP, Hollis JF, Smith KS, *et al*. Effectiveness of the 5-As tobacco cessation treatments in nine HMOs. *J Gen Intern Med* 2009;24:149–54.

127. Schroeder SA. What to do with a patient who smokes. *JAMA* 2005;294:482–7.

128. Gordon JS, Andrews JA, Crews KM, Payne TJ, Severson HH, Lichtenstein E. Do faxed quitline referrals add value to dental office-based tobacco-use cessation interventions? *J Am Dent Assoc* 2010;141:1000–7.

129. Vidrine JI, Shete S, Li Y, *et al*. The Ask-Advise-Connect approach for smokers in a safety net healthcare system: a group-randomized trial. *Am J Prev Med* 2013;45:737–41.

130. Lancaster T, Stead LF. Individual behavioural counselling for smoking cessation. *Cochrane Database Syst Rev* 2017;3:Cd001292.

131. Cahill K, Lancaster T. Workplace interventions for smoking cessation. *Cochrane Database Syst Rev* 2014:Cd003440.

132. Stead LF, Hartmann-Boyce J, Perera R, Lancaster T. Telephone counselling for smoking cessation. *Cochrane Database Syst Rev* 2013:Cd002850.

133. Tobacco Use and Secondhand Smoke Exposure: Quitline Interventions. The Community Guide, 2012. https://www.thecommunityguide.org/findings/tobacco-use-and-secondhand-smoke-exposure-quitline-interventions, accessed July 31, 2019.

134. Results from the 2017 NAQC annual survey of quitlines. North American Quitline Consortium, 2018. https://www.naquitline.org/page/2017survey.

135. Davis KC, Alexander RL, Jr., Shafer P, Mann N, Malarcher A, Zhang L. The dose-response relationship between tobacco education advertising and calls to quitlines in the United States, March-June, 2012. *Prev Chronic Dis* 2015;12:E191.

136. Graham AL, Carpenter KM, Cha S, *et al.* Systematic review and meta-analysis of internet interventions for smoking cessation among adults. *Substance Abuse Rehab* 2016;7:55-69.

137. Bricker JB, Mull KE, McClure JB, Watson NL, Heffner JL. Improving quit rates of web-delivered interventions for smoking cessation: Full-scale randomized trial of WebQuit.org versus Smokefree.gov. *Addiction* 2018; 113:914–23.

138. Etter JF. A list of the most popular smoking cessation web sites and a comparison of their quality. *Nicotine Tobacco Res* 2006;8 Suppl 1:S27–34.

139. Fraser D, Kobinsky K, Smith SS, Kramer J, Theobald WE, Baker TB. Five population-based interventions for smoking cessation: A MOST trial. *Trans Behav Med* 2014;4:382–90.

140. The Community Guide. Tobacco use and secondhand smoke exposure: Mobile phone-based cessation interventions. 2011.

141. Smith A. *U.S. Smartphone Use in 2015* (Washington, DC: Pew Research Center, 2015).

142. Rodgers A, Corbett T, Bramley D, *et al.* Do u smoke after txt? Results of a randomised trial of smoking cessation using mobile phone text messaging. *Tobacco Control* 2005;14:255–61.

143. Free C, Knight R, Robertson S, *et al.* Smoking cessation support delivered via mobile phone text messaging (txt2stop): A single-blind, randomised trial. *Lancet* 2011;378:49–55.

144. Scott-Sheldon LA, Lantini R, Jennings EG, *et al.* Text messaging-based interventions for smoking cessation: a systematic review and meta-analysis. *JMIR mHealth and uHhealth* 2016;4:e49.

145. Perrin A, Turner E. *Smartphones Help Blacks, Hispanics Bridge Some — But not All — Digital Gaps with Whites* (Washington, DC: Pew Research Center, 2019).

146. Krebs P, Duncan DT. Health app use among US mobile phone owners: A national survey. *JMIR mHealth uHealth* 2015;3:e101.

147. Bricker JB, Mull KE, Kientz JA, *et al.* Randomized, controlled pilot trial of a smartphone app for smoking cessation using acceptance and commitment therapy. *Drug & Alcohol Dependence* 2014;143:87–94.

148. Hoeppner BB, Hoeppner SS, Seaboyer L, *et al.* How smart are smartphone apps for smoking cessation? A content analysis. *Nicotine Tobacco Res* 2016;18:1025–31.

149. Haskins BL, Lesperance D, Gibbons P, Boudreaux ED. A systematic review of smartphone applications for smoking cessation. *Trans Behav Med* 2017;7:292–9.

150. Buller DB, Borland R, Bettinghaus EP, Shane JH, Zimmerman DE. Randomized trial of a smartphone mobile application compared to text messaging to support smoking cessation. *Telemed J E Health* 2014;20:206–14.

151. Smith A, Anderson M. Social media use in 2018. Report: Pew Research Center; 2018 March 1, 2018.

152. Prochaska JJ, Pechmann C, Kim R, Leonhardt JM. Twitter=quitter? An analysis of Twitter quit smoking social networks. *Tobacco Control* 2012;21:447–9.

153. Stoddard JL, Augustson EM, Moser RP. Effect of adding a virtual community (bulletin board) to smokefree.gov: Randomized controlled trial. *J Med Int Res* 2008;10:e53.

154. Pechmann C, Delucchi K, Lakon CM, Prochaska JJ. Randomised controlled trial evaluation of Tweet2Quit: A social network quit-smoking intervention. *Tobacco Control* 2017;26:188–94.

155. Ramo DE, Thrul J, Delucchi KL, *et al.* A randomized controlled evaluation of the tobacco status project, a Facebook intervention for young adults. *Addiction* 2018;10.1111/add.14245.

156. Thomas JL, Bengtson JE, Ghidei W, *et al.* Social contingencies and college quit and win contest: A qualitative inquiry. *Am J Health Behav* 2015;39:232–41.

157. Notley C, Gentry S, Livingstone-Banks J, Bauld L, Perera R, Hartmann-Boyce J. Incentives for smoking cessation. *Cochrane Database Syst Rev* 2019;7(7):CD004307.

158. American Lung Association. Tobacco cessation treatment: What is covered? 2020. https://www.lung.org/policy-advocacy/tobacco/cessation/tobacco-cessation-treatment-what-is-covered, Accesssed 10/19/2021.

159. Jacobs EJ, Newton CC, Carter BD, *et al.* What proportion of cancer deaths in the contemporary United States is attributable to cigarette smoking? *Ann Epidemiol* 2015;25:179–82. e1.

160. Walker MS, Vidrine DJ, Gritz ER, *et al.* Smoking relapse during the first year after treatment for early-stage non–small-cell lung cancer. *Cancer Epidemiol Prev Biomarkers* 2006;15:2370–7.

161. Karam-Hage M, Cinciripini PM, Gritz ER. Tobacco use and cessation for cancer survivors: An overview for clinicians. *CA: Cancer J Clin* 2014;64:272–90.

162. Lucchiari C, Masiero M, Botturi A, Pravettoni G. Helping patients to reduce tobacco consumption in oncology: A narrative review. *SpringerPlus* 2016;5:1136.

163. Marin VP, Pytynia KB, Langstein HN, Dahlstrom KR, Wei Q, Sturgis EM. Serum cotinine concentration and wound complications in head and neck reconstruction. *Plastic Reconstr Surg* 2008;121:451–7.

164. Gajdos C, Hawn MT, Campagna EJ, Henderson WG, Singh JA, Houston T. Adverse effects of smoking on postoperative outcomes in cancer patients. *Ann Surg Oncol* 2012;19:1430–8.

165. O'Malley M, King AN, Conte M, Ellingrod VL, Ramnath N. Effects of cigarette smoking on metabolism and effectiveness of systemic therapy for lung cancer. *J Thoracic Oncol* 2014;9:917–26.

166. Peppone LJ, Mustian KM, Morrow GR, *et al.* The effect of cigarette smoking on cancer treatment-related side effects. *Oncologist* 2011;16:1784–92.

167. Parsons A, Daley A, Begh R, Aveyard P. Influence of smoking cessation after diagnosis of early stage lung cancer on prognosis: Systematic review of observational studies with meta-analysis. *BMJ* (*Clin Res Ed*) 2010;340:b5569.

168. Garces YI, Yang P, Parkinson J, *et al.* The relationship between cigarette smoking and quality of life after lung cancer diagnosis. *Chest* 2004;126:1733–41.

169. Shields PG, Bierut L, Herbst RS, *et al.* NCCN clinical practice guidelines in oncology (NCCN Guidelines): Smoking cessation. 2019.

170. Fiore MC, Jaén CR, Baker TB, *et al. Treating Tobacco Use and Dependence: 2008 Update* (Rockville, MD: US Department of Health and Human Services, 2008).

171. Goldstein AO, Ripley-Moffitt CE, Pathman DE, Patsakham KM. Tobacco use treatment at the US National Cancer Institute's designated cancer centers. *Nicotine Tobacco Res* 2013;15.

172. Adsit R, Wisinski K, Mattison R, Bailey H, Fiore M. A survey of baseline tobacco cessation clinical practices and receptivity to academic detailing. *WMJ* 2016;115:143–6.

173. Warren GW, Marshall JR, Cummings KM, *et al.* Addressing tobacco use in patients with cancer: A survey of American Society of Clinical Oncology members. *J Oncol Pract* 2013;9:258–62.

174. Sheeran P, Jones K, Avishai A, *et al.* What works in smoking cessation interventions for cancer survivors? A meta-analysis. *Health Psychol* 2019;38:855.

175. Goldstein AO, Shoenbill KA, Jolly TA. Intensive smoking cessation counseling for patients with cancer. *JAMA* 2020;324:1401–3.

176. Croyle RT, Morgan GD, Fiore MC. Addressing a core gap in cancer care — the NCI Moonshot program to help oncology patients stop smoking. *New Eng J Med* 2019;380:512–5.

177. Green LW. Making research relevant: If it is an evidence-based practice, where's the practice-based evidence? *Family Practice* 2008;25:i20–i4.

178. Gali K, Pike B, Kendra MS, *et al.* Integration of tobacco treatment services into cancer care at Stanford. *Int J Environ Res Public Health* 2020;17(6):2101.

179. Karam-Hage M, Oughli HA, Rabius V, *et al.* Tobacco cessation treatment pathways for patients with cancer: 10 years in the making. *J Natl Compr Canc Netw* 2016;14:1469–77.

180. Abdelmutti N, Brual J, Papadakos J, *et al.* Implementation of a comprehensive smoking cessation program in cancer care. *Curr Oncol* 2019;26:361.

181. Prochaska JJ, Benowitz NL. The past, present, and future of nicotine addiction therapy. *Ann Rev Med* 2016;67:467–86.

182. Teague Jr. CE. Memo to Dr. G. R. DiMarco from C. E. Teague, Jr. *Nordine Study*. Joe Camel Collection, 1982: Bates No. 500915405-7.

183. U.S. Department of Health and Human Services. *The Health Consequences of Smoking — 50 Years of Progress. A Report of the Surgeon General.* (Atlanta, GA: U.S. Dept. of Health and Human Services, Centers for Disease Control and Prevention, National Center for Chronic Disease Prevention and Health Promotion, Office on Smoking and Health, 2014).

https://doi.org/10.1142/9789811239533_0013

Chapter 13

Tobacco Control Policies

Michael P. Eriksen[*,†] and Carrie F. Whitney[*]

1. Introduction

The United States (US) adult smoking prevalence for combusted cigarettes reached a near record low of 13.8%[1] in the first quarter of 2020. Today, tobacco control measures are as popular and accepted as they have been at any point in US history. Despite these achievements, there are still 34 million smokers in the US and effective tobacco control policies have the potential to further decrease cancer morbidity and mortality among those smokers.

Smoking combusted cigarettes is still the leading cause of cancer death in the US, and smoking causes a myriad of cancers including cancers of the lung, oral cavity, larynx, pharynx, esophagus, pancreas, bladder, kidney, cervix, and stomach.[2,3] In the US, 80%[4] of all lung cancer deaths are the result of smoking and more adults die from lung cancer each year than from breast, colon and prostate cancers combined.[5] In 2020 in the US, more than 228,000 individuals will be diagnosed with lung cancer and an estimated 135,000 individuals will die.[6] Tobacco control measures, education, screening and treatment have all contributed to a reduction in lung cancer incidence and mortality in recent

*Georgia State University, USA.
†meriksen@gsu.edu

decades. Since the mid-1980s, the incidence of lung cancer in men has been declining and this trend has been seen among women since mid-2000.[7] As a result of reductions in smoking, early detection and improved treatment, the lung cancer death rate for men has decreased by 51% since 1990 and by 26% for women since 2002.[7] In the American Cancer Society's report, Cancer Facts & Figures 2021, lung cancer accounted for almost half (46%) of the overall decline in cancer mortality for the past 5 years.[8]

Strategic tobacco control policies, such as smoking bans, health warnings, advertising and tobacco taxes, have accelerated the decrease in morbidity and mortality caused by smoking.[9] It is important to understand how current tobacco control policies have evolved and thus set the framework for an array of future policy options. It is the hope that these new policies will provide a comprehensive approach to further reducing the prevalence of cigarette smoking and ultimately reducing the associated cancer burden.

2. Evolution of Tobacco Control Policy in the US

In 1954, Drs. Richard Doll and Bradford Hill published an article in the *British Medical Journal* confirming a link between smoking and lung cancer.[10] This initial finding along with other findings (see Chapter 2) and the resulting concerns led to the first report on smoking in 1964. *Smoking and Health: Report of the Advisory Committee to the Surgeon General of the Public Health Service* recognized and described the evidence between smoking and lung cancer.[11]

As summarized in Chapter 2, the 1964 report concluded that smoking was the cause of lung and laryngeal cancer in men, a probable cause of lung cancer in women and the most important contributor to chronic bronchitis.[12] In summarizing the findings, the Committee made the following judgment: "Cigarette smoking is a health hazard of sufficient importance in the United States to warrant appropriate remedial action."[11] As a result of these findings, many physicians stopped smoking, which contributed to large declines in population smoking rates. Additionally, the 1964 SGR ultimately led to the requirement of warning labels on cigarette packages and a ban on broadcast media advertising, both important initial tobacco regulatory policies in the US.

The first health warnings appeared on cigarette packages in 1966 as a result of Congressional legislation. The warnings read "Caution — cigarette smoking may be hazardous to your health".[13] Even as health concerns relating to smoking began to grow in the general public, the tobacco industry pressed forward with new products, such as light cigarettes, and deceptive marketing campaigns. Popular marketing campaigns included Philip Morris's introduction of the Virginia Slims brand targeted at women in 1968 and the introduction of Joe Camel by RJ Reynolds in 1987, which subsequently attracted millions of youth to smoking cigarettes.[14] These campaigns are further described in Chapter 1.

In 1967, the Federal Communications Commission ruled that the 1947 Fairness Doctrine applied to cigarette advertising.[15] This policy change ensured counter advertisements against smoking were broadcast on television and radio stations that also broadcasted cigarette advertisements. The counter ads had such an impact that the tobacco companies volunteered to remove cigarette advertising. This ultimately resulted in the 1970 Congressional broadcast advertising ban that still exists today and prohibits cigarette ads on television and radio.[16] Somewhat ironically, the Fairness Doctrine no longer exists and the current broadcast advertising ban has not been applied to novel tobacco products, such as e-cigarettes. This means youth and even older generations who have never seen tobacco advertisements on television nor heard them on radio have now been exposed to advertisements for e-cigarettes and other novel tobacco products for the first time in their lifetime.

In 1986, the 19th SGR, *The Health Consequences of Involuntary Smoking,* focused on the harmful effects of secondhand smoke.[17] This SGR was important as it gave momentum to the non-smokers rights movement, which subsequently advanced tobacco control strategies more broadly (see Section 3).

Research has continued to explore the impacts of secondhand smoke and the 2006 SGR on Involuntary Smoking estimated that a non-smoker living with a smoker has a 20–30% increased risk of lung cancer.[18]

One could argue that the US is still waiting for the "appropriate remedial action" that was called for in 1964. If our nation adopts a comprehensive tobacco control policy focused on reducing lung cancer, we will no doubt see further decreases in smoking prevalence and the resultant decrease in morbidity and mortality.

3. Social Action and Tobacco Control Policy

Social action has been an important catalyst for meaningful tobacco control laws, policies and regulations in the US. Even before the harm from secondhand smoke was documented in the 1986 SGR, non-smokers determined that involuntarily exposure to secondhand smoke, and the associated negative externalities, were unacceptable. In the past decades, social action was the impetus for the creation of state and local smoke-free laws, which are generally safe, effective, and inexpensive to implement.[19] Social action played a critical role in diffusing smoke-free laws across the country and most recently again in the Tobacco 21 initiative to raise the minimum age to sell tobacco in the US from 18 to 21.[20]

The best and earliest example of social action creating tobacco control policy change was from California and followed the basic steps of changing social norms as outlined in Figure 1. Social action is typically not prompted by scientific authorities but rather by individual citizens experiencing negative externalities and acting collectively to change the status quo. In the 1980s, local action against smoking in public places and private workplaces began in cities in California, such as Los Angeles, San Francisco, San Diego and Sacramento. Groups of individuals became concerned about the negative externalities of being involuntarily exposed to secondhand smoke and advocated for local and statewide action. At the

Figure 1:   The process of social change in regard to tobacco control.[21]

time, statewide action was essentially blocked by tobacco industry lobby-ing. As evidence of the harm from secondhand smoke grew and local citi-zens formalized their call for change, laws were passed at the local level to ban smoking in public areas to protect non-smokers.

After victory at the local level, the California legislature tried to pass a weaker, preemptive statewide law and ultimately a strong statewide ref-erendum was approved protecting California residents and serving as a model for state and local action elsewhere. The diffusion of smoke-free laws from California across the rest of the country resulted in positive change and protection of non-smokers.[19] As of August 2020, 54% of the US States had 100% smoke-free laws in non-hospitality workplaces, res-taurants and bars.[22]

A more recent example of tobacco control policy change is the Tobacco 21 movement where cities and states across the US increasingly began to raise the minimum sales age of tobacco from 18 to 21 years. The Tobacco 21 movement gained such momentum that it ultimately became a federal law. In late 2019, the Federal Food, Drug and Cosmetic Act was amended to prohibit the sale of tobacco (including cigarettes, cigars and e-cigarettes) to individuals under 21 years of age.[23] In terms of smoking cigarettes, the National Academy of Medicine found in 2015 that raising the minimum age of sale to 21 years would reduce smoking by 25% among those aged 15–17 years and by 15% among those aged 18–20 years. This increase in the minimum age of sale is expected to prevent 223,000 premature deaths, 50,000 lung cancer deaths, and 4.2 million fewer years of life lost among individuals born between 2000 and 2019.[24] Tobacco 21 is also significant as it includes e-cigarettes.

Although cigarette smoking rates among youth have declined over the years, e-cigarettes are now the most commonly used nicotine-containing product among youth. The 2020 National Youth Tobacco Survey found 3.6 million youth currently use e-cigarettes, accounting for 19.6% of high school students and 4.7% of middle school students.[25] The potential to reduce youth consumption of e-cigarettes is significant and important given the current popularity of the products and their potential to serve as a gateway to smoking.[26]

Changing social norms has been critical to tobacco control policy efforts in the US. As a result of social action at the local level, we have seen policy change at the federal level which has allowed more protection of non-smokers from secondhand smoke. Social norms are also important when considering smokers, as changing social norms create an environment that decreases the social acceptability of smoking, which can result in decreased smoking rates, illness and death from smoking. One study quantified the importance of reducing the social acceptability of smoking by finding that increasing the social unacceptability of smoking by 40% would result in a 15% decrease in cigarette consumption.[27]

4. Current and Effective Tobacco Control Policies

4.1. *US tobacco control*

The history of cigarette use and tobacco control in the US represents a unique story of the evolution of research and understanding of addiction, cultural and historical factors, social action, and egregious corporate behavior. As seen in Figure 2, the per capita cigarette consumption in the

Figure 2:   Per capita annual cigarette consumption among adults, 18 years of age and older, and major smoking and health events in the United States, 1900–2019.

Sources: Adapted from Wagner 1985 with permission from Massachusetts Medical Society, 1985; U.S. Department of Health and Human Services, 1989; Creet *et al.*, 1994; U.S. Department of Agriculture, 2000; U.S. Census Bureau, 2020; U.S. Department of Treasury, 2020.

US increased during the first half of the century and began to decline as the links between cigarettes and negative health consequences were documented and the non-smokers rights movement was established, as further discussed in Chapters 1 and 2. The increase in smoking rates was related primarily to social and historical factors and the decline began as proven tobacco control strategies, such as tax increases, smoke-free indoor air laws, health warnings and advertising bans, were implemented in the US.

5. Master Settlement Agreement

As noted in Chapter 1, in the mid-1990s, 46 states, the District of Columbia and five US territories brought suit against four major cigarette manufacturers (Philip Morris, R.J. Reynolds, Brown & Williamson and Lorillard) and the trade association of the tobacco industry. In 1998, the Master Settlement Agreement was entered into and states were awarded more than $200 billion over a 25-year period for costs associated with treating smoking-related illnesses.[28] Additionally, there were provisions forbidding direct and indirect advertising to youth, restrictions on advertising, and marketing and promotions bans (including restricting cartoons, most outdoor advertising and sponsorships, media product placement, branded merchandise and product samples).[29] Although the goals of the lawsuit were to prevent future tobacco harm and provide states with reimbursement for healthcare costs of smokers, the MSA did not mandate that a portion of these revenues be dedicated to tobacco control. The centers for Disease Control and Prevention recommends that spending 12% of annual settlement dollars and tobacco taxes collected by states would fund each state's tobacco control program at their recommended levels.[30] In 2020, states will collect $27.2 billion and will spend only $740 million on tobacco control, representing less than 3% of the recommended costs to prevent new smokers from starting and to help current smokers quit.[31] While the US has access to funding for tobacco control and a blueprint of evidence-based practices for tobacco cessation and prevention,[32] the country is not fully utilizing the available resources and funding tobacco control in a way that allows for further reductions in morbidity and mortality caused by smoking.

If the Master Settlement Agreement were established today, rather than in 1998, it might look very different. Today's version would consider regulatory authority, screening technology and medical advances (see section "A Comprehensive Approach to Lung Cancer") that could dramatically decrease cancer mortality caused by smoking.

6. 2009 Family Smoking Prevention and Tobacco Control Act

Prior to the establishment of the 2009 Family Smoking Prevention and Tobacco Control Act (TCA), the US Food and Drug Administration (FDA) made efforts to regulate tobacco in the 1990s but they were mostly unsuccessful.[33] The efforts of the FDA to regulate tobacco products was challenged by the tobacco industry and other related parties, resulting in a Supreme Court case. In 2000, Chief Justice Sandra Day O'Connor ruled that cigarettes should be regulated, particularly with regard to youth, but that the FDA did not have the authority to regulate tobacco products, and that authority needed to be granted by Congress. Nine years later in 2009, the FDA was statutorily given regulatory authority over tobacco products with a new chapter on tobacco regulation added to the century-old Food, Drug and Cosmetic Act.

The 2009 Family Smoking Prevention and TCA gave the FDA authority over the manufacture, sale and marketing of tobacco products (see Chapter 14 for more details). Specifically, the Tobacco Control Act[34] does the following:

- Restricts tobacco marketing and sales to youth;
- Requires smokeless tobacco product warning labels;
- Ensures "modified risk" claims are supported by scientific evidence;
- Allows FDA to establish product standards on tobacco products;
- Requires disclosure of ingredients in tobacco products;
- Preserves state, local, and tribal Authority.

Since this law was passed, the FDA has prohibited the use of candy and fruit flavorings in cigarettes, free cigarette samples, sales to minors, and the use of unsubstantiated health claims on packaging and in advertising.[35] In 2016, the FDA was given "deeming" authority over all types of tobacco-derived products, including cigars, hookas, pipes, e-cigarettes, gels and dissolvables (oral nicotine products).[63] How the FDA utilizes this deeming authority will directly impact its potential to reduce smoking rates and the role of potentially less harmful tobacco products and how they are utilized (or not utilized) in tobacco control.

6.1. *Global tobacco control*

Internationally, there are several global partnerships associated with the World Health Organization (WHO) to help countries organize their tobacco control efforts and to provide data, directives, goals and measures. These efforts are especially important in low- and middle-income countries where resources are limited and public health priorities are numerous.

7. WHO Framework Convention on Tobacco Control

The WHO Framework Convention on Tobacco Control (WHO FCTC) is an international treaty to respond to the globalization of the tobacco epidemic.[35] In 2003, 192 WHO Member States unanimously adopted the WHO FCTC as the world's first public health treaty,[36] which then needed to be ratified individually by the member states. The WHO FCTC reaffirms the right of all people to the highest standard of health and addressed cross-country issues of tobacco, such as trade, illicit tobacco trade, tobacco advertising, promotion and sponsorship.[37] The WHO FCTC is an important global instrument that recognizes the complex issues of tobacco control and provides countries with guidance for tobacco control efforts. Currently 182 Parties, which account for 90% of the global population, have ratified the WHO FCTC.[38]

8. MPOWER

MPOWER is part of the Tobacco Free Initiative of the WHO. MPOWER provides a package of technical resources and measures that correspond to the demand-reduction provisions of the WHO FCTC.[39] MPOWER stands for and includes the following concepts:

- *M*onitor tobacco use and prevention policies;
- *P*rotect people from tobacco smoke;
- *O*ffer help to quit tobacco use;
- *W*arn about the dangers of tobacco;
- *E*nforce bans on tobacco advertising, promotion and sponsorship;
- *R*aise taxes on tobacco.

Part of the legacy of MPOWER is that it drives the assessment of tobacco activities and monitoring at the country level. By providing regular surveillance and reporting, we now have an understanding of tobacco use, changes over time and how the various MPOWER tobacco control components are being achieved within each country.

9. WHO Best Buys

Tobacco use is one of the world's leading non-communicable disease contributors. WHO has identified "best buy" practices to reduce the economic impact of non-communicable diseases in low- and middle-income countries. Cardiovascular disease, diabetes, respiratory diseases and cancer have been identified as the most economically costly, non-communicable diseases in these countries. Tobacco use, and more specifically the smoking of combustible cigarettes, is a major contributor to cancer and all countries should decrease smoking in order to impact health. WHO best buys for countries to reduce smoking rates include[40] the following:

- Tax increases;
- Smoke-free indoor workplaces and public places;
- Health information and warnings;
- Bans on tobacco advertising, promotion and sponsorship.

10. Future Directions for Cancer-Specific Tobacco Control Policies

10.1. *The current role of regulation*

In this increasingly interconnected world, the regulation of all tobacco and nicotine products needs to be enacted globally. Through the WHO and other global tobacco control initiatives, countries have a strong framework, support and assessment tools to focus on tobacco control. Despite these resources, the implementation of tobacco control measures in many countries is challenged by the competing needs of a country's limited financial resources or infrastructure and even from tobacco industry influence. The framework and support provided by WHO FCTC, MPOWER and "Best Buys" do not work without implementation, guidance and monitoring. Many countries are still working to implement the evidence-based strategies that include tax increases and price policies (see Chapter 14), regulations on where products can be used, requirements for health warnings on packages and bans on tobacco advertising, promotion and sponsorship. The emergence of novel nicotine products are further changing the way nicotine is used throughout the world. Tobacco control advocates must continue to adapt their global strategy and ensure regulation of specific tobacco products commensurate with the harm each causes.

Regulations and policies should guide the use of tobacco products at each stage in the tobacco life cycle — from production to display, purchase and use (see Figure 3). The regulation of tobacco products has been implemented differentially in countries, with individual countries emphasizing specific approaches, but relatively few countries establishing a comprehensive policy framework. One effective and popular tobacco control policy is graphic warning labels and over half of the world's population, accounting for 3.9 billion people in 91 countries, benefit from graphic warning labels on cigarette packages.[41] Australia extended graphic warning labels to require plain packaging in 2012. Australian plain packaging requires cigarette packs to have a certain color, display brand names in specified ways, display the required text and graphic warnings and NOT display logos, brand images or promotional text.[42] Other countries, including France, the United Kingdom and Northern Ireland, have since passed similar laws.[43] Since 2003, the European Union has prohibited

Growing
Governments must help to improve supply and value chains for alternatives to tobacco leaf, and invest in farmers' education/re-training programs.

Manufacturing
Ban all tobacco additives, including flavorings.

Disposal
Get the tobacco industry to bear the cost of cleaning up the environmental devastation from the waste left by tobacco production and use.

Packaging and Labeling
Plain, standardized packaging of all tobacco products.

Product Use
Policies should make all indoor, workplace and public outdoor spaces smoke-free, and find effective, new ways to keep smokers from smoking in their homes with non-smokers.

Marketing
Ban all direct and indirect forms of marketing, including advertising, promotion and sponsorship.

Point-of-Purchase
Eliminate all signs and even hints of tobacco product sales, including keeping them out of sight behind the counter.

Tax Policies
Implement higher excise taxes on all tobacco products and make certain that increases outpace inflation and income growth.

PRODUCTION · DISPLAY · PURCHASE · USE

Figure 3:   Tobacco wheel of regulation.

Source: Drope J, Schluger N, Cahn Z, Drope J, Hamill S, Islami F, Liber A, Nargis N, Stoklosa M. 2018. The Tobacco Atlas. Atlanta: American Cancer Society and Vital Strategies.

cross-border tobacco advertising and sponsorship.[44] In early 2021, Paraguay banned smoking and e-cigarette use in indoor public places and crowded outdoor areas. This was the final country in South America to adopt a smoke-free law, leading to a landmark public health achievement — the citizens of every South American country (430 million total) are now protected by comprehensive smoke-free laws.[45]

In the US, cigarettes are regulated comprehensively at most points of the cigarette life cycle (see Figure 3). This type of regulation and comprehensive approach does not yet exist for novel nicotine products and many public health experts recommend that these regulations and policies be proportionate to the amount of harm caused by the products. For example, combustible cigarettes are deadly to half of all users and should be regulated to the highest degree and regulated in a manner that promotes cessation. In turn, tobacco or novel nicotine products, such as Electronic Nicotine Delivery Systems (ENDS), that are potentially less harmful than combusted cigarettes should be regulated in a way commensurate with the amount of harm they cause.[46]

The US FDA is often looked to as a global example of tobacco product regulation. The FDA has the authority to regulate all tobacco products and thus the potential to be one of the largest driving forces of tobacco control, and in turn, cancer reduction. Since 2015 FDA has begun exercising its authority over novel nicotine and tobacco products. The premarket tobacco application (PMTA) pathway allows for a rigorous, science-based review of products in the US to determine if they are appropriate for the protection of public health prior to the authorization for marketing. For example, in mid-2019, the Philip Morris International IQOS device, Marlboro Heatsticks, Marlboro Smooth Menthol Heatsticks and Marlboro Fresh Menthol Heatsticks received this designation and are allowed to be marketed in the US (under certain restrictions such as preventing youth access and exposure).[47]

In mid-2020, FDA authorized its first health claim for a modified risk tobacco product (MRTP) for IQOS. This designation implicitly indicates that IQOS may provide a net public health benefit even though it is not "FDA-Approved" and it will be subjected to rigorous post-market surveillance.[48]

With the MRTP authorization, marketing efforts for IQOS are allowed to state[48] the following:

- The IQOS system heats tobacco but does not burn it.
- This significantly reduces the production of harmful and potentially harmful chemicals.
- Scientific studies have shown that switching completely from conventional cigarettes to the IQOS system significantly reduces your body's exposure to harmful or potentially harmful chemicals.

This statement and authorization for sale by the FDA gave Altria the authority to sell IQOS in the US and allowed the health claims stated above. There is evidence that Philip Morris International has used the FDA authorization to facilitate marketing of IQOS globally.[49]

All new tobacco products are required to obtain premarket authorization. General Snus, a smokeless tobacco product with relatively low levels of tobacco specific nitrosamines (manufactured by Swedish Snus), and IQOS, a heated tobacco system manufactured by Phillip Morris International, have received authorization to be marketed in the US. E-cigarettes and novel tobacco products that were on the market as of August 8, 2016 were required to submit a marketing application to FDA by September 9, 2020.[50] As a result, there are many novel tobacco or nicotine products currently being evaluated by the FDA in order to secure premarket tobacco authorization which will allow for sale in the US, including JUUL, one of the more popular e-cigarettes.[51] Regulation of novel tobacco products in the US is still evolving and should be based on the differences in products and the potential harm caused by each so as to achieve a net public health benefit (see Chapter 14 for more details).

10.2. *The future role of regulation — FDA example*

As discussed, there are a number of "best buys" for tobacco control policy and these policies have been demonstrated to be effective and have been implemented in the US and elsewhere. However, much of the attention of tobacco control today is devoted to harm reduction as a potential tobacco control policy. As an example, harm reduction has been accepted in the United Kingdom (UK). The UK recognized some level of smoking and nicotine dependence as inevitable and thus encouraged smokers to use non-combustible nicotine products, such as e-cigarettes, that may reduce exposure to many toxic substances.[52]

In the US, harm reduction as a tobacco control effort has been strongly debated and is slowly becoming more accepted (or at least considered) as potentially having a role in reducing the morbidity and mortality from tobacco use. In July of 2017, Scott Gottlieb (then-Commissioner of FDA) and Mitchell Zeller (Director of FDA's Center for Tobacco Products) proposed a plan for the US to further reduce the harm from smoking combustible cigarettes. This two-part plan focused on "reducing the addictiveness of combustible cigarettes while recognizing and clarifying the role that potentially less harmful tobacco products could play in improving public health".[53] The FDA has the ability to establish tobacco product standards, and Gottlieb and Zeller argued an effective regulatory framework for cigarettes would include a nicotine-limiting standard. The addition of very low nicotine content cigarettes has the potential to reduce the addictiveness of cigarettes, and thus the demand or appeal for smoking.[54] The second part of the proposed plan was for the FDA to support the innovation of harm reduction. Nicotine products that are delivered without combustion have the potential to reduce the level of harm compared to smoking cigarettes. Nicotine patches, gum and lozenges have been proven to be safe and effective quit aids for smokers.[55] To further reduce combustion, the continuum of risk for nicotine products should be considered so consumers who will not quit nicotine altogether can utilize other products that are potentially less harmful than cigarettes.

In addition to the FDA's potential to regulate tobacco and nicotine in a way to reduce combustion, the FDA has the potential to reduce the harm caused by tobacco products by restricting the level of harmful or potentially harmful constituents (HPHCs).[56,57] Harmful constituents of tobacco smoke are discussed in Chapter 4. This authority is provided to the FDA through the TCA. When making decisions about which new or modified products should be authorized for marketing, the FDA uses the population health standard which includes the risks and benefits to the population as a whole. Exposure to HPHCs is the basis of health risk to users of tobacco products. Failure to demonstrate a substantive reduction in HPHC exposure can serve as a primary reason for denying authorization of a new product application. Product standards are arguably the most powerful regulatory tool in the TCA. Since population health is the standard which FDA must meet in promulgating a product standard, the TCA specifically lists the "reduction or elimination of other constituents, including smoke constituents, or harmful components of the product" in the list of tobacco product standards that can be established (see Chapter 14 for more information on the process of FDA regulation of tobacco products).

10.3. *A comprehensive approach to lung cancer caused by tobacco products*

When considering lung cancer and today's advances in technology and science, the focus should be on the adoption of a comprehensive policy approach that considers the three levels of disease prevention — primary, secondary and tertiary prevention. Primary prevention methods in regard to traditional tobacco control policies are those proven and effective in preventing individuals from developing lung cancer. This includes the current group of tobacco control measures such as cigarette taxes, smoke-free indoor spaces, health warnings and bans on advertising.

Secondary prevention involves early screening and detection of lung cancer. Since 2013, the US Preventive Services Task Force (USPSTF) has recommended an annual low-dose CT scan for adults aged 55–80 years old who have a 30 pack-year smoking history and currently smoke or have quit within the past 15 years.[58] In 2020, the USPSTF updated its screening recommendation to include individuals 50 years and older with a 20 pack-year or more smoking history.[59] Under the new guidelines of starting screening at age 50 and reducing the pack-year history to 20, the lung cancer mortality rate is estimated to be reduced by 13%.[60] While use of low-dose CT scans scan have the potential to make a difference, uptake in the US has been slow.[60] To have the biggest impact on lung cancer rates, it is important to combine cessation and screening activities so providers are confident and trained to promote smoking cessation while a smoker is participating in lung cancer screening.[61] Molecular changes associated with cancer development can potentially be used to help identify those individuals who could benefit from screening; this is an area of active research.

Finally, advances in lung cancer treatment may be considered a type of tertiary prevention. Advances in genomic and precision medicine can provide lung cancer treatment options that can extend lives in a manner never previously possible. Expanding clinical trials for lung cancer treatment and furthering immunotherapy can result in better treatments and thus outcomes for patients. Precision medicine involves an individualized approach to patient care so that treatments are selected based on what is most likely to help a patient given the genetic understanding of their disease.[62] With expanded, proven treatment options for lung cancer, we can increase the lung cancer survival rate and provide patients with better outcomes.

With the advancement of a comprehensive primary, secondary and tertiary lung cancer policy platform, we have the opportunity to make a meaningful difference in reducing lung cancer mortality.

11. Conclusion

Lung cancer may be the leading cause of cancer deaths in the US, but it is not the only cancer that has benefitted from advancements in technology, medicine and treatment. A comprehensive policy package focused on prevention, screening and treatment should be applied to all cancers caused by smoking. The adoption of such a long-term policy platform will prevent many cancers from occurring and for those that do, it will improve 5-year cancer survival rates, creating a net public health benefit of lives saved.

Complete cessation from all nicotine-containing products should remain the optimal goal. However, a comprehensive policy package is needed that considers prevention, cessation *and* harm reduction. To this end, we must effectively apply the current and newly emerging technologies to reduce the public health burden of all tobacco product use. Policies regulating tobacco and nicotine products should be implemented commensurate with the harm caused by the product. In the current landscape of tobacco products in the US, the primary prevention efforts should be focused on ending the use of combusted tobacco products, which is the best way to impact lung cancer rates and save lives. Although ending combustion is the first priority, there are existing smokers and those with a history of smoking who will benefit from the evolving and already proven secondary and tertiary prevention strategies. The time is right to consider a comprehensive policy package that prevents future disease as well as detects and treats current cancers. Perhaps with the adoption of such a comprehensive policy package the US can finally claim that the 1964 goal of "appropriate remedial action" has been achieved.

References

1. National Center for Health Statistics. Percentage of current cigarette smoking for adults aged 18 and over, United States, 2019 Q1, Jan–Mar 2020 Q1, Jan–Mar. National Health Interview Survey. Generated interactively: Fri Sep 25 2020. Source: National Center for Health Statistics, National Health Interview Survey. Available from: https://wwwn.cdc.gov/NHISDataQueryTool/ER_Quarterly/index_quarterly.html.
2. U.S. Department of Health and Human Services. *The Health Consequences of Smoking: A Report of the Surgeon General.* (Atlanta, GA: U.S. Department of Health and Human Services, Centers for Disease Control and Prevention, National Center for Chronic Disease Prevention and Health Promotion, Office on Smoking and Health, 2004).
3. World Health Organization. 2012. Cancer. Available from: http://www.who.int/mediacentre/factsheets/fs297/en/.
4. American Cancer Society. 2019. Lung Cancer Risk Factors. Available from: https://www.cancer.org/cancer/lung-cancer/causes-risks-prevention/risk-factors.html.
5. American Cancer Society. 2020. Key Statistics for Lung Cancer. Available from: https://www.cancer.org/cancer/lung-cancer/about/key-statistics.html.
6. American Cancer Society. 2020. Cancer Facts & Figures: 2020. *CA: A Cancer Journal for Clinicians.* Available from: https://www.cancer.org/research/cancer-facts-statistics/all-cancer-facts-figures/cancer-facts-figures-2020.html.
7. American Cancer Society. 2020. Cancer Facts & Figures 2020. Atlanta: American Cancer Society. Available from: https://www.cancer.org/content/dam/cancer-org/research/cancer-facts-and-statistics/annual-cancer-facts-and-figures/2020/cancer-facts-and-figures-2020.pdf.
8. American Cancer Society. 2021. Cancer Facts & Figures 2021. Atlanta: American Cancer Society. Available from: https://www.cancer.org/research/cancer-facts-statistics/all-cancer-facts-figures/cancer-facts-figures-2021.html.
9. Flor LS, Reitsma MB, Gupta V, *et al.* The effects of tobacco control policies on global smoking prevalence. *Nat Med* 2021;27:239–243. https://doi.org/10.1038/s41591-020-01210-8.
10. Doll R, Hill B. Smoking and Carcinoma of the Lung. *Brit Med J.* 1950;2:739 doi: https://doi.org/10.1136/bmj.2.4682.739. Available from: https://www.bmj.com/content/2/4682/739.

11. U.S. Department of Health, Education, and Welfare. *Smoking and Health. Report of the Advisory Committee to the Surgeon General of the Public Health Service.* (Washington, DC: U.S. Department of Health, Education, and Welfare. Public Health Service, 1964). Available from: https://profiles.nlm.nih.gov/spotlight/nn/browse.

12. Ruble K. 2014. Read the Surgeon General's 1964 Report on Smoking and Health. PBS News Hour Weekend Available from: https://www.pbs.org/newshour/health/first-surgeon-general-report-on-smokings-health-effects-marks-50-year-anniversary.

13. U.S. Food and Drug Administration. 2020. FDA Proposes New Health Warnings for Cigarette Packs and Ads. Available from: https://www.fda.gov/tobacco-products/labeling-and-warning-statements-tobacco-products/fda-proposes-new-health-warnings-cigarette-packs-and-ads.

14. American Lung Association. 2021. Tobacco Control Milestones. Available from: Timeline https://www.lung.org/research/sotc/tobacco-timeline

15. Centers for Disease Control and Prevention. 2020. Smoking and Tobacco Use: Regulation. Office on Smoking and Health. Available from: https://www.cdc.gov/tobacco/data_statistics/by_topic/policy/regulation/index.htm/.

16. Truth Initiative. 2017. What Do Tobacco Advertising Restrictions Look Like Today? Available from: https://truthinitiative.org/research-resources/tobacco-industry-marketing/what-do-tobacco-advertising-restrictions-look-today.

17. U.S. Department of Health and Human Services. *The Health Consequences of Involuntary Smoking: A Report of the Surgeon General.* (Washington, DC: Department of Health and Human Services, Public Health Service, Office of the Assistant Secretary for Health, Office of Smoking and Health, 1986).

18. U.S. Department of Health and Human Services. *The Health Consequences of Involuntary Exposure to Tobacco Smoke: A Report of the Surgeon General.* (Atlanta, GA: U.S. Dept. of Health and Human Services, Centers for Disease Control and Prevention, Coordinating Center for Health Promotion, National Center for Chronic Disease Prevention and Health Promotion, Office on Smoking and Health, 2006). Available from: https://www.ncbi.nlm.nih.gov/books/NBK44324/pdf/Bookshelf_NBK44324.pdf.

19. Eriksen MP, Cerak RL. The diffusion and impact of clean indoor air laws. *Ann Rev Public Health* 2008;29:171–85. doi:10.1146/annurev.publhealth.29.020907.090920.

20. Tobacco 21. 2020. U.S. Food and Drug Administration. Available at: https://www.fda.gov/tobacco-products/retail-sales-tobacco-products/tobacco-21, accessed July 8, 2020.

21. Eriksen M, Whitney CF. Risk factors: tobacco. *Global Handbook on NCDs and Health Promotion*. Ed. D.V. McQueen. (New York: Springer Press, 2013)

22. American Nonsmokers' Rights Foundation. 2020. U.S. 100% Smokefree Laws in Non-Hospitality Workplaces AND Restaurants AND Bars Map. Available from: https://no-smoke.org/wp-content/uploads/pdf/WRBLawsMap.pdf.

23. US Food and Drug Administration. 2020. Tobacco 21. Available from: https://www.fda.gov/tobacco-products/retail-sales-tobacco-products/tobacco-21.

24. National Academy of Medicine. Annual Report 2015. Available from: https://nam.edu/wp-content/uploads/2016/06/NAM-Annual-Report-2015.pdf.

25. US Food and Drug Administration. 2020. Youth Tobacco Use: Results from the National Youth Tobacco Survey. Available from: https://www.fda.gov/tobacco-products/youth-and-tobacco/youth-tobacco-use-results-national-youth-tobacco-survey.

26. National Institute on Drug Abuse; National Institutes of Health; U.S. Department of Health and Human Services. 2020. What are vaping devices? Available from: https://www.drugabuse.gov/publications/drugfacts/vaping-devices-electronic-cigarettes.

27. Alamar B, Glantz S. Effect of increased social unacceptability of cigarette smoking on reduction in cigarette consumption. *Am J Public Health* 2006;96(8):1359–63. doi: 10.2105/AJPH.2005.069617. Available from: https://www.ncbi.nlm.nih.gov/pmc/articles/PMC1522108/.

28. Centers for Disease Control and Prevention. 2012. State Tobacco Revenues Compared with Tobacco Control Appropriations — United States, 1998–2010. *MMWR* 2012;61(20):370–4. Available from: https://www.cdc.gov/mmwr/preview/mmwrhtml/mm6120a3.htm.

29. Master Settlement Agreement. 1998. Available from: https://www.industrydocuments.ucsf.edu/wp-content/uploads/2016/06/MSA.pdf.

30. Campaign for Tobacco Free Kids. 2020. A State-by-State Look at the 1998 Tobacco Settlement 21 Years Later. Available from: https://www.tobaccofreekids.org/what-we-do/us/statereport/.

31. Campaign for Tobacco-Free Kids. 2020. U.S. State and Local Issues — Broken Promises to our Children. Available from: https://www.tobaccofreekids.org/what-we-do/us/statereport/.

32. Centers for Disease Control and Prevention. 2014. Best Practices for Comprehensive Tobacco Control Programs — 2014. Available from: https://www.cdc.gov/tobacco/stateandcommunity/best_practices/index.htm.

33. Kessler, DA. 2001. A Question Of Intent: A Great American Battle With A Deadly Industry. BBS Publishing, New York.

34. U.S. Food and Drug Administration. 2020. Family Smoking Prevention and Tobacco Control Act — An Overview. Available from: https://www.fda.gov/tobacco-products/rules-regulations-and-guidance/family-smoking-prevention-and-tobacco-control-act-overview.

35. World Health Organization. 2020. WHO Framework Convention on Tobacco Control. Available from: https://www.who.int/fctc/cop/about/en/.

36. World Health Organization. 2003. An International Treaty for Tobacco Control. Available from: https://www.who.int/features/2003/08/en/.

37. World Health Organization. 2020. The WHO Framework Convention on Tobacco Control: an overview. Available from: https://www.who.int/fctc/about/WHO_FCTC_summary_January2015.pdf?ua=1&ua=1.

38. World Health Organization. 2020. Parties to the WHO Framework Convention on Tobacco Control. Available from: https://www.who.int/fctc/cop/en/.

39. World Health Organization. WHO Report on the Global Tobacco Epidemic, 2008: the MPOWER package. Available from: https://apps.who.int/iris/handle/10665/43818

40. World Economic Forum and World Health Organization. 2011. From Burden to "Best Buys": Reducing the Economic Impact of Non-Communicable Diseases in Low- and Middle-Income Countries. Available from: https://www.who.int/nmh/publications/best_buys_summary.pdf.

41. World Health Organization. 2019. WHO Report on the Global Tobacco Epidemic, 2019: Offer help to quit tobacco use — Executive Summary. Available from: https://www.who.int/publications/i/item/WHO-NMH-PND-2019.5

42. Australian Government. 2020. Tobacco Plain Packaging. Australian Government Department of Health. Available from: https://www.health.gov.au/health-topics/smoking-and-tobacco/tobacco-control/tobacco-plain-packaging.

43. World Health Organization. 2016. Plain Packaging of Tobacco Products: Evidence, Design and Implementation. Available from: https://apps.who.int/iris/handle/10665/207478.

44. European Commission. 2020. Ban on Cross-Border Tobacco Advertising and Sponsorship. https://ec.europa.eu/health/tobacco/advertising_en.

45. Myers, M. 12 January 2021. Statement — Landmark for Global Health: With Addition of Paraguay, All of South America is Now Protected by Comprehensive Smoke-Free Laws. Available from: https://www.tobaccofreekids.org/press-releases/2021_01_12_paraguay-south-america-smoke-free?eType=EmailBlastContent&eId=d4cd4ccf-7c6e-4a67-b62d-71d54fc6e71b.

46. Glynn TJ, Hays JT, Kemper K. 2021. E-cigarettes, harm reduction and tobacco control: a path forward? *Mayo Clin Proc* 2021;96(4):856-862 doi: 10.1016/j.mayocp.2020.11.022.

47. US Food and Drug Administration. 2019. FDA Permits Sale of IQOS Tobacco Health System Through Premarket Tobacco Product Application Pathway. FDA News Release. April 30, 2019. Available from: https://www. fda.gov/news-events/press-announcements/fda-permits-sale-iqos-tobacco-heating-system-through-premarket-tobacco-product-application-pathway.

48. US Food and Drug Administration. FDA News Release: FDA Authorizes Marketing of IQOS Tobacco Heating System with 'Reduced Exposure' Information. July 7, 2020. Available from: https://www.fda.gov/news-events/ press-announcements/fda-authorizes-marketing-IQOS-tobacco-heating-system-reduced-exposure-information.

49. Glantz, S. 2019. PMI is using the FDA to sell IQOS outside the US. UCSF Center for Tobacco Control Research and Education. July 16 2019. Available from: https://tobacco.ucsf.edu/pmi-using-fda-sell-IQOS-outside-us.

50. U.S. Food and Drug Administration. 2020. Submit Tobacco Product Applications for Deemed Tobacco Products. Available from: https://www. fda.gov/tobacco-products/manufacturing/submit-tobacco-product-applications-deemed-tobacco-products.

51. Glantz, S. 2020. FDA has "accepted" e-cigarette PMTA submissions: What does that mean and what should we expect after September 9? UCSF Center for Tobacco Control Research and Education. August 27, 2020. Available from: https://tobacco.ucsf.edu/fda-has-%E2%80%9Caccepted%E2%80%9D-e-cigarette-pmta-submissions-what-does-mean-and-what-should-we-expect-after-september-9.

52. Action on Smoking and Health. 2020. Harm Reduction. Available from: https://ash.org.uk/category/information-and-resources/product-regulation/ harm-reduction/.

53. Gottlieb S, Zeller M. Perspective — a nicotine-focused framework for public health. *New Eng J Med* 2017;377:1111–4. doi: 10.1056/NEJMp1707409. Available from: https://www.nejm.org/doi/full/10.1056/NEJMp1707409.

54. Abrams D, Notley C. Invited Commentary — Is Nicotine Reduction in Cigarettes Enough? *JAMA Netw Open*. 2020;3(10):e2019367. doi:10.1001/ jamanetworkopen.2020.19367. Available from: https://jamanetwork.com/ journals/jamanetworkopen/fullarticle/2771865.

55. American Cancer Society. 2017. Nicotine Replacement Therapy for Quitting Tobacco. Available from: https://www.cancer.org/healthy/stay-away-from-tobacco/guide-quitting-smoking/nicotine-replacement-therapy.html.

56. U.S. Department of Health and Human Services Food and Drug Administration Center for Tobacco Products (CTP). 2012. Guidance for Industry — Reporting Harmful and Potentially Harmful Constituents in Tobacco Products and Tobacco Smoke Under Section 904(a)(3) of the Federal Food, Drug, and Cosmetic Act — Draft Guidance. Available from: https://www.fda.gov/media/83375/download.

57. Hecht S. It is time to regulate carcinogenic tobacco-specific nitrosamines in cigarette tobacco. *Cancer Prev Res* 2014;7(7):639–47. doi: 10.1158/1940-6207.CAPR-14-0095. Available from: https://cancerpreventionresearch.aacr-journals.org/content/7/7/639.long.

58. U.S. Preventive Services Task Force. 2013. Final Recommendation Statement Lung Cancer: Screening. Available from: https://www.uspreventiveservicestaskforce.org/uspstf/recommendation/lung-cancer-screening.

59. AAFP. 2020. USPSTF Recommends Lung Cancer Screening With Low-dose CT. Available from: https://www.aafp.org/news/health-of-the-public/20200715uspstfdraftlung.html.

60. Fedewa SA, Kazerooni EA, Studts JL, Smith RA, Bandi P, *et al.* State variation in low-dose computed tomography scanning for lung cancer screening in the United States. *J Natl Cancer Inst* 2021;113(8):1044–1052. doi: https://doi.org/10.1093/jnci/djaa170. Available from: https://academic.oup.com/jnci/advance-article/doi/10.1093/jnci/djaa170/5970481.

61. Cadham CJ, Cao P, Jayasekera J, Taylor KL, Levy DT, Jeon J, Elkin E, Foley KL, Joseph A, Kong CY, Minnix JA, Rigotti NA, Toll BA, Zeliadt SB, Meza R, Mandelblatt J. Cost-effectiveness of smoking cessation interventions in the lung cancer screening setting: a simulation study. *J Natl Cancer Inst.* 2021;113:1065–73. CISNET-SCALE Collaboration. Available from: https://academic.oup.com/jnci/advance-article-abstract/doi/10.1093/jnci/djab002/6117330

62. U.S. Department of Health and Human Services. National Institute of Health. National Cancer Institute. 2017. Precision Medicine in Cancer Treatment. Available from: https://www.cancer.gov/about-cancer/treatment/types/biomarker-testing-cancer-treatment.

63. US Department of Health and Human Services. Food and Drug Administration. 2016. Deeming Tobacco Products To Be Subject to the Federal Food, Drug, and Cosmetic Act, as Amended by the Family Smoking Prevention and Tobacco Control Act; Restrictions on the Sale and Distribution of Tobacco Products and Required Warning Statements for Tobacco Products. Federal Register, Vol. 81, No. 90. Tuesday, May 10, 2016. Available from: https://www.govinfo.gov/content/pkg/FR-2016-05-10/pdf/2016-10685.pdf.

https://doi.org/10.1142/9789811239533_0014

Chapter 14

The Role of Tobacco Regulation in Addressing Cancer from Tobacco Products

David L. Ashley*

1. Introduction: What Is Tobacco Regulation?

The WHO Framework Convention on Tobacco Control (FCTC) encourages countries to implement comprehensive tobacco control policies under the acronym of MPOWER[1] (see Chapter 13) which has six components: (1) Monitor tobacco use and prevention policies, (2) Protect people from tobacco smoke, (3) Offer help to quit tobacco use, (4) Warn about the dangers of tobacco, (5) Enforce bans on tobacco advertising, promotion, and sponsorship, and (6) Raise taxes on tobacco. These policies can be implemented in various ways including performing surveillance, educating the public, providing services, or enacting laws that require individuals and/or corporations to act in a specified manner, i.e., regulation. Regulation is different from other forms of persuasion because it carries the force of law and may penalize non-compliance through warnings, monetary penalties, loss of operating permission or license, or incarceration. Because penalties may be imposed and the force of law supports these penalties, regulation can be an effective means of change, if

---

*Georgia State University, USA. dashley4@gsu.edu

successfully enforced. In the United States, regulatory authority encompasses two levels. Primary legislation is a statutory instrument enacted by an elected body such as the United States Congress or individual state, county or city governments, which, when signed into force, becomes enforceable law. Delegated legislation is drafted by subject matter experts to enforce primary legislation and is commonly referred to as Rules or Regulations. Once delegated legislation is in force, it carries authority equivalent to primary legislation. Rules or Regulations often provide explicit details explaining how more general aspects of a law will be carried out and enforced. Regulations require notice-and comment rulemaking, providing the public and all interested parties opportunity to comment on the regulation and requiring the agency developing the regulation to respond to comments. The rulemaking process may consist of an Advanced Notice of Proposed Rule Marking (ANPRM), a Proposed Rule, and a Final Rule. Due to the notice-and-comment nature of rulemaking, the process for developing and finalizing a regulation may require an extended period of time.

In the United States in June 2009, President Obama signed into law the Family Smoking Prevention and Tobacco Control Act (TCA),[2] which gave the US Food and Drug Administration (FDA) authority to regulate tobacco products including components and parts with the objective of reducing harm from use of these products. This authority, which originally encompassed cigarettes, cigarette tobacco, roll-your-own tobacco, and smokeless tobacco, was expanded through notice-and-comment rulemaking in 2016 to include all products meeting the statutory definition of tobacco products including e-cigarettes, all cigars, pipe tobacco, waterpipe tobacco, and any future tobacco products. In the United States, tobacco products are defined as any product that is made or derived from tobacco and is not a therapeutic drug or device. The TCA includes a wide range of authorities including legal requirements that determine which specific products can be sold and how they can be sold (marketing decisions) and what specifications apply to all or a subset of products if they are to be sold to consumers (product standards). These two authorities encompass the most effective *regulatory* means of addressing cancer caused by use of tobacco products. This chapter will describe the type of authorities that have been given to the US FDA to regulate tobacco products, the process of review of tobacco products, how marketing decisions are made for new products, and the scientific considerations for proposing specific standards for tobacco products.

2. What Authorities Have Been Given to Regulate Tobacco Products?

2.1. *Marketing decisions*

Marketing decisions are the heart and soul of FDA regulatory authority. Many products under FDA's regulatory authority, including drugs, medical devices and tobacco products must pass a rigorous evaluation process *before* they are allowed to be sold to consumers. This evaluation is intended, under the statutory authority, to promote public health. Marketing decisions are made for each separate product based on scientific data collected by the product's manufacturer and submitted to FDA for review and evaluation. In the case of marketing decisions, evidence that adequately demonstrates that the product meets the statutory standard is the responsibility of the manufacturer. Due to the product-by-product nature of marketing decisions, significant change is a slow and arduous process, requiring substantial resources from both the applicants and the regulators.

Under the authority of the TCA, for products that are not grandfathered (were on the market on February 15, 2007 and have not been modified since that date) to be marketed, there are four pathways by which tobacco products can be marketed. These are pre-market tobacco product applications (PMTAs), substantial equivalence reports, exemptions from substantial equivalence, and modified risk tobacco product (MRTP) applications. These pathways are intended for different purposes and require the products to meet different statutory standards (see Table 1 for summary).

The PMTA is considered by FDA to be the primary pathway by which new products should be introduced onto the market and can be submitted by any person seeking to market a tobacco product. The standard for marketing authorization for PMTA is "appropriate for the protection of public health", a requirement that is used commonly throughout the TCA. In

Table 1:   Statutory requirements for tobacco product marketing given to the US FDA.

Type of review	Review criteria
Marketing	
Pre-Market Tobacco Product Applications	• "Risks and benefits to the population as a whole, including people who would use the proposed new tobacco product as well as nonusers; • Whether people who currently use any tobacco product would be more or less likely to stop using such products if the proposed new tobacco product were available; • Whether people who currently do not use any tobacco products would be more or less likely to begin using tobacco products if the new product were available; • The methods, facilities, and controls used to manufacture, process, and pack the new tobacco product."
Substantial Equivalence	• "Has the same characteristics (materials, ingredients, design, composition, heating source or other features of tobacco product) as the predicate tobacco product, or • Has different characteristics and the information submitted contains information, including clinical data if deemed necessary by FDA, that demonstrates that it is not appropriate to regulate the product under (the premarket tobacco application or "PMTA" provisions) because the product does not raise different questions of public health."
Substantial Equivalence Exemption	• "The new tobacco product is modified by adding or deleting a tobacco additive or increasing or decreasing the quantity of an existing tobacco additive; • The proposed modification is minor compared to a legally marketed tobacco product; • An SE Report is not necessary; • An exemption is otherwise appropriate"
Modified Risk Tobacco Product Application	• "Significantly reduces harm and the risk of tobacco related disease to individual tobacco users; • Benefits the health of the population as a whole taking into account both users of tobacco products and persons who do not currently use tobacco products."

considering whether a product meets the population health standard, FDA considers, among other things, the following:

• "Risks and benefits to the population as a whole, including people who would use the proposed new tobacco product as well as non-users;

- Whether people who currently use any tobacco product would be more or less likely to stop using such products if the proposed new tobacco product were available;
- Whether people who currently do not use any tobacco products would be more or less likely to begin using tobacco products if the new product were available; and
- The methods, facilities, and controls used to manufacture, process, and pack the new tobacco product."[3]

This definition identifies the three ways that tobacco product use can affect public health: the health risk from using the product, the likelihood that people will stop using tobacco products, and the likelihood that people will start using tobacco products. Any of these aspects could alter the prevalence of cancer resulting from tobacco product use. Due to the harm from tobacco product use, FDA has interpreted the PMTA standard to mean that marketing authorization of the new tobacco product is likely to reduce the tremendous burden of death and disease currently resulting from tobacco product use. Therefore, a product that receives a PMTA should demonstrate (1) lower health risk compared to products that are alternatively used by those likely to use the new product, (2) that it is likely that users will switch from more harmful to the less harmful product, and (3) that it is unlikely that non-tobacco users or users of less harmful products will start using this product. This will include accounting for the toxicity of the product, the appeal of the product to youth and non-users, the addictiveness of the product relative to current products on the market and how the product would be marketed, promoted, advertised and distributed. For a PMTA to be authorized, the combination of these considerations should be likely to result in a net population reduction in the death and disease resulting for tobacco use. If this is not likely, the PMTA should be denied.

Substantial equivalence (SE) is an alternative to the PMTA, still recognizes the inherent harm in using tobacco products, but allows new or modified products that are not more harmful than those that have been traditionally marketed to be introduced. A product that has been traditionally marketed is termed a "predicate product" and can be either a product that was on the market on February 15, 2007 (grandfathered) or a product previously found substantially equivalent. It is important to note that products that have been removed from the market because they are misbranded or adulterated or products that are authorized for marketing through authorities other than grandfathered or previously found SE (e.g., PMTA) are not eligible to be used as predicate products. Products that either have the same characteristics as a predicate product or have different characteristics, but FDA has found that the new product does not raise different questions of public health, are deemed to be substantially equivalent. In August[4] 2016, Judge Amit Mehta of the US District Court for the District of Columbia ruled that, for SE purposes, a change in tobacco product labeling does not result in a new product, but a change in the quantity of tobacco in the product does result in a new product. This finding sets a legal precedent that allows tobacco companies to change the product name, pack colors, or other features of labeling without requiring an SE report as long as the consumed product is not modified. "Characteristic" under SE authority means the materials, ingredients, design, composition, heating source, or other features of a tobacco product. This list provides broad authority for FDA to consider all changes to the formulation of the product when making SE decisions. According to FDA's proposed SE regulation,[5] other features "include harmful and potentially harmful constituents and any other product characteristics that relate to the chemical, biological, and physical properties of the tobacco product and are necessary for review". SE is the pathway for marketing authorization by which tobacco companies have applied for the vast majority of combusted tobacco products.

An alternative to SE is an exemption from substantial equivalence (EX). Products can be found to be EX if FDA determines the following:

- "The new tobacco product is modified by adding or deleting a tobacco additive or increasing or decreasing the quantity of an existing tobacco additive;
- The proposed modification is minor compared to a legally marketed tobacco product;
- An SE Report is not necessary;
- An exemption is otherwise appropriate."[2]

Few products have been submitted for review through this pathway. While FDA has not provided specific categories of exemption from SE at this time, they may do so in the future. Products that have received marketing authorization through this pathway have been modified in a minor way such that only limited data are required to be submitted and reviewed. An example from 2020 of a modification found exempt from SE is the substitution of one type of Fire Standard Compliant cigarette paper for another.[6]

A MRTP application is not a means to obtain authorization to put a new product on the market, but allows the manufacturer or other person to make modified risk or exposure claims in statements to the public, typically on packaging or in advertising. As with PMTA, SE, and EX, an order permitting MRTP claims refers to a single specific product and not to a class of products as a whole. For example, in October 2019, separate modified risk orders were issued for General Dry Mint Portion Original Mint and General Portion Original Large, two distinct products from Swedish Match USA, Inc.[7] Thus, even if a single brand and sub-brand of snus were found to be modified risk, modified risk claims could not be made for other products in this class (e.g., snus). An MRTP application must demonstrate that the product as marketed and used by consumers will or is expected to benefit the health of the population as a whole. Different from PMTA, SE, and EX, the TCA requires FDA to make MRTP applications available for public comment, except information regarding trade secrets or otherwise commercially confidential information. MRTP applications also must be referred to the FDA Tobacco Products Scientific Advisory Committee. FDA's review of an application evaluates whether the product, as proposed to be marketed and actually used by consumers, will (see Table 1) do the following:

- "significantly reduce harm and the risk of tobacco related disease to individual tobacco users;
- benefit the health of the population as a whole taking into account both users of tobacco products and persons who do not currently use tobacco products."

Two types of MRTP applications may be filed. One is for applicants seeking to make modified risk claims. The other is for applicants seeking to make modified exposure claims. The modified exposure claim is intended to provide a pathway for products for which scientific evidence is not available and cannot be made available without long-term epidemiological studies to meet the standards for modified risk, but there is evidence that it is reasonably likely that, if the long-term epidemiological studies were conducted, the product would meet the standard. Thus, likelihood that a product will reduce cancer in tobacco users may be a critical factor in determining whether a product meets the requirements as either modified risk or modified exposure. To minimize misunderstanding of modified exposure claims, authorization under this pathway requires additional findings including that the reductions in exposure are substantial, exposure to other harmful substances will not be higher, and consumers will not be misled by the claims. Applicants must agree to conduct post-market surveillance to determine the impact of the order on consumer perception, behavior and health. Different from PMTA, SE or EX, an MRTP authorization is limited to 5 years under a modified exposure order or a specified period of time for a modified risk order. Applicants can apply to have the order renewed, but must provide additional evidence that the finding of modified risk is supported; the required post-market surveillance data will have a substantial impact on the decision to renew the order.

The authority and resources given to the US FDA under the TCA is unique compared to other nation's tobacco regulatory authority. While other nations have instituted graphic health warnings and plain packaging, steps still facing legal challenges in the US, pre-market authorization is exclusive to the US. Some countries, including those in the European Union, require companies that introduce new products to report information to the regulatory authorities. The Tobacco Products Directive (TPD) of the European Union requires notification before marketing (6 months for novel tobacco products and 1 day for traditional tobacco products[8]). Companies must provide data on sales volume, preferences of consumer groups, mode of sale, and summaries of market surveys after marketing. When required by the government, companies must also carry out health studies. However, companies do not have to apply for and receive authorization for marketing. The immense resources required to review evidence for individual products is likely to limit the expansion of pre-market review authority to other countries. In the US, the FDA collects fees from the tobacco industry to fund the infrastructure for these reviews.

2.2. *Product standards*

Product standards are one of the most powerful public health tools provided by the TCA that could be used to address cancer resulting from tobacco use. Product standards are requirements set forth by regulation, thus requiring notice-and-comment rulemaking. Product standards are based on the finding that the standard is appropriate for the protection of public health as for the PMTA marketing decisions described above. As described in the TCA, product standards may include provisions for the following[2]:

- "nicotine yields of the product";
- "the reduction or elimination of other constituents, including smoke constituents, or harmful components of the product"; or
- "the construction, components, ingredients, additives, constituents, including smoke constituents, and properties of the tobacco product";
- "the testing (on a sample basis or, if necessary, on an individual basis) of the tobacco product";
- "the measurement of the tobacco product characteristics of the tobacco product";
- "the results of each or of certain of the tests of the tobacco product required to be made" to "show that the tobacco product is in conformity with the portions of the standard for which the test or tests were required"; and
- restricting "the sale and distribution of the tobacco product" but under a limited extent.

Products standards, as described in the TCA, have certain limitations to the range of actions that can be taken:

- "banning all cigarettes, all smokeless tobacco products, all little cigars, all cigars other than little cigars, all pipe tobacco, or all roll-your-own tobacco products"; or
- "requiring the reduction of nicotine yields of a tobacco product to zero".

Thus, product standards that reduce the number of users of tobacco products, reduce the adverse health effects (including cancer) resulting from the use of tobacco products, or encourage a substantial number of current users of more harmful products to switch completely to use of less harmful products could meet the statutory requirements for enacting a product standard. Any of these changes, when accomplished thoughtfully and adequately enforced, could reduce the burden of cancer from tobacco use.

Because product standards are issued as a regulation, the evidentiary burden falls upon FDA to demonstrate through notice-and-comment rule-making that the evidence demonstrates that the product standard is likely to meet the statutory standard, appropriate for the protection of public health. In formulating this evidence, FDA addresses the inherent uncertainty in the available science, unintended consequences of the action, and unexpected modifications made by product manufacturers seeking to meet the letter of the law but maintain product appeal and addictiveness.

Different from the individual-product nature of marketing decisions, product standards can be applied to all tobacco products, all products of a certain type (e.g., cigarettes, smokeless tobacco), or a subset of products (e.g., menthol cigarettes) if the evidence supports this. Thus, even though product standards may require a substantial time to enact, they can affect broad sweeping changes and limit alternatives to which users might switch. For example, if a product standard limits concentration of a known carcinogen in tobacco smoke and, because of this change, reduces the appeal of the product, the possibility of smokers switching to products to which the standard was not applied is eliminated because this standard is applied to all combusted products. This is likely to accomplish a more substantial reduction in cancer than one-by-one marketing decisions, which allow grandfathered products to remain on the market.

Globally, product standards are included in the regulatory authority for several countries. However, enforcing this authority has met with mixed results. Canada bans flavors in cigarettes, small cigars, and blunt wraps based on appeal to adolescents, but provides an exception for additives that impart a flavor of port, wine, rum, or whiskey, which appeal more to adults.[9] The EU TPD includes a ban on flavorings in cigarettes and roll-your-own tobacco and a ban on the use of flavor capsules in tobacco products. This legislation is focused on discouraging young people from starting tobacco use and ensuring accurate understanding on the harm that results from tobacco use.[10] In 2013, Chile's Ministry of Health took action to ban menthol tobacco products based on its authority to restrict additives that increase addiction, harm, or risk. However, the Office of the Comptroller General determined that the Ministry had failed to demonstrate the direct association between menthol and harm. A new bill was introduced in 2015 linking the ban of menthol and other distinctive cigarette flavors to their high levels of use among youth.[11,12] To date, globally, regulatory authorities have been more successful in instituting product standards intended to reduce appeal to children rather than the toxicity or carcinogenicity of the product.

3. FDA Review Process — Different Scientific Considerations

FDA regulatory review, both for making marketing decisions and developing product standards is a complex process that assimilates scientific findings from a wide spectrum of scientific disciplines aimed at evaluating the evidence for the appropriate protection of public health standard upon which most of these decisions are based. Evidence typically includes information based on studies of the product itself (design, engineering, chemistry, microbiology, and emissions), the likely health impact on individual users (exposure biomarkers, pharmacokinetics, toxicology, clinical outcomes, abuse liability, and use behavior) and influence on the population as a whole (epidemiology, appeal, harm perception, initiation, cessation, and statistical modeling). The characteristics of the product as designed by the manufacturer are evaluated in terms of how they may influence population morbidity and mortality. To accomplish this goal, scientific studies are considered and evaluated that link the product's characteristics (what is directly regulated) to likely health outcomes (the measure of outcome).

With any new or modified product, differences in characteristics can alter the three primary measures (risk, initiation, and cessation) in different directions. For example, IARC considers there to be sufficient evidence in humans for the carcinogenicity of formaldehyde.[13] Formaldehyde is generated in e-cigarette aerosols at higher concentrations when the battery output voltage is higher and when vegetable glycerin is included in the solvent.[14] A review decision that limits the formaldehyde concentrations in e-cigarette aerosol may require the manufacturer to limit the voltage applied in their product. This action could also reduce the nicotine delivered, making the product less satisfying (addictive) to smokers and reducing the likelihood that these products would be effective in helping smokers stop smoking combusted products[15] by switching completely to e-cigarettes. Thus, a review decision aimed at reducing the delivery of carcinogenic chemicals to users of one product could influence the likelihood that current users of a different more harmful product completely stop use. Conversely, designing a product that is more effective at encouraging smokers to stop smoking could deliver more of the carcinogen, formaldehyde. These considerations must be integrated into an overall estimation of impact on population health.

Unintended consequences should also be considered when making marketing or product standard decisions. For example, because much of the population falsely believes that nicotine in cigarette smoke is an important cause of the cancer caused by smoking, reducing nicotine could have the unintended halo effect[16] of encouraging the belief that reduced nicotine cigarettes are less carcinogenic than current cigarette. The reduction in nicotine, intended to make it easier for smokers to quit and less likely that experimenters would become regular smokers, could increase experimentation by non-users due to decreased concern about the carcinogenicity of cigarette smoke. A different example of a possible unintended consequence is the relationship between the carcinogenic tobacco-specific nitrosamines (TSNAs) and polynuclear aromatic hydrocarbons (PAHs). IARC has determined that the TSNAs 4-(methylnitrosamino)-1-(3-pyridyl)-1-butanone (NNK) and N'-nitrosonornicotine (NNN), and the PAH, benzo[a]pyrene, are carcinogenic to humans (Group 1) and that several other PAHs are either probably carcinogenic to humans (Group 2A) or possibly carcinogenic to humans (Group 2B).[17,18] Studies have shown that nitrogen levels in fertilizer and in the air during the curing process can be a factor in the relative levels of TSNAs and PAHs in tobacco smoke.[19–21] In addition, Burley tobacco contains substantially higher levels of TSNAs compared to Bright tobacco. However, Bright tobacco contains much higher levels of PAHs than Burley tobacco.[22] Reducing levels of TSNAs by reducing nitrogen in fertilizer or during curing or adjusting the variety of tobacco used may increase levels of PAHs. Thus, efforts to reduce the carcinogenicity of tobacco smoke should address levels of both TSNAs and PAHs in order to prevent the unintended consequence of shifting from one carcinogen to another. These issues should be evaluated in population health modeling and included in assessing population health impact decision-making. Steps should be undertaken to identify and remove or minimize these unintended consequences as part of the regulatory process.

4. Marketing Decisions

Ideally, marketing decisions would include validated measures of carcinogenic risk from long-term use of the product which is the subject of the application. But, in reality, because these products (or the current modified version) have not been marketed before, there are typically no data available that provide the preferred evidence upon which to evaluate the carcinogenicity of the particular product. Instead, surrogate measures, such as HPHC delivery from machine smoking of combusted products, electronic nicotine delivery systems, or heated tobacco products; HPHC extraction efficiency from oral tobacco products; *in vitro* assays; animal carcinogenicity studies; biomarkers of exposure or effect; cellular mutagenicity studies; or cancer epidemiology of similar products are used to predict the likely cancer outcomes from use of the product. These measures are discussed in more detail in other chapters in this book. This chapter will focus on examples of how FDA has evaluated the evidence applicants have used to argue that their new product meets the statutory standard required for marketing, and their strengths and limitations.

In May 2017, Philip Morris Products S.A. (PMI) applied for PMTA authorization to market four components of their heated tobacco product IQOS: Marlboro Heatsticks, Marlboro Smooth Menthol Heatsticks, Marlboro Fresh Menthol Heatstick, and IQOS System Holder and Charger. In April 2019, FDA granted the marketing authorization.[23] Heatsticks are plugs of reconstituted tobacco sheet blended with glycerin and rolled and bound by a hollow acetate tube and outer cigarette paper with a polylactic acid filter on the mouth end. To obtain nicotine from the product, the Heatsticks are inserted into the IQOS Holder, which contains a blade that pierces into the tobacco plug. Pressing a button causes the blade to heat to temperatures not exceeding 300 °C, releasing nicotine and other chemical constituents in an aerosol, which is inhaled by the user.

The concentrations of several HPHCs of carcinogenic concern were significantly lower in the aerosol generated from IQOS compared to the typical range in smoke for commercial or reference cigarettes from data reported by the manufacturer, when analyzed in the FDA Southeast Tobacco Laboratory, and reported in peer-reviewed publications.[23] For example, PMI reported that concentrations of formaldehyde were 14.1 ± 0.43 μg/cig in aerosol from Marlboro Heatsticks and 98.23 ± 35.09 μg/cig in smoke from 31 brands of commercial cigarettes. Concentrations of NNN were 10.1 ± 0.205 ng/cig in aerosol from Marlboro Heatsticks and 178.67 ± 57.79 ng/cig in smoke from 31 brands of commercial cigarettes. Concentrations of NNK were 7.80 ± 0.423 ng/cig in aerosol from Marlboro Heatsticks and 128.32 ± 34.76 ng/cig in smoke from 31 brands of commercial cigarettes. Concentrations of benzo[a]pyrene were 0.736 ± 0.0973 ng/cig in aerosol from Marlboro Heatsticks and 14.95 ± 3.12 ng/cig in smoke from 31 brands of commercial cigarettes. These results are in agreement with peer-reviewed literature.[24] From these results, FDA concluded that "When normalized to nicotine yield, the yields of HPHCs that were measured were reduced by 24.8–99.8% compared to the smoke from the CC [commercial cigarettes] evaluated by the applicant."

PMI also reported the presence of four possible carcinogens (glycidol, 3-chloro-1,2-propanediol [3-MCPD], 2-furanmethanol, and furfural) which are not typically measured in tobacco smoke. PMI stated that these compounds do not pose a toxicological concern because the levels are below recognized dietary or occupational exposure limits (OELs). They supported their position by comparing to OELs, OSHA's permissible exposure limit (PEL), and maximum dietary intake. In spite of this explanation, FDA did not consider PMI's assessment of these compounds to be adequate because of their reliance on comparison to OELs and PELs, measures that are not directly applicable to tobacco use.

PMI performed *in vitro* tests of possible mutagenicity, both an Ames test and a mouse lymphoma assay. In both cases, treatment of cell cultures with total particulate matter (TPM) isolated from IQOS aerosol produced lower effects compared to cigarette smoke. The IQOS TPM did not demonstrate any mutagenic activity in the Ames assay, but PMI did not provide a rationale for testing the TPM only and not including the vapor phase of the aerosol. When using the complete IQOS aerosol for the mouse lymphoma assay, cytotoxicity was observed, but only at levels substantially lower than found in cigarette smoke. FDA concluded that these evaluations were not adequate to evaluate the relative carcinogenicity of IQOS aerosol and cigarette smoke because the level of substances may not be an accurate indicator of mutagenic potency.

PMI performed a 90-day nose-only rat exposure and an 18-month carcinogenicity study with A/J mice. The incidence of basal cell hyperplasia (nose and larynx) and squamous cell hyperplasia (nose and larynx) in rats exposed to either Heatstick aerosols or 3R4F were not significantly different, while goblet cell hyperplasia/hypertrophy (lung) and macrophage aggregation (lung) were not observed in the rats exposed to smoke from the reference cigarette. The incidence of bronchioloalveolar adenoma after 10 months of exposure was similar in mice exposed to aerosol from either IQOS or the reference cigarette. FDA concluded that there was a potential for carcinogenic effects from IQOS aerosol, but these effects would require much higher exposure levels than from conventional cigarettes.

From combined confined and ambulatory clinical studies on IQOS, PMI reported the results of 16 HPHC biomarkers of exposure of which 13 are considered carcinogenic. The studies found that biomarkers of exposure were significantly reduced by between 34% and 92% or 15% and 82% ($p < 0.05$), respectively, among smokers completely switching to a IQOS developmental product (THS 2.2). For example, 4-(methylnitrosamino)-1-(3-pyridyl)-1-butanol (total NNAL), a major metabolite of NNK, decreased between 48% and 61% following 5 days in a confined setting using THS 2.2, similar to subjects in a smoking-abstinence arm (59–64%). Urine mutagenicity, also evaluated in samples taken from the clinical studies, decreased by 42.8–72% for those participants who used THS 2.2 exclusively versus 37–74% for those in the smoking-abstinence arm. FDA concluded that the biomarkers of exposure and urine mutagenicity data supported the finding of reduced likelihood of smoking-related disease. But, they also noted several limitations including the absence of data on dual users of cigarettes and IQOS. Since other data indicated that this was the most common use behavior, this deficiency could be substantial. Data on the likelihood of disease causation including cancer should reflect actual consumer use and not only a best-case scenario. In spite of these concerns, FDA authorized the products for marketing based primarily on the decreased exposure when used exclusively and required the applicant to monitor use behavior after marketing.

Because IQOS has only been on the market for a limited number of years in countries outside the US, it is not possible to perform epidemiological studies to evaluate the long-term carcinogenicity of these products. However, this is not true for Swedish snus, which has been marketed for decades in Sweden. In 1970, the Swedish government imposed foodstuff criteria for snus production and, in 1973, the first portioned snus was introduced in Sweden.[25] Thus, for this product, there is a substantial history of use by consumers. This history of use provides an opportunity for epidemiological studies to be included as part of the marketing decision-making. In June 2014, Swedish Match submitted to FDA both a new product PMTA application and an MRTP application. The applications sought marketing authorization and modified risk claims for eight separate Swedish Match snus products. One of the original modified risk requests was that the required warning statement "WARNING: This product can cause mouth cancer" be removed.

The original 2014 Swedish Match application provided several cancer-related lines of evidence. The application provided data on constituent standards including carcinogens such as benzo[a]pyrene, NNN and NNK; concentrations of other HPHCs, including carcinogens in the products; a review of toxicological studies, and epidemiological studies including biomarkers of exposure. These data led to the FDA authorization to market these Swedish Match products because they were evaluated to be appropriate for the protection of public health. However, evidence provided by Swedish Match and reviewed by FDA showed that even though the products contained significantly lower levels of harmful carcinogens, the products contained nitrosamines, NNN and NNK, which have been demonstrated to cause cancer. Therefore, since there is no established threshold for cancer risk, the products pose an increased risk of mouth cancer compared to non-use. Six epidemiological studies examined the relationship between snus use and mouth cancer using three cohort and three population-based case-control studies. The cohort studies had 20–30 years of follow-up using national cancer and death registries. While the results of the studies were mixed, the most recent epidemiological study found a statistically significant increased oral cancer risk (RR = 3.1, 95% CI = 1.5–6.6) after adjusting for possible confounders.

In its decision of December 14, 2016, FDA refused to issue a modified risk order for this change. However, FDA suggested that Swedish Match adjust their claims and amend their application. In September 2018, Swedish Match provided an amended request to use the claim "Using General Snus instead of cigarettes puts you at a lower risk of mouth cancer, heart disease, lung cancer, stroke, emphysema, and chronic bronchitis." This amendment did not contain any additional health-related information but addressed the claim itself. FDA granted this claim for these eight snus products in October 2019 predominantly based on the epidemiological studies that showed that Swedish snus was associated with these reduced health risks compared to cigarette smoking.

Data from product analysis, emissions testing, toxicology determinations, and epidemiological studies all influence final regulatory decisions. Data that demonstrate lower concentrations of carcinogens in the product, emissions, and biomarkers of exposure; decreased *in vitro* effects and lower incidence of cancer in animal models; and reduced cancer prevalence in populations using that product or a surrogate support that the new product is appropriate for the protection of public health or will benefit the population as a whole. However, this must be evaluated in light of other concerns such as use behavior, addictiveness, and harm perceptions which can alter the likelihood that marketing of the product will achieve overall population health benefits and reduce the death and disease now resulting from tobacco use.

5. FDA Product Standards — Different Scientific Considerations

Product standards should address a set of issues demonstrating that there is adequate evidence that the standard is likely to meet the statutory objective in the most beneficial and least costly manner while being une-quivocal and enforceable. Under the TCA, FDA must provide convincing evidence that the product standard is appropriate for the protection of public health and be able to determine whether a specific marketed prod-uct meets the standard. This evidence is then described in a proposed rule which is subject to notice and comment rulemaking.

To answer these questions, the standard should be as follows:

- Justifiable — is there adequate evidence?
- Necessary — is this the least costly alternative to achieve the goal?
- Appropriate — will it do what it claims to do?
- Unambiguous — is the requirement clear?
- Measurable — are there methods to measure the standard?
- Quantifiable — can the methods distinguish products that meet the standard from products that do not?

To address these questions, FDA gathers or develops scientific data that indicate the following:

- An adverse impact on population health of the existing product with-out a product standard;
- Causality or association of the item proposed to be regulated with the adverse impact;
- Termination or reduction in the adverse impact due to the proposed (quantitative) requirement;
- Viability of technical means of meeting the requirement;
- Quantitative estimate of the public health benefit;
- Costs associated with meeting the requirement;
- Quantitative impact of other related changes that may limit the benefit of the requirement;
- Alternative ways which were considered to address the adverse impact along with estimated benefit and cost;
- Possible unintended/secondary consequences of the requirement, their costs, and benefits.

In January 2017, FDA issued a proposed rule requiring the mean level of NNN in any batch of smokeless tobacco products (any tobacco products that consists of cut, ground, powdered, or leaf tobacco that is intended to be placed in the oral or nasal cavity) not to exceed 1.0 μg/g of tobacco (on a dry weight basis) at any time through the product's labeled expiration date as determined by specific product testing.[26] Through supporting evidence, FDA systematically addressed all of the questions and topics described above.

In 2007,[17] and again in 2012,[27] IARC has determined that there is sufficient evidence in humans that smokeless tobacco is carcinogenic. In 1986, the report of the Surgeon General of the US Public Health Service stated "users of smokeless tobacco products face a strongly increased risk of oral cancer".[28] Also, the Scientific Committee on Emerging and Newly Identified Health Risks of the European Commission evaluated the cancer risks of smokeless tobacco products and concluded that smokeless tobacco causes esophageal and pancreatic cancer in humans and identified evidence in the United States that demonstrated an increased risk of oral cancer among smokeless tobacco users.[29]

NNN is the predominant driver of excess oral cancer risk in users of smokeless tobacco. In smokeless tobacco, TSNAs are present at a level capable of causing cancer. Animal studies have demonstrated that NNN causes oral and esophageal tumors in a dose-dependent manner.[30] The mechanism of action of NNN-induced carcinogenicity is known.[31] NNN's carcinogenic effects have been documented in the esophagus, oral, and nasal cavities. In contrast, NNK is a powerful lung carcinogen, but no oral or esophageal tumors have been reported in animals exposed only to NNK. Epidemiological studies have identified an association of NNN with greater risk of head, neck, and esophageal cancer in tobacco users,[32] but not lung cancer.

Comparison of international epidemiological studies shows that oral cancer rates are higher when NNN levels are higher. Comparison of cancer risk in India and Pakistan (high NNN and oral cancer risk), Sudan, the US, and Scandinavia (low NNN and oral cancer risk) shows an association of cancer risk with differing NNN concentrations.[26]

Current limits in Swedish snus for NNN and NNK combined are about 2 μg/g dry weight.[33] The limit established in the NNN proposed rule are based on epidemiological evidence that populations that use smokeless tobacco with lower levels of NNN (particularly Sweden compared to the US) have reduced incidence of oral and esophageal cancer. FDA used

EPA's guidance for carcinogen risk assessment and assumed a linear model in the low-dose region of the dose-response curve. Limited data on use of smokeless tobacco below the proposed standard and limited evidence of technical achievability suggested that the most appropriate standard would be 1.0 μg NNN/g tobacco (on a dry weight basis), as noted above.

FDA used modeling to estimate the percent reduction in cancer risk instead of the absolute cancer risk. They used estimates of the current range of smokeless tobacco NNN concentrations to compare to the likely range after implementation of the rule. They found that in the 20 years following implementation, 12,700 new cases of oral cancer and 2,200 oral cancer deaths would be prevented. As a result, 15,200 life years would be gained. While other cancers were not included in these estimates, the rule is expected to also reduce esophageal cancer, and it may reduce the risk of pancreatic, laryngeal, prostate, and lung cancer.

NNN levels vary substantially across and within different subcategories of smokeless tobacco products (e.g., moist snuff, chewing tobacco, dry snuff). The levels of NNN in smokeless tobacco on the US market can vary by several orders of magnitude. One study reported a range from below the limit of detection (0.02 μg/g) to 14.4 μg/g per dry weight.[34] A wide variety of factors, including tobacco type, growing conditions, curing techniques, and storage conditions can influence the levels of NNN in tobacco.[17] This provides manufacturers several different ways for them to reduce concentrations of NNN. In this proposed rule, FDA did not prescribe the steps manufacturers must take, but allowed them to determine the best way to achieve the standard. The range of concentrations of NNN in smokeless tobacco and multiple options for accomplishing reductions shows that the potential exists to reduce the concentration of NNN in all smokeless tobacco supporting the technical achievability of the regulation.[35]

The NNN proposed rule specified testing methodology for both stability testing and batch testing. Batch testing verifies that each batch conforms to the standard before that batch is sold to the consumer. Because cancer risk is due to long-term repeated exposure, FDA chose to set a standard based on batch mean instead of a standard based on all units for the entire batch. Sampling plans were required and would ensure that samples taken were representative, random, and account for the variability of NNN in smokeless tobacco. Stability testing verifies that the product would remain in compliance with the standard throughout its shelf life until it reaches its expiration date. An analytical method is available and was validated by FDA's Southeast Regional Laboratory. Requiring the use of a single method ensures that the regulatory standard has been met and allows comparison of test results among products. Requirements for using an alternative analytical method also were established in the proposed rule along with the description of numerous other possible methods.

The evidence provided in the proposed rule addresses each of the evidentiary needs for establishing a product standard, appropriate for the protection of public health. Reduction of NNN is expected to reduce oral and esophageal cancer in users, not increase the likelihood that non-users will start tobacco use, not substantially decrease the likelihood that current users will stop using tobacco products, and will not encourage current users to switch to more harmful products.

Along with the immediate evidentiary needs, in the NNN proposed product standard, FDA addressed several ancillary issues in order to ensure the rule effectively accomplishes the objective of reducing cancer caused by use of smokeless tobacco.

In some smokeless products, NNN concentrations change over time during storage. Thus, an expiration date was necessary that ensures that products sold to customers continue to meet the standard. Manufacturers have several ways that they can address the increasing NNN concentrations during sample storage including reducing NNN concentrations well below the limit so that the time-dependent increase would not exceed the standard before the expiration date, taking steps to reduce the rate at which NNN concentrations increase over time, or reducing the time between manufacture and the expiration date. The proposed regulation required the manufacturer to indicate the proper storage conditions (room temperature or refrigerated) that is required so that the product continues to meet the standard while stored.

Manufacturers must include a manufacturing code, expiration date and storage conditions on labeling. The manufacturing code is intended to provide traceability of individual products and to link to the manufacturing and testing history. Record-keeping is required to ensure that the products are not misbranded or adulterated and to assist in enforcing the regulation. Record-keeping includes batch-testing results, alternative testing validation results, and sampling plans.

FDA considered including NNK in the proposed rule. However, because no oral or esophageal tumors have been reported in animals exposed only to NNK, the decision was made to regulate NNN levels only. It is likely that actions taken by manufacturers to reduce concentration of NNN will reduce concentrations of NNK also.

All products that are modified to meet the regulatory requirements would be new products and required to obtain authorization for marketing. FDA determined that SE is appropriate if manufacturer's changes are solely to bring the product in compliance with the standard. FDA is considering requiring an SE Report with a reduced, specific set of information that focuses only on these changes and does not increase concentrations of other HPHCs. The requirement that new product authorization is required for products changed in order to comply with the product standard enables FDA to combine the strengths of the two primary regulatory authorities. A product that is modified to meet the standard but will raise new questions of public health or not be appropriate for the protection of public health can be denied marketing authorization.

Using a wide range of evidence from scientific disciplines ranging from chemistry to statistical modeling, FDA is able to address all of the evidentiary needs for supporting product standards aimed at reducing cancer caused by tobacco products. Because these product standards, when finalized and effectively enforced, can apply to a wide range of products, they can be effective tools for reducing morbidity and early mortality resulting from tobacco product use, including cancer.

6. Conclusions

The regulatory authority given the FDA under the TCA provides an opportunity to substantially reduce the cancer resulting from tobacco use. Although the focus has been on US tobacco product regulations, through Articles 9 and 10 of the Framework Convention on Tobacco Control, signatory countries (which do not include the US) are also provided regulatory authority over tobacco products. Article 9 allows for the regulation of the contents and emissions of tobacco products. Article 10 requires manufacturers and importers of tobacco products to disclose information on the tobacco product contents and emissions to governmental authorizers. New product review and product standards can serve as effective tools if these authorities are implemented and enforced successfully. While FDA regulatory authority over drugs and medical devices has been established through decades of legal decisions, FDA's ultimate authority over tobacco products, used recreationally with no medical benefit, is still to be determined. Only time will tell whether this regulatory authority can be used effectively to reduce the cancer that results from tobacco use.

References

1. World Health Organization. Tobacco free initiative (TFI) (https://www.who. int/tobacco/mpower/en/, accessed 9/4/2020).
2. U.S. Government Publishing Office. H.R. 1256 (ENR) — Family Smoking Prevention and Tobacco Control Act (https://www.govinfo.gov/app/details/ BILLS-111hr1256enr/summary, accessed 9/4/2020).
3. United States Food and Drug Administration. Premarket tobacco product applications (https://www.fda.gov/tobacco-products/market-and-distribute-tobacco-product/premarket-tobacco-product-applications, accessed 9/4/2020).
4. Court Listener. MEMORANDUM OPINION: Civil No. 15-cv-1590 (APM), Philip Morris USA Inc. v. United States Food and Drug Administration (https://storage.courtlistener.com/pdf/2016/08/16/philip_morris_usa_ inc._v._united_states_food_and_drug_administration.pdf, accessed 9/4/2020).
5. U.S. Food and Drug Administration. Content and format of substantial equivalence reports; Food and Drug Administration actions on substantial equivalence reports. *Federal Register* 2019;84:12740-91.
6. U.S. Food and Drug Administration. Exemption Letter from FDA CTP to R.J Reynolds Tobacco Company (EX0000747, EX0000748, EX0000749, EX0000750) (https://www.fda.gov/media/135726/download, accessed 9/4/2020).
7. U.S. Food and Drug Administration. Modified Risk Orders (https://www.fda. gov/tobacco-products/advertising-and-promotion/modified-risk-orders, accessed 9/4/2020).
8. European Commission. Revision of the Tobacco Products Directive (https:// ec.europa.eu/health/tobacco/products/revision_en, accessed 9/4/2020).

9. Government of Canada Justice Laws Website. Tobacco and Vaping Products Act (S.C. 1997, c. 13), SCHEDULE 1 (Sections 5.1, 5.2, 7.1 and 23.1), Prohibited Additives (https://laws.justice.gc.ca/eng/acts/T-11.5/page-12. html, accessed 9/4/2020).

10. Official Journal of the European Union. Directive 2014/40/EU of the European Parliament and of the Council of 3 April 2014 on the approxima- tion of the laws, regulations and administrative provisions of the Member States concerning the manufacture, presentation and sale of tobacco and related products and repealing Directive 2001/37/EC Text with EEA relevance (https://eur-lex.europa.eu/legal-content/EN/ALL/?uri=CELEX: 32014L0040, accessed 9/4/2020).

11. World Health Organization. Case Studies for Regulatory Approaches to Tobacco Products: Menthol in Tobacco Products. (Geneva: World Health Organization, 2018).

12. Institute for Global Tobacco Control. Technical Report on Flavored Cigarettes at the Point-of-Sale in Latin America: Availability and Marketing around Primary and Secondary Schools in Five Countries. (Baltimore, MD: Johns Hopkins Bloomberg School of Public Health, 2017.

13. International Agency for Research on Cancer. A review of human carcino- gens: chemical agents and related occupations. In *IARC Monographs on the Evaluation of Carcinogenic Risks to Humans*, vol. 100F, 401–36. (Lyon, FR: IARC, 2012).

14. Kosmider L, Sobczak A, Fik M, Knysak J, Zaciera M, Kurek J, Goniewicz ML. Carbonyl compounds in electronic cigarette vapors-effects of nicotine solvent and battery output voltage. *Nicotine Tobacco Res* 2014;16:1319–26.

15. Lopez AA, Hiler MM, Soule EK, Ramoa CP, Karaoghlanian NV, Lipato T, Breland AB, Shihadeh, AL, Eissenberg, T. Effects of electronic cigarette liquid nicotine concentration on plasma nicotine and puff topography in tobacco cigarette smokers: A preliminary report. *Nicotine Tobacco Res* 2016;18:720–3.

16. Epperson AE, Henriksen L, Prochaska JJ. Natural American Spirit brand marketing casts health halo around smoking. *Am J Public Health* 2017;107:668–70.

17. International Agency for Research on Cancer. Smokeless tobacco and some tobacco-specific N-nitrosamines. In *IARC Monographs on the Evaluation of Carcinogenic Risks to Humans*, vol. 89. (Lyon, FR: IARC, 2007).

18. International Agency for Research on Cancer. Some non-heterocyclic poly- cyclic aromatic hydrocarbons and some related exposures. In *IARC*

Monographs on the Evaluation of Carcinogenic Risks to Humans, vol. 92. (Lyon, FR: IARC, 2010).

19. Fischer S, Spiegelhalder B, Preussmann R. Preformed tobacco-specific nitrosamines in tobacco — role of nitrate and influence of tobacco type. *Carcinogenesis* 1989;10:1511–7.

20. Hoffmann D, Hoffmann I. The changing cigarette, 1950–1995. *J Toxicol Environ Health* 1997;50:307–64.

21. Adams JD, Lee SJ, Hoffmann D. Carcinogenic agents in cigarette smoke and the influence of nitrate on their formation. *Carcinogenesis* 1984;5:221–3.

22. Ding YS, Zhang L, Jain RB, Jain N, Wang RY, Ashley DL, Watson CH. Levels of tobacco-specific nitrosamines and polycyclic aromatic hydrocarbons in mainstream smoke from different tobacco varieties. *Cancer Epidemiol Biomarkers Prev* 2008;17:3366–71.

23. U.S. Food and Drug Administration. Premarket Tobacco Product Marketing Orders (https://www.fda.gov/tobacco-products/premarket-tobacco-product-applications/premarket-tobacco-product-marketing-orders, accessed 9/4/2020).

24. Bekki K, Inaba Y, Uchiyama S, Kunugita N. Comparison of chemicals in mainstream smoke in heat-not-burn tobacco and combustion cigarettes. *J UOEH* 2017;39:201–7.

25. Swedsnus. History of Swedish Snus (https://www.swedsnus.com/swedish-snus-history/, accessed 9/4/2020).

26. U.S. Food and Drug Administration. Tobacco product standard for N-nitrosonornicotine level in finished smokeless tobacco products. *Federal Register* 2017;82:8004–53.

27. International Agency for Research on Cancer. Personal habits and indoor combustions. In *IARC Monographs on the Evaluation of Carcinogenic Risks to Humans*, vol. 100E. (Lyon, FR: IARC, 2012).

28. U.S. Department of Health and Human Services. *The Health Consequences of Using Smokeless Tobacco. A Report of the Advisory Committee to the Surgeon General.* (Bethesda, MD: Department of Health and Human Services, Public Health Service, 1986).

29. European Commission Scientific Committee on Emerging and Newly Identified Health Risks. Health effects of smokeless tobacco products. European Commission, Brussels, 2008.

30. Balbo S, James-Yi S, Johnson CS, O'Sullivan G, Stepanov I, Wang M, Bandyopadhyay, D, Kassie, F, Carmella, S, Upadhyaya, P, Hecht, SS.

(S)-N'-nitrosonornicotine, a constituent of smokeless tobacco, is a powerful oral cavity carcinogen in rats. *Carcinogenesis* 2013;34:2178–83.

31. Hecht SS. Biochemistry, biology, and carcinogenicity of tobacco-specific N-nitrosamines. *Chem Res Toxicol* 1998;11:559–603.

32. Yuan JM, Knezevich AD, Wang R, Gao YT, Hecht SS, Stepanov, I. Urinary levels of the tobacco-specific carcinogen N'-nitrosonornicotine and its glucuronide are strongly associated with esophageal cancer risk in smokers. *Carcinogenesis* 2011;32:1366–71.

33. Swedish Match AB. GOTHIATEK limits for undesired components (https://www.swedishmatch.com/Snus-and-health/GOTHIATEK/GOTHIATEK-standard/, accessed 9/4/2020).

34. Borgerding MF, Bodnar JA, Curtin GM, Swauger JE. The chemical composition of smokeless tobacco: a survey of products sold in the United States in 2006 and 2007. *Regul Toxicol Pharmacol* 2012;64:367–87.

35. Hecht SS, Stepanov I, Hatsukami DK. Major tobacco companies have technology to reduce carcinogen levels but do not apply it to popular smokeless tobacco products. *Tobacco Control* 2011;20:443.

https://doi.org/10.1142/9789811239533_0015

Chapter 15

Tobacco Endgame

Kenneth E. Warner*

1. Introduction

Progress against the leading cause of cancer death among both men and women, cigarette smoking, has been striking. In the mid-1960s, smoking prevalence among American adults exceeded 40%, including more than half of all men. By 2018, prevalence had plummeted to under 14%. In 1963, the year before the first Surgeon General's report on smoking and health,[1] adult per capita cigarette consumption — total cigarettes purchased divided by the population 18 years and older — stood at 4,345 cigarettes. That means that the average smoker that year smoked about 9,600 cigarettes, or 26/day. By 2019, annual adult per capita cigarette consumption had fallen by 80% to 876. The average smoker consumed 6,400 cigarettes, 17.5/day (see Figure 1). Research has credited tobacco control with avoiding the premature deaths of 8 million Americans from 1964 to 2012,[2] a large proportion representing avoided lung and other smoking-related cancers.

Progress against smoking has energized prominent tobacco control activists and researchers to call for a tobacco endgame within their countries. Leading endgame proponent Ruth Malone has described the strategies articulated to achieve the endgame as "big-picture radical ideas that

---

* University of Michigan, USA. kwarner@umich.edu

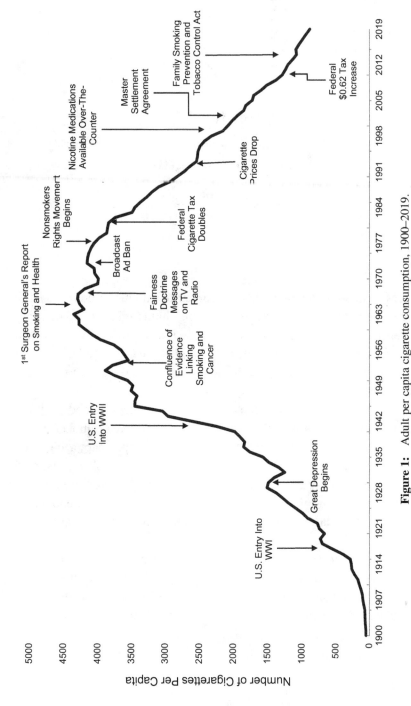

Figure 1: Adult per capita cigarette consumption, 1900–2019.

Source: Office on Smoking and Health, Centers for Disease Control and Prevention.

seek to propel the tobacco control movement more quickly towards a time when the global tobacco disease pandemic…will be ended." She considers endgame thinkers "the visionaries of the tobacco control movement".[3]

But what, specifically, would constitute the end of tobacco envisioned by endgame proponents? How do proponents propose to achieve that outcome? That is, what are the strategies and interventions they have identified that they believe can expedite the end of the tobacco pandemic? Are these strategies and interventions feasible? Why or why not? What is the receptivity of governments to adopting a tobacco endgame plan? Governments are the organizations that ultimately will determine whether endgame proposals are converted into practice.

While it is not possible to date its origins specifically, and some endgame concepts predate the use of the term in tobacco control circles,[4] the endgame "movement" is less than two decades old. The latter half of that period has witnessed the emergence of a series of novel alternative nicotine delivery systems (ANDS), the most familiar of which is the electronic- or e-cigarette. These products' increasing presence in the nicotine marketplace raises an additional question: Do these products represent a threat to the endgame, or could they assist its realization?

These are the questions that will be addressed in the remainder of this chapter.

2. How Is "The End" Defined?

Conceptually, defining the goal of the endgame is simple: It is just that, the end of tobacco use. Practically, however, defining a goal against which success or failure will be measured is far more challenging and, it turns out, arbitrary. Under the best of circumstances, some degree of tobacco use will persist for decades to come. Even the most draconian of tobacco control policies — declaring tobacco smoking punishable by death, as did 17th century Ottoman Empire Sultan Murad IV — failed to quash smoking.[5] In the present era, the Kingdom of Bhutan banned smoking, yet the behavior continued, albeit at very low levels.[6]

Recognizing the inevitability of some degree of tobacco use, and the need for a measurable, attainable "end", endgame proponents have typically defined the goal as reducing the prevalence of tobacco use (in one or more forms) to a very low level, generally 5%. For some proponents, that level applies to all forms of tobacco use. For others, it refers to tobacco smoking, specifically cigarette smoking, by far the largest cause of tobacco-related illness and death. For a few, the goal applies to use of all nicotine products. Along with the product category and the maximum prevalence, endgame goals include a date by which the goal is to be achieved. Endgame goals articulated thus far have commonly selected a decade to three decades hence. Thus, the specific category of tobacco (or nicotine) products, the prevalence level indicating success, and the date by which the goal is to be attained vary across the views of proponents and also across the relatively few countries that have articulated a commitment to a tobacco endgame.

3. Endgame Strategies/Interventions

McDaniel and colleagues[7] have defined the tobacco endgame as "Initiatives designed to change/eliminate permanently the structural, political and social dynamics that sustain the tobacco epidemic, in order to end it within a specific time." Broadly, endgame strategies can be grouped into four categories, each of which is described in this section. Obstacles to endgame strategies are considered later in the chapter. The four categories are as follows:

1. General supply-side interventions;
2. Product-specific interventions;
3. Consumer-specific interventions;
4. Combinations of interventions.

As noted above, some endgame proponents focus exclusively on ending the use of cigarettes (or combusted tobacco products), while others seek to end the use of all tobacco products; a few expand the latter category to include all nicotine products (thus including products like e-cigarettes, which contain no tobacco, and even, in theory, government-sanctioned nicotine replacement products, like nicotine gum and patch). In what follows, reference to tobacco products (and the tobacco industry, etc.) should be construed as referring to all tobacco products. However, many of the same endgame interventions could be applied specifically to solely cigarettes (and other combusted tobacco products) or to all nicotine-yielding products.

3.1. *General supply-side interventions*

Supply-side interventions focus on controlling the availability of tobacco products, either through prohibitions on the manufacture and/or sale of certain product categories or by establishing new institutional approaches to regulating the manufacture or sale of tobacco products.

3.1.1. *A ban on tobacco products*

The most direct and obvious supply-side intervention would be a governmental prohibition of manufacture and/or sale of tobacco products, either a class of products (specifically the most dangerous, those that are combusted) or all tobacco products. While the specter of prohibition has limited calls for such bans, they do have advocates.[8,9]

As of 2021 only one country, the Kingdom of Bhutan, has banned the manufacture and sale of tobacco. The country's Tobacco Control Act of 2010, amended subsequently, does permit importation of small amounts of tobacco for personal use, given payment of a substantial tax and with restrictions on where tobacco can be used.[6] In California, two cities (Beverly Hills and Manhattan Beach) have passed ordinances to prohibit tobacco sales as of January 1, 2021.[10,11]

A variation on the theme, proposed by endgame proponents in New Zealand,[12] envisions governments establishing annual quotas on the manufacture and importation of tobacco products, with the quotas declining annually for a defined period of time (e.g., 10 years) until all tobacco product sales would be prohibited. This "sinking lid" approach would be supported by rising product prices as supply is increasingly restricted. Rising prices, in turn, would reduce demand.

3.1.2. *Institutional approaches*

Several endgame proponents have introduced tobacco product manufacturing and sales regulation models, ranging from a governmental takeover of the industry to the creation of powerful incentives for private sector companies to reduce tobacco use.

Callard and colleagues[13] have introduced one of the more radical concepts on this spectrum: A nation's government would require the sale of tobacco companies to a government-sanctioned not-for-profit organization that would thereafter control the manufacture, marketing, and sale of tobacco products. The organization would have a health promotion mandate.

While not proposing a take-over of tobacco product manufacturing *per se*, Borland[14] described a similar concept, which he dubbed a regulated market model, that entails making a government-sanctioned agency the exclusive buyer of tobacco products. The agency could establish manufacturing standards and regulate retail practices. These standards and practices could include many of those discussed below under the headings of product-specific and demand-side interventions.

A regulatory notch down from direct ownership of the tobacco industry or sole power to purchase and distribute tobacco products would be establishment of an agency that would have the authority to set product manufacturing standards, regulate marketing methods and content, and control sales practices. One unorthodox but intriguing regulatory approach would be for such an agency to have the power to set time-specific and company-specific targets for reductions in smoking prevalence or cigarette sales, with companies fined for failure to achieve the targets. The fines would have to exceed the profits companies could make by failing to meet their targets. This proposal, called performance-based regulation, would leave it to the individual companies to determine how they would meet their goals, whether by increasing prices, restricting supplies, reducing marketing, or whatever.[15] The regulatory agency could use revenues from fines for non-compliance to fund media antismoking campaigns or other activities designed to reduce the demand for cigarettes.

A further notch down would be limiting tobacco product sales to government stores with requirements designed to reduce product-related harms (e.g., analogous to those in government-run alcohol stores, with limited opening hours, strict limitation of sales to legal-age adults, and not selling to inebriated adults). Alternatively, governments could employ a licensing system for tobacco retailers to create incentives to discourage tobacco consumption. While tobacco retail licensing systems exist in many jurisdictions, in general they involve a very modest annual license fee and little to no monitoring of compliance with license requirements. The endgame variation on retailer licensing would impose substantial licensing fees and ensure frequent monitoring, with hefty penalties for non-compliance with license requirements. Penalties might begin with a large fine for the first offense and follow with loss of license for a second offense. The cost of managing the system would be covered by licensing fees and penalties. The system could also restrict the number of licensees, thereby reducing easy access to purchasing tobacco products, and possibly impose additional limits (e.g., hours of sale of tobacco products; locations a minimum distance from schools; minimum prices).[7]

While few governments have adopted strict limitations on tobacco retailing, in 2020, the House of Representatives in the Netherlands passed a bill that would prohibit sales of tobacco products in retail outlets other than tobacco-only, adult-only specialty stores. If signed into law, the policy would require other retailers to cease tobacco sales by the end of 2022.[16]

3.2. *Product-specific interventions*

A tobacco regulatory agency could be authorized to set manufacturing standards that relate to the composition of a tobacco product. Such regulations could address the ability of the product to addict or harm its user, or it could make the product less desirable to consumers (see Chapter 14).

3.2.1. *Reducing the cigarette's ability to addict*

Much of the attention in this group of interventions has focused on the idea of making tobacco products, and specifically cigarettes, less capable of producing or maintaining addiction. This would be achieved by mandating a maximum nicotine delivery at a level incapable of sustaining addiction. Introduced in 1994 by Benowitz and Henningfield,[4] the idea predates discussion of the concept of a tobacco endgame, but it is certainly one of its most important contributions. In the US, the Food and Drug Administration (FDA), which has the authority to establish product standards, was actively considering the policy.[17] More recently, it has put that consideration on the back burner. The FDA's proposal focused exclusively on cigarettes, although the agency's Advanced Notice of Proposed Rulemaking asked whether other combusted products should be included as well. With a cigarette-only nicotine reduction mandate, small cigars and cigarillos could replace a significant component of the market for cigarettes. The expectation, therefore, is that if active consideration of the regulation is resurrected, it will have to cover all combusted tobacco products.

The FDA's own research has concluded that a nicotine-reduction regulation would substantially reduce smoking and greatly diminish its toll of disease and death.[18] In particular, while it likely would assist many adult smokers with quitting, it would substantially reduce future generations' dependence on smoking. The original idea was to phase in reductions in allowable nicotine delivery over a number of years,[4] but recent research has indicated that a more instantaneous implementation could be reasonable and possibly more effective (with smokers given ample notice of the date of policy implementation).[19]

3.2.2. *Reducing the cigarette's ability to harm*

A tobacco regulatory agency could require the reduction or removal of specific toxins from tobacco product smoke. That this is feasible has been demonstrated by the tobacco industry itself. Twenty years ago, Vector Tobacco Ltd. introduced a brand of cigarettes called Omni. The manufacturer used the catalyst palladium to improve the cigarette's burning efficiency, which, according to Hughes and colleagues,[20] should reduce carcinogen exposure. In its ads, the manufacturer claimed that their process significantly reduced polycyclic aromatic hydrocarbons (PAHs), tobacco specific nitrosamines (TSNAs) and catechols, which the company described as "the major causes of lung cancer in smokers"[21] (studying the product, Hatsukami *et al.* found decreases in exposure to TSNAs but not to PAHs).[22]

While the brand was unsuccessful in the marketplace, its existence demonstrated that important toxins in cigarette smoke can be substantially reduced. A recent World Health Organization (WHO) report provides a detailed discussion of major toxicants in tobacco smoke and develops a regulatory strategy for reducing exposure to toxicants.[23] Whether reducing a specific subset of toxins would significantly reduce the disease risks associated with smoking is unknown, but an agency could adopt a regulation working with the presumption that there should be benefit. An associated risk, of course, is that smokers would interpret the plausible risk reduction as meaning that smoking had become safe or at least significantly safer. That in turn could reduce intentions to quit.

3.2.3. *Reducing the desirability of smoking*

The desirability of smoking could be reduced by either altering the physical characteristics of the product in a manner that makes it less physically appealing to smoke or by altering the presentation (appearance) of the product with the same intention.

Altering the physical characteristics of the product dominates endgame discussions of reducing the desirability of smoking. Beginning about a century ago, a series of technological achievements made the inhalation of tobacco smoke relatively easy.[24] That, in turn, expanded the popularity of cigarette smoking and, with it, the addiction to nicotine that has driven much of the global pandemic (see Chapter 1). A tobacco regulatory agency could mandate a pH of ≥ 8 in cigarette smoke, a level that makes the smoke difficult to inhale.[24] Less inhalation, or less deep inhalation, could reduce the desirability of smoking and, with it, the amount of lung cancer and other diseases resulting from the behavior.

Cigarette companies add literally hundreds of chemicals in manufacturing their products. The chemicals' purposes vary, from enhancing nicotine inhalation to improving the "taste" of the cigarette. A regulatory agency could prohibit the use of some or all of these additives, again reducing the desirability of the product.

One such additive has been the subject of regulation in multiple national and sub-national jurisdictions: menthol.[25] Advertising for menthol cigarettes emphasizes that they are "cool" on the throat and "soothing", in effect making smoking easier. Large proportions of American youth begin smoking with menthol cigarettes, and the US industry has marketed menthol cigarettes to African Americans in particular. Menthol smokers find it easier to initiate smoking and harder to quit, which may increase the smoking-related death toll even in the absence of evidence that menthol cigarettes *per se* are more dangerous than non-menthol cigarettes.

If endgame discussions have focused more on altering the physical characteristics of the cigarette, *alteration of how the cigarette is presented* has been more common in practice. For example, since Canada first required large graphic warnings on cigarette packs in 2001, well over 100 countries have followed suit. In 2012, Australia became the first country to adopt plain packaging, meaning that all cigarette packs have the same unappealing color, with no imagery and brand names presented in the same font. Researchers have studied the effect of altering the appearance of the cigarette itself — changing its color to an unappealing olive green or brown, or printing messages on the rod of the cigarette, including "Smoking kills" and, in one particularly creative approach, printing a "ruler" along the rod showing how many minutes of life are lost the further down the cigarette is smoked.[26]

3.3. *Consumer-specific interventions*

A number of endgame strategies involve efforts to directly influence individual consumers (or specific groups) to stop using tobacco products or to avoid it in the first place. In essence, they are intended to reduce and hopefully eliminate consumers' demand for tobacco products.

3.3.1. *Price-based disincentives*

A robust body of research[27] demonstrates that the most rapidly effective means of reducing tobacco use is by substantially raising its price. Scores of studies from around the world have concluded that a 10% price increase reduces the demand for cigarettes (the most studied tobacco product) by 4–5%. The impact can be considerable. For example, doubling the price of a pack of cigarettes would decrease the demand for cigarettes by 40–50%. A portion of the decrease would result from people quitting smoking or not starting in the first place, while the balance would reflect continuing smokers reducing the number of cigarettes they smoke daily. The limited research on how much of the price effect represents reduced daily consumption and how much quitting suggests the decreased demand comes roughly equally from each of these responses. Price increases have a greater impact on the demand for cigarettes by young people than they do for middle-aged and older adults, thus serving as a deterrent to the initiation of smoking.

Raising tobacco product prices through government policy generally involves raising product excise taxes. A long-standing common practice throughout the world, taxing tobacco products does not itself qualify as an endgame strategy. Indeed, tax increases often reflect governments' desire to raise revenues rather than decrease tobacco product use. However, variations on the theme have been introduced as endgame interventions. For example, governmental units could establish a minimum legal price for sale of tobacco products, well above the free-market price, with that price rising each year at a rate greater than inflation, thus making tobacco products increasingly expensive over time. In a similar vein, governments could adopt annual increases in tobacco product excise taxes that are well in excess of inflation, having the same effect of systematically making tobacco use more expensive year after year.[7]

One problem with a minimum retail price, above the going market price, is that it creates a positive financial incentive for the retailer in that profit per unit of product would increase. That could be addressed by another pricing policy that ensures a maximum rate of return to the retailer (and to manufacturers and wholesalers, before retailers), with the amount above the retailer's return going to the government. Modest returns to manufacturers, wholesalers, and retailers could kill the golden goose model of tobacco manufacture, distribution, and sale, thereby reducing the industry's political influence. A drawback: It would increase the government's dependence on revenues from tobacco product sales.

3.3.2. *Require certification of the right to buy tobacco products*

Two endgame notions would change the status of tobacco products from that of conventional consumer goods to something akin to a medication. One would require a physician's prescription to purchase cigarettes. In 2013, an Oregon legislator proposed legislation classifying all nicotine products as controlled substances, requiring a prescription for purchase.[28]

Little discussed is whether physicians would be willing to write such pre-scriptions, and for what reasons.

A relative of requiring a prescription, albeit a more complicated one, is the idea of a "smoker's license".[29] A smoker could apply for an annual license that would allow the smoker to purchase a maximum number of cigarettes during a 2-week period. The higher the maximum, the larger the licensing fee. The license would be renewable annually, and the smoker could adjust the maximum number of cigarettes whenever he or she wished to do so, paying the higher fee if raising the limit. Purchases would be monitored by means of a smart card. Application for a license by a new adult (with the age of adulthood defined by the country in question) would require passing a test on the dangers of smoking (analogous to the written test associated with getting a driver's license).

The heart of the proposal lies in the incentives it creates to quit smok-ing. Anyone quitting could apply for a refund of the life-time entirety of his/her license fees plus interest. If the individual relapsed to smoking, they could regain the license (returning the license fees and interest) for up to 6 months. Beyond 6 months they would no longer be eligible to reverse their decision. The possibility of the refund might be limited to people under a certain age (the proposal suggests 40) to greatly increase the incentive to quit.

Thus far neither the prescription nor licensing concept has translated into legislation.

3.3.3. *Prohibit sales to people born after a certain year*

Scholars in Singapore proposed to phase out tobacco use over time by making it illegal to sell tobacco products to anyone born after a given year (2000 in the original proposal, published in 2010). Referred to as the tobacco-free generation,[30] the concept amounts to gradual implementation of a complete prohibition of tobacco sales. Individuals would know from a very young age that they would never be eligible to buy tobacco prod-ucts legally. Retailers would be on notice as well, and as more annual birth cohorts fell into the prohibited category, selling to "underage" buyers would be increasingly difficult.

A tobacco-free generation bill was introduced into the Tasmanian parliament in 2014 but lapsed in 2018. No other state or national legislative body has entertained similar legislation.

3.4. *Combinations of interventions*

Many of the proposed endgame interventions could be combined into a grand endgame strategy, either within or across the categories of interventions. For example, a tobacco regulatory agency could mandate all of the product standards discussed above in the product-specific interventions section, requiring manufacturers of combusted tobacco products to do the following: (i) reduce the nicotine yield of their combusted products to an agency-defined level that would not be capable of sustaining addiction; (ii) reduce the yields of PAHs, TSNAs, and catechols; (iii) raise the products' pH to ≥ 8; and (iv) prohibit the use of menthol (and all other characterizing flavors).

In some categories, proposed interventions are not combinable; they are alternatives to each other. The institutional approaches discussed under general supply-side interventions constitute an obvious example. Of course, interventions from different categories could be combined. For example, the product-specific standards just noted could be implemented by one of the alternative institutional structures mandated by government to run or regulate the industry.

An excellent illustration of combining interventions comes from New Zealand, a leading voice in the endgame discussion. New Zealand's endgame planning is likely most well recognized for its sinking lid proposal,[12] which, as noted above, entails annually declining quotas on the manufacture and importation of tobacco products, with all tobacco product sales prohibited after a number of years. Accompanying the sinking lid would be substantial annual price increases, which themselves would decrease demand. The mix of policy measures would include plain packaging, enhanced mass media campaigns, and product standards regulation to reduce the appeal of the product (requiring the removal of additives and flavors) and its addictiveness (limiting nicotine delivery to levels not capable of sustaining addiction). Most countries' endgame proponents envision using multiple interventions, but New Zealand has best articulated the multiple intervention approach.

4. Novel Alternative Nicotine Delivery Systems (ANDS): Threat or Assist to the Endgame?

Beginning in the late 1980s, cigarette manufacturers introduced a variety of novel products that, their ads alluded, posed less danger to smokers than did conventional cigarettes. Prominent among these were Premier, Eclipse, and Accord, devices that looked like cigarettes but yielded nicotine by heating rather than burning tobacco or by heating encapsulated nicotine directly. In the early 2000s, another company brought a novel cigarette to market, claiming substantial reduction in the yields of important carcinogens (Omni). At various points cigarette manufacturers have attempted to sell extremely low nicotine cigarettes, including Next in 1989 and, a little over a decade later, Quest, a series of three cigarettes with which smokers could "step down" from low to near-zero levels of nicotine. All of these products failed their market tests and were withdrawn.[31]

The future of alternative products changed dramatically with the invention in China of the electronic- or e-cigarette in 2004. Introduced to the US 3 years later, e-cigarettes began to take off in the next decade. Expenditures on e-cigarettes in the US in 2018 equaled about 10% of expenditures on conventional cigarettes.

E-cigarettes are not the only form of ANDS gaining in popularity in the US and around the world. Heated tobacco products (HTPs) — a much-improved variation on the theme first introduced 30 years ago — are catching on in several countries, most notably including Japan. In 2015, prior to the availability of HTPs, Japanese smokers consumed 182.3 billion cigarettes. Four years later, HTPs had captured 23.5% of the nicotine marketplace, while cigarette sales had decreased by a third, a likely unprecedented rate of decline in a major country.[32] (E-cigarettes are uncommon in Japan.) In addition to e-cigarettes and HTPs, entrepreneurs have recently introduced novel oral nicotine products, nicotine (derived from tobacco) in a pouch or lozenge containing no tobacco *per se*.[33]

These novel products have created considerable controversy in many countries. Proponents of the harm reduction potential of novel products focus on evidence that they are assisting a subset of smokers in quitting smoking, thereby significantly reducing the toll of tobacco. Further, the evidence is strong that the products are substantially less dangerous to health than is smoking, although these reduced-risk products are certainly not risk-free[34,35] (see Chapter 6). In England, both leading medical and public health organizations and the government support the use of e-cigarettes as an aid to smoking cessation.[36,37]

In other countries, including the US, much of the public health establishment is unified in opposition to the novel products. Many health professionals and organizations express concern that the products, used by large numbers of young people in some countries (notably including the US), may entice non-tobacco-using youth into lives of nicotine addiction, with some "graduating" to cigarette smoking. They worry as well that dual use of cigarettes and one or more of these products may sustain smoking, rather than smokers quitting smoking. Opponents of e-cigarettes and HTPs believe that the health risk associated with use of these products may be substantial.[38,39]

An additional source of opposition to the novel products lies in the fact that many are produced and marketed by the tobacco industry. Allowing or even encouraging their production and sale could profit company shareholders and, more generally, keep the industry afloat. Tobacco control advocates who consider the demise of the industry an essential priority would find any industry involvement in the endgame repugnant. However, one can envision endgame strategies that would include industry involvement while hastening the demise of smoking. For example, the industry could be permitted to market the newer products, subject to appropriate governmental regulation of manufacturing standards and marketing practices, so long as the industry ceased its sale of combusted tobacco products over a specified period of time.

As the preceding may suggest, the marketplace emergence of ANDS, a phenomenon of the second half of the era of the tobacco endgame movement, raises questions as to how ANDS might affect pursuit (and attainment) of the endgame. In part, of course, the answer depends on the specific goal. If the objective is to end use of nicotine in any form, the novel products are incompatible with attainment of the goal. If, on the other hand, the goal seeks to eliminate use of cigarettes (or perhaps all combusted tobacco products), the novel products could increase momentum in that direction if they function as substitutes for adults addicted to combusted products. While the evidence is not yet conclusive, increasingly research points to a substitution effect. The experience with HTPs in Japan is consistent with a strong substitution effect.[32] Further, a variety of studies indicate that e-cigarettes are assisting a subset of smokers to quit smoking.[40,41]

While FDA never labeled it an endgame strategy *per se*, as noted above the agency proposed consideration of perhaps the most visionary radical proposal to come out of a governmental agency to expedite the end of smoking. In July 2017, the agency announced a plan to reduce allowable nicotine in cigarettes to levels incapable of sustaining addiction, while facilitating the process of smokers' transitioning away from cigarettes by ensuring the availability of nicotine-yielding products that are substantially lower in risk for those smokers unable or unwilling to cease using nicotine.[17] A complementary intervention would be to greatly increase the price of cigarettes, through excise taxation, while taxing the lower-risk alternative products at a lower rate.[42] However, in the face of the rapid growth in vaping among American youth in 2018 and 2019, the agency changed its focus to discouraging youth use of e-cigarettes. The nicotine-reduction plan was no longer on the agency's current agenda.

5. Countries Committing to a Tobacco Endgame

To date, the governments of only seven countries have committed to achieving an endgame. As noted previously, specific objectives vary, as do deadlines. All countries define attainment of their endgame as achieving prevalence of smoking or tobacco use <5%. The countries and their endgame goals are as follows:

- Finland[43]: Tobacco- and nicotine-free by 2030;
- New Zealand[44]: Smoke-free by 2025;
- Scotland[45]: Smoke-free by 2034;

- Ireland[46]: Smoke-free by 2025;
- Sweden[47]: Smoke-free by 2025;
- Canada[48]: Tobacco-free by 2025;
- England[49]: Smoke-free by 2030.

With one exception, all of the countries have pledged allegiance to a tobacco endgame for several years now. Other than England, which joined the group in 2019, endgame advocates have not been successful in recruiting additional nations to make an endgame commitment. Examination of each country's adoption of their commitments and subsequent actions to realize their goals reveals the following general findings:

1. None of the countries' governments has called for, much less implemented, any of the more radical endgame strategies identified earlier in this chapter. Rather, all have focused on conventional, evidence-based tobacco control measures, including raising taxes, prohibiting smoking (and in some instances other nicotine and tobacco product use) in public places and workplaces, requiring plain packaging and graphic warning labels, mounting sizable media anti-smoking campaigns, and restricting marketing and sales practices.[50]
2. None of the countries' governments has developed an explicit plan to achieve the endgame goal by the established deadline. Nor have the governments devoted significant resources toward attaining the goal. Rather, many call upon NGOs to pursue the goal.
3. In most countries, studies indicate that the countries' goals will not be achieved by the stated deadline. This seems especially clear for the four countries with endgame deadlines of 2025.
4. The envisioned role for alternative nicotine delivery devices varies widely across the countries. In Finland, for example, its goal of ending the use of all tobacco and nicotine products precludes a role for e-cigarettes. The country's Tobacco Act of 2016 declared that regulations that apply to conventional tobacco products apply to e-cigarettes as well. In contrast, both England and New Zealand envision a positive role for e-cigarettes in achieving their smoke-free goals. In the UK, medical authorities encourage use of e-cigarettes as a smoking

cessation tool, consistent with evidence that they have outperformed government-approved nicotine replacement products in clinical trials.[51,52] To date, no endgame-committed government has addressed other ANDS, including heated tobacco products and the new oral nicotine products.

6. The Future of the Endgame Movement — Challenges and Reasons for Optimism

The only reasonable conclusion to draw from the evidence regarding country commitments to a tobacco endgame is that, thus far, the idea has drawn only nominal support from only a small number of national governments. Why is this? What are the obstacles to governments' establishing endgame commitments and developing and pursuing explicit endgame plans that incorporate the novel endgame interventions described earlier in the chapter? And at the same time, what factors might suggest a brighter future for the endgame movement?

One obstacle is embedded in the very idea underlying the concept of the endgame: the endgame interventions and strategies represent, by design, "outside the box" thinking. Tobacco control has progressed effectively, if gradually, through almost six decades, relying on more conventional evidence-based interventions. Governments, and perhaps people in general, often exhibit a conservative, even adverse reaction to radically different ideas. They need time to sink in.

The endgame movement is less than two decades old. While its most prominent concepts might seem prohibitively radical today, the history of tobacco control suggests we should not dismiss such concepts so fast. Consider, for example, that as recently as the turn of the present century, proponents of completely smoke-free workplace laws, including all restaurants and bars, would have been laughed out of a state or national legislature. The idea was preposterous. Then, in 2004, Ireland made the audacious move of declaring the country smoke-free in all workplaces and public places, including their smoke-filled pubs. The public complied with the new law immediately and other countries followed suit in the years thereafter. Today, in countries around the world, smoke-free restaurants and bars are the norm.

Similarly, before the 2000s, few would have anticipated a country requiring cigarette packs to have warning labels covering fully half the front and back of the pack, with graphic imagery depicting the devastation wrought by smoking. In 2001, Canada became the first country to require graphic warnings. Today, over 100 countries require pictorial warnings. It is not inconceivable that one or more of today's radical endgame concepts will become "the new normal" in the foreseeable future.

The novelty of endgame ideas is not the only impediment to their adoption. All would require substantial political courage, as all would certainly face serious political opposition from the powerful tobacco industry and its allies, and possibly also from a significant subset of the public. The law establishing the Center for Tobacco Products within the US FDA specifically required the agency to ban all "characterizing flavors" in cigarettes except menthol, which it did. The agency investigated the role of menthol in smoking, corroborating the finding that menthol increases smoking, making smoking both easier to start and more difficult to quit.[25] Given menthol's prominence in the American cigarette marketplace, banning menthol could have a significant effect on smoking and disease, but the political opposition to a ban is substantial. Indeed, one would assume that banning menthol would be the low-hanging fruit of cigarette regulation. The FDA's inability to do so to date vividly demonstrates the challenge posed by political opposition to potentially effective regulations.

Another obstacle to adoption of endgame ideas is that they would require governmental commitment to long-term plans, along with the resource commitment to carry out those plans. However mundane it may seem, it is always difficult to get government to invest scarce public resources in a new, discretionary initiative, especially one unlikely to meet with universal enthusiasm.

Some important endgame ideas clearly require substantial government investments, such as some of the institutional regulatory approaches to tobacco products discussed above. By creating new bureaucracies, such agencies would require a lot of attention on the part of (other) government authorities. Governmental bureaucracies confront multiple challenges to carrying out their missions, ranging from political opposition to the sheer complexity of the organizations. The US FDA's Center for Tobacco

Products illustrates the challenges that impede governmental bureaucracies from accomplishing their missions. Any tobacco regulatory agency would confront similar challenges. For those given a harm reduction mandate, what incentive structures would ensure their adhering to their mandate?

Other endgame ideas confront philosophical barriers. The most obvious example is the idea of banning one or more categories of tobacco products, most commonly combustible tobacco products. Even the idea of mandating nicotine reduction in combusted products is decried by opponents as a de facto form of prohibition.[53] Opponents also suggest that smokers could "doctor" reduced-nicotine cigarettes with injectable or spray-on nicotine, although it is unclear that such approaches could produce a palatable cigarette. Effective regulations could mitigate the potential of such "end-runs" around the policy, including minimizing the size of a black market. In many countries, banning primarily self-affecting behaviors meets with profound philosophical objection. And bans promote black markets and the accompanying crime, the practical concern opponents raise.

Yet here too counter-arguments can address both philosophical and practical concerns. Robert Proctor has presented an articulate response to philosophical objections to prohibition (which he prefers to call abolition).[9] A practical consideration in favor of a future ban derives from survey data indicating that sizable proportions of the population in several countries favor the idea. For example, in 2013, Gendall and colleagues[54] reported that half of survey respondents agreed with the proposition that "Cigarettes and tobacco should not be sold in New Zealand in 10 years' time." Only a quarter disagreed. Edwards *et al.* found much the same.[55] Three years earlier a similar proportion (44.5%) of respondents to a survey in England supported the same proposition.[56] However, the sentiment is not universal, and the substantial support may be highly dependent on the wording of the proposal. It might rest on deferred adoption of the policy, for example, or on the notion of banning sales, rather than making smoking illegal *per se*. In the US, a 2018 Gallop Poll found that only a quarter of respondents favored making smoking illegal, with no qualification as to when, with three-quarters opposed.[57] Similarly, while Gendall *et al.* found half of their respondents agreeing that "cigarettes and tobacco should not be sold in New Zealand in 10 years' time", the rate of agreement rose to nearly 80% when the statement was "I support the goal of reducing smoking from around 20% of the population to 5% or less by 2025," in essence the endgame goal.

A regulation like a ban or nicotine reduction could benefit from the availability of consumer-acceptable reduced-risk nicotine delivery products. Such products could facilitate addicted smokers dealing with a policy that would remove the principal product that satisfies their addiction. As noted above, England and New Zealand, committed to a smoke-free future, have explicitly endorsed this idea as a component of the drive toward a smoke-free future. In contrast, Finland, with its commitment to end use of all nicotine and tobacco products, specifically precludes the idea.

Each of the endgame proposals has its unique idiosyncrasies. One of the more intriguing endgame concepts — the smoke-free generation[30] (prohibiting the sale of tobacco products to anyone born after a given year) — has the political appeal that, at the time of its adoption, it would not affect the behavior of anyone of legal age. But therein lies a limitation of the proposal: It would rid the country of tobacco very gradually. With other forces reducing smoking in many countries around the world, would the smoke-free generation policy truly expedite the demise of tobacco use?

7. Conclusion: Is an End in Sight?

Tobacco use has been with us since Native Americans first inhaled tobacco smoke centuries before Columbus arrived in what would become known as the Americas. In contrast, cigarette smoking, the most lethal form of tobacco use, is a product primarily of the 20th century. Its role in everything from the development of modern advertising to the creation of the global epidemic of lung cancer inspired a prominent social historian to dub the 20th century "the cigarette century".[58] Figure 1, found at the beginning of this chapter, captures the remarkable rise and fall of the cigarette in the US throughout the century, surely one of the century's most important public health stories. But while smoking has dropped substantially since the mid-1960s, in the early 21st century it is far from ended in the US or anywhere else in the world. Smoking still kills over 7 million of the globe's citizens every year. That's the bad news.

The good news is that, with a few exceptions, smoking is declining around the globe. Aggregate global cigarette consumption, which rose annually for decades, peaked at close to 6 trillion cigarettes in 2012 and has been declining since then.[59] And while no country's government has detailed an explicit tobacco endgame plan to which it has committed significant resources, several countries are experiencing decreases in smoking prevalence that make attainment of the goal of ≤5% a realistic possibility in the not-too-distant future. Among western countries, Australia, Canada, New Zealand, the UK, and the US report smoking rates in the vicinity of 14–15%. (One problem with comparing prevalence across countries is that some report the prevalence of daily smoking, while others report daily plus non-daily smoking.) Sweden's rate is about 10%, likely the lowest in Europe and perhaps among all Western countries. (To many observers, the very low prevalence of smoking in Sweden owes to a significant degree to Swedish males having switched, beginning decades ago, from smoking cigarettes to using snus, a low-nitrosamine smokeless tobacco that appears to have a very low risk of disease associated with its use.[60] In Norway, where rapid growth of snus use is a relatively more recent phenomenon, smoking rates of both men and women have dropped by more than half in the two decades from 1995–1999 to the present.)

The only countries that are very close to the goal of ≤5% smoking prevalence are several countries in Africa and a handful in the Americas. All of the following report smoking prevalence less than 10%: Ethiopia, Panama, Ghana, Barbados, Ecuador, Nigeria, Benin, Niger, and Uganda.[61] Particularly for the African countries, low smoking rates reflect the nations' poverty and the relatively recent entry of multinational tobacco companies into the region. Unlike the Western countries with relatively low smoking rates, most of these countries have never experienced high rates. Indeed, much of Africa represents the only place on earth that the epidemic of smoking-produced disease can still be avoided.

Tobacco control is working, worldwide. In the six WHO regions, smoking is declining over time, with the exception of slight increases in (and projected for) parts of the Eastern Mediterranean and African regions.[62]

Spawned in part by the very success of tobacco control in so many middle- and high-income countries, the tobacco endgame movement reflects a frustration with the pace of progress. As is discussed elsewhere in this book, convincing research demonstrated that smoking caused lung cancer, as well as a host of other diseases, beginning 70 years ago. Yet today this addictive behavior accounts for an eighth of all deaths worldwide every year. Whether an effective endgame movement can take hold remains to be seen. It appears inevitable that smoking will become a thing of the past. The notion that energizes the tobacco endgame is that the demise of smoking can and should be realized sooner rather than later.

Postscript

After this chapter was completed, in April 2021 the government of New Zealand announced a specific draft action plan to achieve a smoke-free country by the year 2025, a goal the country first announced in 2011. The plan incorporates a sizable number of strict regulations that include many of the endgame concepts discussed in this chapter. New Zealand has thus become the world's first country to define and commit to a serious endgame strategy.[63]

Also in April 2021, the U.S. Food and Drug Administration announced its commitment to proceed with developing product standards banning menthol in cigarettes and all flavors in cigars, including menthol. While far from an endgame measure, this represents a courageous step forward for an agency plagued by powerful political and legal opposition to effective regulation of tobacco products.[64]

Acknowledgment

A leader of the endgame discussion, Dr. Ruth Malone of the University of California San Francisco, kindly offered helpful suggestions as I was organizing this chapter. The opinions expressed herein are exclusively my own and should not be interpreted as reflecting those of Dr. Malone.

References

1. U.S. Department of Health, Education, and Welfare. *Smoking and Health. Report of the Advisory Committee to the Surgeon General of the Public Health Service.* (Washington, DC: U.S. Department of Health, Education, and Welfare. Public Health Service, 1964).
2. Holford TR, Meza R, Warner KE, *et al.* Tobacco control and the reduction in smoking-related premature deaths in the United States, 1964–2012. *JAMA* 2014;311:164–71.
3. Malone RE. Imagining things otherwise: new endgame ideas for tobacco control. *Tobacco Control* 2010;19:349–50.
4. Benowitz NL, Henningfield JE. Establishing a nicotine threshold for addiction. The implications for tobacco regulation. *N Engl J Med* 1994; 331:123–5.
5. Murad IV:Ottoman sultan. Britannica. July 23, 2020. (https://www.britannica.com/biography/Murad-IV)
6. Legislation by country: Bhutan. March 9, 2020. (https://www.tobaccocontrollaws.org/legislation/country/bhutan/summary)
7. McDaniel PA, Smith EA, Malone RE. The tobacco endgame: a qualitative review and synthesis. *Tobacco Control* 2016;25:594–604.
8. Daynard RA. Doing the unthinkable (and saving millions of lives). *Tobacco Control* 2009;18:2–3.
9. Proctor RN. Why ban the sale of cigarettes? The case for abolition. *Tobacco Control* 2013;22(Suppl. 1):i27–30.
10. Sharp S. Beverly Hills becomes the first U.S. city to end most tobacco sales. *LA Times.* June 4, 2019 (https://www.latimes.com/local/lanow/la-me-ln-beverly-hills-ends-tobacco-sales-20190604-story.html).
11. Holland E. Manhattan Beach to ban all tobacco sales within the city. Patch. February 24, 2020 (https://patch.com/california/manhattanbeach/manhattan-beach-ban-all-tobacco-sales-within-city).
12. Thomson G, Wilson N, Blakely T, *et al.* Ending appreciable tobacco use in a nation: using a sinking lid on supply. *Tobacco Control* 2010;19:431–5.
13. Callard C, Thompson D, Collishaw N. Transforming the tobacco market: why the supply of cigarettes should be transferred from for-profit corporations to non-profit enterprises with a public health mandate. *Tobacco Control* 2005;14:278–83.
14. Borland R. A strategy for controlling the marketing of tobacco products: a regulated market model. *Tobacco Control* 2003;12:374–82.

15. Ioannidis JP, Henriksen L, Prochaska JJ. Endgame: engaging the tobacco industry in its own elimination. *Eur J Clin Invest* 2013;43:1366–70.

16. Action on Smoking and Health. Dutch parliament moves to drastically reduce tobacco sales. March 3, 2020 (https://ash.org/dutch-parliament-moves-to-reduce-tobacco-sales/).

17. Food and Drug Administration. FDA announces comprehensive regulatory plan to shift trajectory of tobacco-related disease, death. July 27, 2017 (https://www.fda.gov/news-events/press-announcements/fda-announces-comprehensive-regulatory-plan-shift-trajectory-tobacco-related-disease-death).

18. Apelberg BJ, Feirman SP, Salazar E, *et al.* Potential public health effects of reducing nicotine levels in cigarettes in the United States. *New Engl J Med* 2018;378:1725–33.

19. Hatsukami D, Luo X, Jensen JA, *et al.* Effect of immediate vs gradual reduction in nicotine content of cigarettes on biomarkers of smoke exposure: A randomized clinical trial. *JAMA* 2018;320:880–91.

20. Hughes JR, Hecht SS, Carmella SG, Murphy SE, Callas P. Smoking behaviour and toxin exposure during six weeks use of a potential reduced exposure product: Omni. *Tobacco Control* 2004;13:175–9.

21. Omni cigarette ad. Circa 2001 (https://tobacco-img.stanford.edu/wp-content/uploads/cigarettes/filter-safety-myths/reduced-carcinogens/carcinogens_03.jpg).

22. Hatsukami DK, Lemmonds C, Zhang Y, *et al.* Evaluation of carcinogen exposure in people who used "reduced exposure" tobacco products. *JNCI* 2004;96:844–52.

23. WHO Study Group on Tobacco Product Regulation. *Report on the scientific basis of tobacco product regulation: Seventh report of a WHO study group.* (Geneva: World Health Organization 2019). WHO Technical Report Series, No. 1015 (https://apps.who.int/iris/bitstream/handle/10665/329445/9789241210249-eng.pdf?ua=1).

24. Proctor RN. *Golden holocaust: Origins of the cigarette catastrophe and the case for abolition.* (Berkeley CA: University of California Press, 2011).

25. Food and Drug Administration. Preliminary scientific evaluation of the possible public health effects of menthol versus non-menthol cigarettes, nd (https://www.fda.gov/media/86497/download).

26. Hoek J, Gendall P, Eckert C, Louviere, J. Dissuasive cigarette sticks: The next step in standardised ('plain') packaging? *Tobacco Control* 2016;25:699–705.

27. Chaloupka FJ, Powell LM, Warner KE. The use of excise taxes to reduce tobacco, alcohol, and sugary beverage consumption. *Ann Rev Public Health* 2019;40:187–201.

28. Perez S. One Wonders if government agencies ever learn anything from history and the failed, alleged War on Drugs. Reuters. January 25, 2013 (https://familysurvivalprotocol.wordpress.com/2013/01/25/big-brother-gone-wild-new-oregon-law-might-make-cigarettes-prescription-only/).

29. Chapman S. The case for a smoker's license. *PLOS Med* 2012;9:e1001342.

30. Khoo D, Chiam Y, Ng P, *et al.* Phasing-out tobacco: proposal to deny access to tobacco for those born from 2000. *Tobacco Control* 2010;19:355–60.

31. U.S. Department of Health and Human Services. *How Tobacco Smoke Causes Disease: The Biology and Behavioral Basis for Smoking-Attributable Disease: A Report of the Surgeon General.* (Atlanta, GA: Centers for Disease Control and Prevention, National Center for Chronic Disease Prevention and Health Promotion, Office on Smoking and Health, 2010, Chapter 2).

32. Cummings KM, Nahhas GJ, Sweanor DT. What is accounting for the rapid decline in cigarette sales in Japan? *Int J Environ Res Public Health* 2020;17:3570. Published online 2020 May 20. doi: 10.3390/ijerph17103570

33. Robichaud MO, Seidenberg AB, Byron MJ. Tobacco companies introduce 'tobacco-free' nicotine pouches. *Tobacco Control* 2019; online first (https://tobaccocontrol.bmj.com/content/early/2019/11/21/tobaccocontrol-2019-055321).

34. National Academies of Sciences, Engineering, and Medicine. *Public health consequences of e-cigarettes* (Washington, DC: The National Academies Press, 2018). doi:10.17226/24952.

35. Zuck K. Evidence related to the health risk of IQOS use: evaluation of product chemistry. Presentation to FDA's Tobacco Products Scientific Advisory Committee, January 24–25, 2018 (https://www.fda.gov/media/110744/download).

36. Royal College of Physicians. Nicotine without smoke: Tobacco harm reduction. London: RCP, 2016 (https://www.rcplondon.ac.uk/projects/outputs/nicotine-without-smoke-tobacco-harm-reduction).

37. McNeill A, Brose LS, Calder R, Bauld L, Robson D. Evidence review of e-cigarettes and heated tobacco products 2018. A report commissioned by Public Health England. London: Public Health England, 2018 (https://www.gov.uk/government/publications/e-cigarettes-and-heated-tobacco-products-evidence-review/evidence-review-of-e-cigarettes-and-heated-tobacco-products-2018-executive-summary).

38. Bach L. Electronic cigarettes and youth. Washington DC: Campaign for Tobacco Free Kids, January 28, 2020 (https://www.tobaccofreekids.org/assets/factsheets/0382.pdf).

39. Glantz SA, Bareham DW. E-cigarettes: use, effects on smoking, risks, and policy implications. *Ann Rev Public Health* 2018;39:215–35.
40. Mendez D, Warner KE. A magic bullet? The potential impact of e-cigarettes on the toll of cigarette smoking. *Nicotine Tobacco Res* 2021;23:654–61.
41. Balfour D, Benowitz N, Hatsukami D, *et al.* Balancing consideration of the risks and benefits of e-cigarettes. *Amer J Public Health* 2021;111(9):1661–1672. doi:10.2105/AJPH.2021.306416.
42. Chaloupka FJ, Sweanor D, Warner KE. Differential taxes for differential risks — toward reduced harm from nicotine-yielding products. *New Engl J Med* 2015;373:594–7.
43. Tobacco-Free Finland 2030. Tobacco Act (https://savutonsuomi.fi/en/towards-tobacco-free-finland/tobacco-act/).
44. Edwards R, Thornley L. Achieving endgames: Lessons from the international endgames comparison project and New Zealand's Smokefree 2025 goal. Presented at Tobacco Endgame Sweden 2025, June 12–13, 2018, Stockholm, Sweden (https://www.folkhalsomyndigheten.se/contentassets/fc67eab06cf14313b34ea55566a9ac57/12-06-lessons-international-endgames-comparison-project-new-zealand.pdf).
45. Action on Smoking and Health Scotland. Tobacco endgames (https://www.ashscotland.org.uk/what-we-do/supply-information-about-tobacco-and-health/key-topics/tobacco-endgames.aspx).
46. Department of Health, Ireland. Tobacco Free Ireland. April 4, 2019 (https://www.gov.ie/en/policy-information/5df1e7-tobacco-free-ireland/).
47. Tobacco Endgame 2025. Mobilizing public opinion for a Swedish Tobacco Endgame strategy (https://tobaksfakta.se/wp-content/uploads/2017/10/Folder-ENGELSK.pdf).
48. Getting to less than 5% by 2035: the 2019 tobacco endgame report (https://www.lung.ca/sites/default/files/EndGameReport-final.pdf).
49. Barr S. England could become 'smoke-free' by 2030 under new government pledge. Independent. July 23, 2019 (https://www.independent.co.uk/life-style/health-and-families/smoking-ban-uk-end-cigarettes-tobacco-health-green-paper-a9016636.html).
50. World Health Organization. WHO Report on the Global Tobacco Epidemic, 2008: the MPOWER package. https://apps.who.int/iris/handle/10665/43818).
51. Hajek P, Phillips-Waller A, Przulj D, *et al.* A randomized trial of e-cigarettes versus nicotine-replacement therapy. *New Engl J Med* 2019;380:629–37.
52. Walker N, Parag V, Verbiest M, Laking G, Laugesen M, Bullen C. Nicotine patches used in combination with e-cigarettes (with and without nicotine) for

smoking cessation: a pragmatic, randomised trial. *Lancet Respir Med* 2020;8:54–64.

53. Bates C, Wade C. Reducing nicotine in cigarettes: challenges and opportunities. October 24, 2017 (https://clivebates.com/documents/Reduced NicotineOct2017.pdf).

54. Gendall P, Hoek J, Maubach N, Edwards R. Public support for more action on smoking. *NZMJ* 2013;126(1375):85–94.

55. Edwards R, Wilson N, Peace J, Weerasekera D, Thomson GW, Gifford H. Support for a tobacco endgame and increased regulation of the tobacco industry among New Zealand smokers: results from a National Survey. *Tobacco Control* 2013;22(e1):e86–93.

56. Shahab L, West R. Public support in England for a total ban on the sale of tobacco products. *Tobacco Control* 2010;19:143–7.

57. McCarthy J. One in four Americans support total smoking ban. Gallup. July 23, 2018 (https://news.gallup.com/poll/237767/one-four-americans-support-total-smoking-ban.aspx).

58. Brandt AM. *The cigarette century: The rise, fall, and deadly persistence of the product that defined America* (New York, NY: Basic Books, 2007).

59. The global cigarette industry. Campaign for Tobacco Free Kids. December 2019 (https://www.tobaccofreekids.org/assets/global/pdfs/en/Global_Cigarette_Industry_pdf.pdf).

60. Clarke E, Thompson K, Weaver S, Thompson J, O'Connell G. Snus: A compelling harm reduction alternative to cigarettes. *Harm Reduct J* 2019;16:62 (https://doi.org/10.1186/s12954-019-0335-1).

61. Smoking rates by country 2020. World Population Review, nd (https://worldpopulationreview.com/country-rankings/smoking-rates-by-country).

62. Prevalence of tobacco smoking. World Health Organization, nd (https://www.who.int/gho/tobacco/use/en/).

63. Ministry of Health, New Zealand Government. Proposals for a Smokefree Aotearoa 2025 Action Plan: Discussion document. Wellington: Ministry of Health, 2021. (https://www.health.govt.nz/system/files/documents/publications/proposals_for_a_smokefree_aotearoa_2025_action_plan-final.pdf).

64. U.S. Food and Drug Administration. FDA commits to evidence-based actions aimed at saving lives and preventing future generations of smokers. Press release, April 29, 2021. (https://www.fda.gov/news-events/press-announcements/fda-commits-evidence-based-actions-aimed-saving-lives-and-preventing-future-generations-smokers).

Index

CPSIA information can be obtained
at www.ICGtesting.com
Printed in the USA
JSHW041649110222
22710JS00003BB/8